THE NATIONAL ACADEMIES
Advisers to the Nation on Science, Engineering, and Medicine

The **National Academy of Sciences** is a private, nonprofit, self-perpetuating society of distinguished scholars engaged in scientific and engineering research, dedicated to the furtherance of science and technology and to their use for the general welfare. Upon the authority of the charter granted to it by the Congress in 1863, the Academy has a mandate that requires it to advise the federal government on scientific and technical matters. Dr. Ralph J. Cicerone is president of the National Academy of Sciences.

The **National Academy of Engineering** was established in 1964, under the charter of the National Academy of Sciences, as a parallel organization of outstanding engineers. It is autonomous in its administration and in the selection of its members, sharing with the National Academy of Sciences the responsibility for advising the federal government. The National Academy of Engineering also sponsors engineering programs aimed at meeting national needs, encourages education and research, and recognizes the superior achievements of engineers. Dr. Wm. A. Wulf is president of the National Academy of Engineering.

The **Institute of Medicine** was established in 1970 by the National Academy of Sciences to secure the services of eminent members of appropriate professions in the examination of policy matters pertaining to the health of the public. The Institute acts under the responsibility given to the National Academy of Sciences by its congressional charter to be an adviser to the federal government and, upon its own initiative, to identify issues of medical care, research, and education. Dr. Harvey V. Fineberg is president of the Institute of Medicine.

The **National Research Council** was organized by the National Academy of Sciences in 1916 to associate the broad community of science and technology with the Academy's purposes of furthering knowledge and advising the federal government. Functioning in accordance with general policies determined by the Academy, the Council has become the principal operating agency of both the National Academy of Sciences and the National Academy of Engineering in providing services to the government, the public, and the scientific and engineering communities. The Council is administered jointly by both Academies and the Institute of Medicine. Dr. Ralph J. Cicerone and Dr. Wm. A. Wulf are chair and vice chair, respectively, of the National Research Council.

www.national-academies.org

D0002795

PANEL ON NEW RESEARCH ON POPULATION AND THE ENVIRONMENT

Barbara Entwisle *(Chair)*, Carolina Population Center and Department of Sociology, University of North Carolina, Chapel Hill

Myron P. Gutmann, Inter-university Consortium for Political and Social Research (ICPSR), University of Michigan, Ann Arbor

Wolfgang Lutz, International Institute for Applied Systems Analysis, Laxenburg, Austria

Emilio Moran, Department of Anthropology, Indiana University

Dennis Ojima, Natural Resource Ecology Laboratory, Colorado State University

Steward Pickett, Institute of Ecosystem Studies, Millbrook, NY

Peter J. Richerson, Division of Environmental Studies, University of California, Davis

Mark R. Rosenzweig, John F. Kennedy School of Government, Harvard University

Susan C. Stonich, Department of Anthropology and Environmental Studies, University of California, Santa Barbara

Paul C. Stern, *Study Director*
Deborah Johnson, *Senior Program Assistant*

Preface

The interactions of human population growth and migration with environmental quality have long been a topic of debate among demographers, natural scientists, and other observers. A recent expansion of empirical research on the topic made it timely to review the state of the field to set an agenda for research in the coming decade. To this end, with the support of the William and Flora Hewlett Foundation and the National Institute of Child Health and Human Development and with input from the Committee on the Human Dimensions of Global Change, the Panel on New Research on Population and the Environment of the National Research Council (NRC) organized a workshop to bring together social and natural scientists to discuss results from ongoing research projects, as well as to find ways to enhance the exchange of knowledge among disciplines.

Empirical research on population and environment can be divided into four major categories. Studies have focused on population effects that operate either primarily via change in land and water use (e.g., deforestation, habitat fragmentation, water pollution, introduction of exotic species) or primarily via industrial processes (e.g., emissions of pollutants to atmosphere or waterways). Studies below the global scale have tended to focus either on processes in developing countries or on processes in wealthy countries. Research exists in each cell of the implied table, although more attention has been given to some cells than others. In particular, recent empirical research has emphasized population-environment linkages that operate via change in land use. In order to adequately reflect and incorporate a full range of disciplinary diversity and variability in field site and situation, the committee decided to focus the workshop on this linkage.

Given a focus on land use as the link between population and environment, the 1993 NRC volume *Population and Land Use in Developing Countries* was a natural point of departure. Since its publication, the National Institute of Child Health and Human Development at the National Institutes of Health developed a program on population, land use, and environment and funded a number of research projects, some of which are represented in the papers assembled for the workshop and this volume. Related programs at the National Science Foundation and at the National Aeronautics and Space Administration were also important sources of support. These projects, too, are represented. The research on population, land use, and environment in the 1990s and early 2000s was scientifically much stronger than in the past. It also began to open new research directions and suggest new hypotheses that should be pursued. This is why the time was ripe for an effort to collect some of the best recent research, review its strengths and weaknesses, and discuss the implications for future directions.

Through consultations with experts in population and environment, including experts from both the behavioral and social sciences and the biological and ecological sciences, the committee identified an interdisciplinary group of researchers who could contribute to assessing and advancing research on interrelations between population, land use, and the environment.

The first task of the Panel on New Research in Population and the Environment was to organize the workshop. Its overall goal was to assess and advance research on interrelations between population and the environment, with a particular focus on environmental effects of population changes mediated by land use change. More specific goals of the workshop were to

- present research reflecting the state of the art in empirical work and conceptual and integrative research that promises to advance empirical knowledge;
- point toward more sophisticated analysis of population and environmental variables in research on human-environment interactions;
- demonstrate modes of collaboration between social scientists and natural scientists on population-environment research by including joint presentations by social scientists and natural scientists from the same research groups;
- examine closely how particular demographic processes interact with environmental processes, particularly separating effects of natural increase from those of migration;
- examine the multiple determinants of population behavior, consider-

ing the effects of cultural, economic, and biophysical context on population-environment relations; and

   • examine the empirical research in light of available integrative concepts in order to define research directions that can lead to more rapid accumulation and integration of knowledge.

The second task of the panel was to synthesize the results of the workshop, describing the progress that has been made, evaluating strengths and weaknesses, and identifying unanswered questions and to make recommendations about directions for future research in this area. The panel organized the workshop around a set of interdisciplinary studies of population, land use, and environment in a wide variety of settings. Of particular interest were detailed, ongoing, longitudinal, site-based studies being done by research teams that include both social and natural scientists. The selection of studies to include was guided by a rubric that distinguished between disciplinary starting point and research setting. The studies selected represent different starting points in social science (primarily demography) and natural science (primarily ecology) yet include both perspectives. Research settings for the studies cover urban and rural contexts in developing and wealthy countries. Some cells of the implied 2 × 2 × 2 table are populated by many excellent studies that met our criteria (especially rural site-based studies in developing countries), whereas other cells are sparser (e.g., urban site-based studies in developing countries). In some instances, the choice of which study to include was difficult. Selections were made in such a way as to feature disciplinary diversity and regional variability. The panel also thought that it was important to include a global perspective. In the workshop, the strengths and limitations of the studies were discussed from social science and natural science perspectives to identify potentially fruitful areas for future progress and collaboration.

Representatives of the research projects were invited to attend a two-day workshop, which was held January 14-16, 2004, at the Beckman Center of the National Academies in Irvine, California. Authors were asked to write papers that identified the important research questions for their project and study site; explained how they conceptualized connections between population, land use, and environment; described the research designs and statistical techniques they have used; provided an overview of their major findings; and reflected on the challenges and benefits of integrating social science and natural science perspectives. Authors were asked to tell the story of their projects and to summarize the major findings, citing more technical reports of the research that are available. Revised versions of these papers appear as chapters in Part II of this volume, in the order that they are cited in Part I, the panel's report itself.

The workshop was organized around groupings of papers and related discussion. The papers by John Weeks and colleagues on Cairo, Egypt, and by Charles Redman on metropolitan Phoenix, Arizona, were paired. Both address rapid demographic and land use change in urban areas in desert environments, but they do so from sharply different perspectives. The papers by Pamela Matson and colleagues on the Yaqui Valley, Mexico, and Myron Gutmann and colleagues on the U.S. Great Plains both address change in agricultural regions with considerable dependence on irrigation, but the initial orientation and questions differ. The papers by Jack Liu and colleagues on Wolong Nature Reserve, China, and Andrew Foster on rural India have in common an interest in tensions between economic development and the maintenance of common-pool resources (bamboo forest and endangered pandas in China and commonly held forest lands in India), but they differ dramatically in methods and approach. The papers by Karen Seto on the Pearl River Delta in China and Red River Delta in Vietnam, by Stephen Walsh and colleagues on Nang Rong, Thailand, and by Emilio Moran and colleagues on the Brazilian Amazon, all focus on land use change to and from agriculture, although in vastly different cultural, historical, social, and economic contexts. The paper by Günther Fischer and Brian O'Neill addresses issues of global modeling.

Discussion at the workshop was lively and covered a wide variety of topics, including a few discussions of larger issues and integrative challenges. A discussion of the difficulties of joining social science and natural science approaches addressed a range of concerns, from the absence of a fully developed conceptual model of the coupled human-natural system to very practical issues related to the time and resources needed for integrative research. A discussion of the challenges of linking the site-based studies to regional and global models addressed the issue of the generalizability of site-based studies. Another cross-cutting discussion addressed how spatial, temporal, and institutional contexts relate to cross-scale linkages and to the integration of different approaches to the study of population, land use, and environment. Yet another considered the roles of social institutions in mediating population–land use–environment relationships, which arose in every paper prepared for the workshop. A final panel discussion addressed data and methods needed for further progress in the modeling of complexity and answering questions about cause and effect.

This volume would not have been possible without resources provided by the National Institute of Child Health and Human Development and the William and Flora Hewlett Foundation and the generous contribution of time and energy from many experts in the field. In addition to standing members of the NRC Committee on the Human Dimensions of Global Change, Rebecca Clark, Pamela Matson, Fred Myerson, and Holly Reed participated in the initial framing of the project. Each signed paper in this volume, regardless of orientation, was sent to a social scientist and to a natural scientist for review. The goal was a collection of papers that would be viewed as useful to a broad audience. We are most grateful to the following reviewers for their comments on the papers and for their critiques and suggestions as to how papers might be improved: Deborah Balk, Columbia University; Lawrence Brown, Ohio State University; Sara R. Curran, Princeton University; Erle C. Ellis, University of Maryland, Baltimore County; Christine Goodale, Cornell University; Flora Lu Holt, University of North Carolina; Richard Houghton, Woods Hole Research Center; Lori Hunter, University of Colorado; Marc Imhoff, NASA Goddard Space Flight Center; Leiwen Jiang, Brown University; Randall Kuhn, University of Colorado; Landis MacKellar, The International Institute for Applied Systems Analysis (IIASA); George Malanson, University of Iowa; William Moomaw, Tufts University; Barry R. Noon, Colorado State University; Diane Pataki, University of Utah; Pete Richerson, University of California, Davis; Cynthia Rosenzweig, NASA Goddard Space Flight Center; Donald Worster, University of Kansas; and Xingming Xiao, University of New Hampshire. We are grateful for their thoughtful comments and suggestions as well as their attention to detail.

The review process for the panel's overview and recommendations chapters followed formal NRC procedures.

This report has been reviewed in draft form by individuals chosen for their diverse perspectives and technical expertise, in accordance with procedures approved by the Report Review Committee of the NRC. The purpose of this independent review is to provide candid and critical comments that will assist the institution in making the published report as sound as possible and to ensure that the report meets institutional standards for objectivity, evidence, and responsiveness to the study charge. The review comments and draft manuscript remain confidential to protect the integrity of the deliberative process.

We thank the following individuals for their participation in the review of this report: Richard Bilsborrow, Carolina Population Center, University of North Carolina, Chapel Hill; Thomas H. Dietz, College of Agriculture and Natural Resources, College of Natural Science and College of Social Science, Michigan State University; Robert Kates, independent scholar, Trenton, Maine; Geoffrey McNicoll, Population Council, New York; Harold A. Mooney, Department of Biological Sciences, Stanford University; Robert Repetto, Stratus Consulting, Inc., Boulder, Colorado; Barbara Boyle Torrey, Population Reference Bureau, Washington, DC; and Billie Lee Turner, Graduate School of Geography, Clark University.

Although the reviewers listed above have provided many constructive comments and suggestions, they were not asked to endorse the conclusions or recommendations nor did they see the final draft of the report before its release. The review of this report was overseen by John Bongaarts, Population Council, New York. Appointed by the NRC, he was responsible for making certain that an independent examination of this report was carried out in accordance with institutional procedures and that all review comments were carefully considered. Responsibility for the final content of this report rests entirely with the authoring committee and the institution.

Barbara Entwisle, *Chair*
Panel on New Research on
Population and the Environment

Contents

xiii

PART I

PANEL REPORT

Executive Summary

The relationships between human population dynamics and natural resources have been of interest at least as far back as Malthus, who argued that human population growth could outstrip the ability of the Earth to provide food. More recent scholars have noted that population-environment relationships are much more complex and are influenced by many more human activities than just procreation. About a decade ago, the National Institute of Child Health and Human Development, the William and Flora Hewlett Foundation, and other research sponsors began providing concerted support of research to understand connections between human population and environmental quality that are mediated by changes in land use. This volume focuses on research in which land use or land cover change is a key mediator of human-environment interactions, in which demographic variables figure prominently among the driving forces investigated, and in which efforts are made to investigate the causal mechanisms by which human population changes affect land use and environmental outcomes. It takes stock of the progress that has been made in such research to see what has been learned, to identify gaps and problems that remain, and to develop a set of recommendations about future research directions.

The main areas of research progress have been refining the broad concepts of population, land use, and environment into more specific and illuminating concepts; developing sustained research on the relationships among these factors over time at specific sites; identifying ways in which population–land use–environment relationships depend on the scale at which observations are made and in which relationships at one scale affect processes at others; and developing some effectively functioning interdisciplinary research teams. Recent research has clarified how population effects depend not only on total numbers, but also on migration, household size, and other demographic variables. It has shown how the causes of change in forest cover look different depending on how secondary forest is treated in the analysis. Current research challenges include linking social with environmental data, collecting data at the appropriate levels of resolution, achieving comparability of data across sites and time, and moving from descriptive studies to ones that can reasonably be used for causal inference. Interdisciplinary collaboration remains a challenge despite the progress that has been made.

The Panel on New Research on Population and the Environment makes the following recommendations:

1. Research should be increasingly coordinated to promote creation of a body of integrated knowledge that links demographic, land use, and environmental variables and seeks to move beyond site-based observations toward the development of general knowledge. To accomplish such coordination,

• *Organizations that support population–land use–environment research should work with researchers to develop minimum reporting standards for data collected and analyzed in site-based studies.*

• *Individual projects should provide an inventory of important contextual variables for their study sites.*

• *Efforts should be made to coordinate definitions of variables measured and research designs chosen in different site-specific studies to enhance the creation of a body of integrated knowledge in the field.*

• *Research should be pursued at this time in two substantive areas that hold promise for building knowledge of generic processes—the study of new settlement ("frontier") areas and of regions of rapid urban (including suburban) development.*

2. Research should continue to decompose or "unpack" the complex, general phenomena of population, land use, and environment and examine causal relationships among their more specific component factors. Such refined analyses will improve understanding of the mechanisms and feedbacks that connect population, land use, and environment, clarify assumptions and theoretical structures, and facilitate interdisciplinary communication and integration. Population–environment research on land use should include research with a substantive focus on water because of the special importance of coastal and riparian regions to marine productivity, storm and flood impacts, and the transformation of wetland habitats.

3. Research should investigate the dynamic interactions involving population *and* land use *and* environmental variables, coupling all three classes of variables and remaining attentive to contextual factors that may influence these relationships.

4. Research should increasingly explore scale dependencies and cross-scale interactions. In particular:

• *Researchers focused on population–environment relationships should pay explicit attention to spatial, temporal, and social scale in framing their studies and offering explanations. They should be explicit about the scales at which they are working.* Research funders should use their influence to develop gridded approaches that can place local studies within spatial matrices and to encourage levels of temporal resolution (including of remotely sensed images) adequate to understanding dynamic processes.

• *Researchers should be encouraged to address explicitly the extent to which the population–land use–environment relationships they study vary by scale of analysis, how these scale dependencies may vary by place or time, and how relationships at one scale may influence those at another scale, for example, by using appropriate modeling techniques.*

5. Organizations that support population–land use–environment research should support and encourage continued development of linked data sets that include information about population, land use, and environmental variables and that are spatially explicit, multilevel, and longitudinal.

• *Continued investment should be made in existing linked longitudinal data sets and in developing similar datasets at new sites in understudied regions and in places that offer unique research opportunities.*

• *Continued investment is warranted in developing methods for data and process integration.*

• *Guidelines must be developed for use of linked data sets and for making data available to researchers beyond the original research team.*

6. Increased effort should be devoted to modeling and quantifying causal relationships among population, land use, and environment using a variety of approaches, as well as to analyzing uncertainties in models of these complex systems. Mathematical models have considerable value for addressing dynamic relationships of population, land use, and environment; for structuring discussion across disciplines; for identifying open questions; and for providing forecasts for policy analysis.

7. A research effort should be made to identify highly effective mechanisms to facilitate interdisciplinary research. Specifically, organizations that support population-environment research should support a systematic assessment of which approaches seem to result in the best and most rigorously trained young scholars in this field and the most productive research collaborations.

1

The State of Knowledge

Intellectual debate about the relationships between human population dynamics and natural resources goes back at least 200 years (Malthus, 1798, 1803; Lloyd, 1833). The most intense focus was on human demands on land because of the simple Malthusian argument that population growth would eventually outstrip the productive capacity of lands. Analysis of population–environment relationships became broader in the second half of the twentieth century, when recognition became widespread that human activity posed major environmental threats not only through land use, which among other effects can degrade the food-producing capacity of lands, but also through pollution resulting from industrial activities that supported economic growth. Among the landmarks in this broadening of focus were the arguments raised in the early 1970s by Ehrlich and colleagues (Ehrlich and Ehrlich, 1970; Ehrlich and Holdren, 1971) and in the "limits to growth" models of Meadows and colleagues (1972).

This newer thinking was broader not only in the range of environmental effects linked to population growth but also in its attention to the relationships among population growth and other factors, such as economic growth, technological development, and change in human institutions. A famous formulation of these relationships is the I = PAT or Kaya identity, which defined environmental impact as the product of total population (P); economic output per capita, or affluence (A); and all other human activities per unit of output (symbolized by T, for technology) (Holdren and Ehrlich, 1974). This identity became both controversial and potentially useful analytically when used as a model of the social forces that cause environmental degradation, or what later came to be called driving

7

forces of environmental change (National Research Council, 1990, 1992; for reviews of work using the equation analytically, see Dietz and Rosa, 1994; Chertow, 2001). Debates about the relative importance of population vis-à-vis other driving forces, about whether the effects of population growth are always negative, and about whether effects are uniform across settings were common in the 1970s and 1980s, but they have since largely receded from the scientific literature. Researchers' interests have focused increasingly on understanding the driving forces, including not only population, affluence, and technology, but also human values, social institutions, public policies, and more; their effects and interactions; the mechanisms by which they affect environmental outcomes; and feedbacks from environmental conditions to human activity. Just as demographic driving forces may lead to environmental outcomes in various ways, environmental conditions and changes may also influence population size, structure, and change.

By the early 1990s, human influences on the natural environment were understood to occur through two main processes: change in land cover and land use (including use of waters) and "industrial metabolism," that is, the transformation of materials and energy for industrial production and economic consumption (National Research Council, 1988, 1990). Population and other driving forces operate through these processes to generate specific outcomes that act as proximate causes of environmental change (National Research Council, 1992). Proximate causes tied to land use and land cover change include conversion of forests into agricultural lands, of farm fields and pastures to urban uses, and of wetlands to agricultural or urban uses, all of which transform habitats for nonhuman species and alter biogeochemical cycles. Industrial metabolism generates other proximate causes, including releases of phosphates and heavy metals into waterways and of nitrogen, sulfur, and carbon oxides into the atmosphere. Accordingly, research on population-environment relationships has been dominated by two rather distinct streams of work: one focusing on effects mediated by changes in land use or land cover, and another focusing on effects mediated by materials and energy transformations. Efforts to integrate both kinds of human influence have been far less common (e.g., Lutz, 1994; Curran et al., 2002; York, Rosa, and Dietz, 2003; Rosa, York, and Dietz, 2003).

SCOPE OF THIS BOOK

The limited resources available for this study have led us to select only part of this large field for coverage. This volume focuses on research in which change in land use or land cover is a key mediator of human–environment interactions, in which demographic variables figure prominently among the driving forces investigated, and in which efforts are made to investigate the causal mechanisms by which human population changes affect land use and environmental outcomes. Clearly, this is only part of a large and complex picture in which institutions, public policies, market conditions, technological changes, and other factors also figure. In the conceptual framework developed for the Millennium Ecosystem Assessment, for instance, changes in land use and land cover figure among the "direct drivers" affecting ecosystem services, demographic factors among the "indirect drivers" (Alcamo, Bennett, and the Millennium Ecosystem Assessment Project, 2003). The chain of causality leading from population to land use to environmental effect that is of primary interest in this volume is embedded in the Millennium Ecosystem Assessment framework, although the main focus of that assessment is on ecosystems services and human well-being rather than any particular strand of interconnected effects.

Population–land use–environment relationships have great environmental significance, both locally and globally. Human activity has changed the face of the Earth, particularly in the past few hundred years, with major environmental consequences. About 50 percent of the Earth's land surface has been transformed by direct human action, mainly for farming, pasturing, and forestry, and also for industry, urban development, and transport (Turner et al., 1990; Steffen et al., 2004). More than half of all accessible fresh water is used directly or indirectly by humankind, and ancient and often nonrenewable underground water resources are being depleted rapidly in many areas (Gleick, 1999, 2003). Human use of land and fresh water has transformed global precipitation regimes and altered ecosystems worldwide, reducing the diversity of the world's biota and affecting the overall ability of the biosphere to sustain life (Steffen et al., 2004; Vitousek et al., 1997a). Intensification and diversification of land use, together with advances in technology, have also led to rapid changes in the global cycles of carbon, nitrogen, and other critical elements (Melillo, Field, and Moldan, 2002). More nitrogen is now fixed synthetically and applied as fertilizers in agriculture than is fixed naturally in all terrestrial ecosystems, resulting in fundamental ecological changes in lakes and rivers and in leaching of other nutrients from soils (Vitousek et al., 1997b). Land use change, mainly through its effects on the global carbon and nitrogen cycles, is also responsible for a significant proportion of the phenomenon of global climatic change (National Research Council, 1992).

Demographic factors, including population growth, density, fertility, mortality, and the age and sex composition of households, are known to be important influences on land use and land cover change. Human migration, including shifts from rural to urban areas, movements between countries for economic or political reasons, and large-scale planned resettlements, as in Amazônia and Indonesia, also significantly affect land cover and land use. Although overall population numbers are sometimes strongly related to land cover changes, such as deforestation (Allen and Barnes, 1985), recent research shows that this overall relationship depends on many factors, including land settlement policies and market forces (Geist and Lambin, 2002), cultural and institutional factors, and characteristics of the biophysical environment itself. In other words, the impacts of demographic factors need to be understood in the context of other drivers of land use and land cover change. Moreover, some of these factors affecting land use and the environment also influence demographic variables. For example, land tenure can affect fertility at the household level, with more secure tenure (all else being equal) resulting in lower fertility rates (Moran, 1993; Bilsborrow, 1994). Thus, the relationships among demographic changes, changes in land use and management, and the states, properties, and functions of environmental systems are complex (Alcamo et al., 2003; Turner et al., 2003a). They are also matters of scientific and practical interest (e.g., Kates et al., 2001; National Research Council, 1999a, 1999b).

The land use branch of population-environment research has received more attention in recent years than the industrial metabolism branch (Pebley 1998).[1] Over the past decade, catalyzed in part by an international land use/land cover research program (Turner et al., 1995; Lambin et al., 1999) and organized programs of research support from the National Institute of Child Health and Human Development (NICHD), the John D. and Catherine T. MacArthur Foundation, the William and Flora Hewlett Foundation, the National Aeronautic and Space Administration (NASA), and some other sources, significant progress has been made in understanding the land use connection between population and environment. Site-based studies, in particular, have flourished over the past decade. These studies, as well as the broader field, have set the foundation for even more progress to be made. The connections between population, land use, and environment have been identified as an area in which significant research gains are expected over the next decade (National Research Council, 1999a, 2002).

Much of the recent research devoted to identifying causal mechanisms and processes has examined changes in population characteristics, land uses, and environmental conditions over time at specific sites. This volume

---

[1]One reason for limited research attention to processes linking demographic and other human variables to environmental consequences through production and consumption of industrial products has been the absence of targeted funding for this research in the United States. Industrial metabolism has become a focus of interest in the engineering field (see, e.g., Williams, Larson, and Ross, 1987; National Academy of Engineering, 1994; Graedel and Allenby, 1995; National Research Council, 2004b), but much less has been done to integrate social scientific analysis (however, see, e.g., National Research Council, 1984, 1997; Grossman and Krueger, 1995; York, Rosa, and Dietz, 2003; Rosa, York, and Dietz, 2003).

focuses heavily, although not exclusively, on these site-based studies, especially those integrating multiple methodologies and perspectives. Research that fully incorporates population *and* land use *and* environment must cross disciplines—indeed, it must cross the social and natural sciences. Focusing on a specific site is one approach to achieving this integration. In addition, site-specific studies have been a particular emphasis of research supported by the population-environment programs of the sponsors of this study. For these reasons, we have looked closely at site-specific studies and also other studies that have tried to clarify the mechanisms linking demographic variables, land use change, and environmental outcomes. The notion of demographic factors as driving forces suggests one-way causation, and indeed the primary emphasis in many studies has been on the effects of human activities on environmental variables, including research undertaken as part of the Intergovernmental Panel on Climate Change (Fischer and O'Neill, Chapter 3) and the Millennium Ecosystem Assessment (Alcamo et al., 2003). Feedbacks from environmental variables to demographic and land use change are also important, although less studied.

The panel organized a workshop in Irvine, California, on January 14-15, 2004, at which we discussed the insights from research on population-land use–environment interactions and the challenges of conducting this kind of research with researchers in the field. We invited representatives of several research programs that included both natural scientists and social scientists to prepare papers summarizing the progress of their programs and the challenges they confronted in doing their research. Revised versions of the papers appear as appendixes to this volume. We selected researchers who would provide a variety of intellectual perspectives; diversity in focus by world region, level of economic development, and rural or urban setting; and representation of individuals whose initial research questions were primarily environmental and others whose initial questions were primarily demographic. Most of the research discussed at the workshop was site-focused, but also discussed global-level modeling issues to enhance discussions of issues of scale, modeling, and causal analysis.

This volume takes stock of the progress that has been made in understanding population–land use–environment linkages and causal mechanisms to see what has been learned, to identify gaps and problems that remain, and to develop a set of recommendations for future research. It is worth noting that we have emphasized scientific criteria for making our recommendations rather than criteria of practical importance. Thus, we have recommended research directions that would strengthen knowledge of the ways that demographic and land use variables affect environmental conditions, but we have not offered judgments on which environmental conditions are most worthy of this kind of analysis or which areas of research are most likely to yield results of practical importance in the near term. Our review and recommendations complement other efforts, such as the Millennium Ecosystem Assessment, for which the goal is to inform the decisions of policy makers as they might affect ecosystems (Alcamo et al., 2003:12).

This chapter provides a synthetic overview of progress in population–land use-environment research over the past decade, showing the current state of knowledge, the areas of rapid development, and the major challenges for research. Chapter 2 presents our conclusions and recommendations for further development of research on the population–land use–environment relationships that are our focus. The main audiences for our recommendations are researchers working in the field and the sponsors of their research. We have not made recommendations for research on other questions of human–environment interaction. In particular, we have not offered recommendations for research on population–environment relationships that are mediated by industrial production or consumption, despite the obvious importance of the topic, nor for research on the connections between land use and industrial metabolism as they affect population–environment relationships.

AREAS OF RESEARCH PROGRESS

A useful reference point for the present work is a volume published a little more than a decade ago, *Population and Land Use in Developing Countries* (National Research Council, 1993), which summarized the state of science at that time. It addressed one major question: What are the effects of population growth on land use change? It focused on one aspect of human demography (population growth) and concentrated on a subset of land use changes associated with expansion of agriculture. The potential environmental consequences of land use change, a strong motivator for the workshop that produced the volume, were addressed by some of the participants. At the end of the workshop, the participants identified two key areas in which research was needed (Jolly and Torrey, 1993). One was to develop better and more detailed data, over time, on population and land use variables. The other was for case studies that clearly analyze the roles of the various factors, such as property rights institutions, market conditions, and soil and climate characteristics, that condition population–land use relationships. It was expected that such studies could explain why population growth does not have uniform effects on the land and help develop a causal understanding of population–land use relationships. Research since then has made progress in these and other directions (e.g., O'Neill, MacKellar, and Lutz, 2001; Lutz, Prskawetz, and Sanderson, 2002). In the process, it has opened up additional areas of inquiry.

Unpacking Concepts

A major area of progress over the past decade has been in adding nuance to earlier arguments about population–environment relationships. Some of this research is "unpacking" or decomposing broad concepts of population, land use, and environment into more refined elements and thereby producing deeper understandings.

Knowing that population size, density, or growth is associated with land use change and environmental change is just the beginning of analysis (e.g., Fischer and O'Neill, Chapter 3). For example, population growth might be caused by natural increase, a surplus of births over deaths, or migration. The former was a major focus of research for many years, in part due to high fertility in many parts of the world combined with dramatic decreases in death rates after World War II. Indeed, much of the early work was at the national level, where natural increase dominates as a component of population growth (e.g., Allen and Barnes, 1985). More recent work has focused subnationally, where the role of migration in population change is likely to be particularly pronounced.

Researchers investigated a series of hypotheses regarding effects of fertility on land use in rural areas dependent on subsistence agriculture: that larger families require more food in order to subsist when children are young, have more labor with which to cultivate land when children are older but still living in the home household, and require more land when children grow up and need a place of their own to farm (i.e., the developmental cycle of domestic groups; see Goody, 1958, 1976). Households may adjust to increasing family size and subsistence needs in a variety of ways (Bilsborrow, 1987; Davis, 1963), including enlarging the area under cultivation (e.g., Cruz, 1996; Mortimore, 1993; Paulson, 1994; Pichon, 1993, 1997; Pichon and Bilsborrow, 1999; Umezaki et al., 2000) or putting pressure on lands held in common (e.g., Axinn, Barbar, and Biddlecom, 2002; Foster et al., 2003, Shivakoti et al., 1999). They may also adjust by intensifying land use. Societies dependent on swidden agriculture may increase frequency of cultivation, thereby reducing fallow time. Studies found a correlation between fertility-driven high rates of population growth and shortened periods of fallow (Saikia, 1998; Umezaki et al., 2000). Increasing frequency of cultivation was of particular interest to Chayanov (1966) and to Boserup (1965), who first developed a theory of intensification. Intensification may occur in many ways, including multiple cropping; use of fertilizers, pesticides, herbicides, and high-productivity seeds; and improved irrigation.

A notable feature of recent research is increased analytic attention to migration as a component of population growth and change. Migrations can have a substantial impact on land use (United Nations Population

Fund, 2001). These effects arise not only from relatively permanent migrations to frontiers (e.g., Gutmann et al., Chapter 4; Moran, Brondizio, and VanWey, Chapter 5; Walsh et al., Chapter 6) or to urbanizing areas (Redman, Chapter 7; Seto, Chapter 8), but also from shorter term and more temporary movements. Examples of the latter include "floating workers" in China (Seto, Chapter 8), seasonal and circular migrants in Thailand (Walsh et al., Chapter 6), tourists (Liu et al., Chapter 9), and commuters. There is also the issue of possible environmental effects of policy-driven migrations, often aimed at replacing indigenous peoples, as in forced migrations or population dilutions of such peoples in North America in the nineteenth century and in the Soviet Union, Tibet, and elsewhere in the twentieth. These policy interventions tend to replace adapted indigenous land use systems with ones imported from other ecological zones. On long time scales, migration can have substantial impacts through land use on the environment (Gutmann et al., Chapter 4). Recent studies are showing how a more nuanced treatment of migration gives better understanding than simple analyses of population numbers.

Research has also expanded to include population effects on coastal and marine as well as terrestrial ecosystems. Demographic changes are increasingly affecting the environment through human migration to coastal areas. During the past 50 years, there has been a dramatic increase in human migration to coastal zones, related urbanization of many coastal areas, increased linkages between coastal and inland populations, and a transformation in the use and management of coastal and marine resources. A recent set of studies completed under the John D. and Catherine T. MacArthur Foundation Program on Population, Consumption, and Environment focused on these ecosystems (*Ambio* Vol. 31, Number 4, 2002). Migration as a driving factor has been a major focus of this research, which has also addressed governance institutions for such common pool resources as productive estuaries, as well as policy interventions, for example to promote shrimp aquaculture (McCay and Acheson, 1987; Ostrom, 1990; National Research Council, 2002; Matson et al., Chapter 10; Seto, Chapter 8).

Another shift in research focus is increasing attention to households. Changes in fertility, mortality, marriage, and migration have produced smaller households in many parts of the world. The detailed impact of household and family dynamics on land use and the environment is increasingly well understood (Galvin et al., 2002; Moran et al., Chapter 5; Walsh et al., Chapter 6; Liu et al., Chapter 9). In some contexts, growth in the number of households is at least as important as growth in the number of persons (MacKellar et al., 1995; Liu et al., 2003). There is some evidence from various sites that the number of households and their composition in terms of family cycle or life course significantly influences land use and environmental change (Moran et al., Chapter 5; Walsh et al., Chapter 6). The more complete the understanding of households and their dynamics, the better one will understand and be able to predict the associated change in land use and the environment.

Unpacking the concept of land use has also been productive. Land use and land cover are typically organized into a small number of major classes (e.g., urban or rural; forest, cropland, desert, tundra, water; permeable or impermeable surface). Finer distinctions can be very informative, however. For example, uses of space may differ greatly, even in seemingly uniform urban or rural settings (Redman, Chapter 7). Areas classified as uniformly urban in fact have widely differing intensities of population and land use within them (Grove et al., 2004; Pickett et al., 2001; Redman, Chapter 7; Weeks, Larson, and Fugate, Chapter 11). A given area revealed in remote-sensing data as containing little or no permeable surface might consist mainly of low-density uses, such as single-family or small multifamily dwellings, or it might be covered by high-density housing or nonresidential office, manufacturing, service, or commercial facilities. Each of these land uses has its own signature in terms of population composition and environmental impacts. Similarly, an area that appears as uniformly rural may include dispersed or clustered settlement; also, it may have large areas of undifferentiated habitat or be divided up into a multitude of tiny patches. These differences can be closely tied to both population and environmental variables (Kaufman and Marsh, 1997). For instance, tree cover may be primary forest or secondary forest (Moran and Ostrom, 2005), with different implications for biodiversity loss. The variation in land uses within major classes suggests the importance of developing similarly nuanced classification systems for remote imaging based on efforts to identify spectral signatures for land use types that correspond to systematic variations observed on the ground.

In much of the early research on population and land use, little attention was given to environmental outcomes beyond those involving land cover. Recent research is beginning to specify environmental variables in much more detail. For example, in this volume, Matson and colleagues (Chapter 10) describe a complex study of two interconnected ecosystems in the Yaqui Valley (in Sonora State, Mexico), one an inland wheat-growing region and the other a coastal area devoted to shrimp aquaculture. The project is particularly strong in documenting the effects of land use change on the environment, for instance, the consequences of agricultural intensification in the form of increasing fertilizer inputs for the functioning of both the surface water systems draining the valley and for the coastal ecosystems of the Sea of Cortez. The study makes clear that population growth is both cause and consequence of land use change, but the population–land use connection is not developed in detail.

The Yaqui Valley study also illustrates the added value of decomposing broadly defined population, land use, and environment variables into more refined ones. This study was able to identify fertilizer runoff as a key mechanism driving environmental impacts. For anyone concerned with alleviating these impacts, the study suggests that it might be more productive to address the issue of fertilizer application directly than to focus on birth rates, human settlement patterns, or even rates of land conversion to agriculture. Such conclusions can be only tentative, though, in the absence of research that considers the roles of all these factors together.

At present, research that completely bridges population, land use, and environment is rare. Most studies have focused either on connections between population and land use, with environment relatively deemphasized, or on connections between land use and environment, with population relatively deemphasized. This is true of all of the studies included in this volume.

Site-Based Studies

Researchers have responded to the call in *Population and Land Use in Developing Countries* (National Research Council, 1993) for better and more detailed data by conducting detailed and sustained studies at many sites around the world. As the authorized chapters in this volume illustrate, such studies have been a major source of scientific progress over the past decade. They have carefully collected and analyzed multilevel, longitudinal, and spatially explicit data on population, land use, and environmental processes for specific localities, large and small (Galvin et al., 2002; Gutmann et al., Chapter 4; Matson et al., Chapter 10; Moran et al., 1994, 2003, Chapter 5; Walsh et al., Chapter 6; Redman, Chapter 7; Thornton et al., 2003; Turner, Geoghegan, and Foster, 2004). Over time, as the breadth, depth, and detail of these studies has grown, the study sites have come to represent "microcosms" (Matson et al., Chapter 10) and "laboratories" (Entwisle et al., 1998) for the interdisciplinary study of social and environmental change. The addition of new data over time as projects have extended and expanded their purviews has greatly enhanced the value of the overall data sets.

Although site-specific studies have become much more common, the studies are uneven in terms of the world regions, types of population and land use changes, and institutional and environmental contexts they cover. In terms of regional representation, the studies represent Asian and Latin American settings better than African and Middle Eastern ones, although of course there are exceptions (e.g., Weeks et al., Chapter 11; Tiffen, Mortimore, and Gichuki, 1994; Turner, Hyden, and Kates, 1993; Geist and Lambin, 2002; Laney, 2002; Galvin et al., 2002). Also, although the balance is shifting, it remains the case that rural settings are better represented than urban and urbanizing ones, shifts from one type of land use to another more frequently dealt with than changes within types, and terrestrial ecosystems more than coastal and marine ones.

Scale

Site-based studies vary considerably in their scale. The concept of scale can be confusing because it has at least two distinct meanings. In one meaning, scale is a study's coverage or extent. A study of the U.S. Great Plains over more than a century (e.g., Gutmann et al., Chapter 4) has a broader spatial and temporal scale in this sense than a study of metropolitan Phoenix over 30 years (Redman, Chapter 7). In another meaning, scale corresponds to the unit of analysis or level of organization. In this meaning, studies that analyze data on countries or major subnational political divisions (e.g., Fischer and O'Neill, Chapter 3; Gutmann et al., Chapter 4) work at a larger scale than studies that use data on individuals or households (e.g., Moran, et al., Chapter 5; Walsh et al., Chapter 6).

Often, these two meanings of scale go together. Thus, studies at local levels frequently involve research on small decision-making units, such as individuals or households, and small land units, such as plots. Regional and national studies are often concerned with larger units, such as counties. Studies of individuals or households typically cover relatively short temporal scales, often 5 or 10 years, at most 20 or 30 years. Studies of counties, states, or provinces may cover a century or more (Gutmann et al., Chapter 4). Increasingly, studies are departing from the norm in which coverage matches units of analysis. For instance, there are studies of individuals and households that are national in scope (Foster, Chapter 12). There are studies of pixels covering fractions of a square kilometer (km^2) that track seasonal and annual variation in land cover over long periods of time (Walsh et al., Chapter 6; Redman, Chapter 7) and of villages that extend back at annual time steps 50 years or more (Entwisle et al., 2004).

The studies in this volume indicate that current research represents a broad range in terms of spatial coverage and level of organization. They range from intensive studies of small sites such as Nang Rong district in Thailand (1,300 km^2), the Wolong Nature Reserve in China (2,000 km^2), and the development areas along the road in Altimira in the Brazilian Amazon (3,800 km^2); to larger ecologically defined areas such as the Yaqui Valley in Mexico (23,500 km^2 in the irrigated area), the Red River Delta in Vietnam (16,000 km^2), and the Pearl River Delta in China (26,000 km^2); to large metropolitan areas (Cairo, Phoenix); to very large ecologically defined areas (the U.S. Great Plains); to countries (India, China); to the entire world. As studies of broader coverage begin to use data at finer levels of analysis, it becomes possible for research to address the question of whether phenomena that are visible at large scales appear the same at lower levels of analysis. This question is important because generalizations across spatial scales are difficult and often flawed.

The studies in this volume also illustrate the variety in current research with respect to units of analysis in space and time. Social science data may be analyzed for individuals, households, villages or neighborhoods, districts or counties, a region, or countries as a whole. Spatial data may be analyzed at the observational levels of pixels and scenes; at ecological levels of plots, ecosystems, communities, and landscapes; by socially defined spatial units, such as field plots and village territories; or in environmentally defined units, such as watersheds and bioregions. Temporal analysis may involve observations daily, weekly, seasonally, annually, or at longer intervals. Often practical constraints dictate choices about the spatial or temporal resolution of observations. Resolution is often equivalent to the level of analysis because studies at finer levels of analysis (e.g., individual, plot) require data at those levels of social and spatial resolution. But studies at coarser levels of analysis may use coarser or finer resolution data. For example, a national-level study might use census or survey data on individuals and aggregate them to local, regional, or national levels for analysis. Similarly, a study that covers a century might use frequently collected (i.e., high temporal resolution) environmental data at the highest available resolution, or it might use averages for each decade.

Scale Dependence and Cross-Scale Interactions

Population–land use–environment relationships exhibit scale dependence; that is, relationships observed at one level of analysis often look quite different when analyzed at a different level. For example, Walsh et al. (1999, 2001) examined the relationships of a measure of landscape greenness (a vegetation index derived from remotely sensed data) to population and environment variables measured at multiple spatial scales and organized within a geographical information system (GIS), to identify social and biophysical processes that affect landscape conditions and spatial structure at fine to coarse scales. They compared the strength of relationships measured at pixel sizes ranging from 30 to 1,000 m. Relationships between landscape greenness and sociodemographic variables were strongest at the finest resolution. The reverse was true of relationships between landscape greenness and biophysical variables. Other studies, however, have found that population variables are more prominent at increasingly large scales (e.g., Meyer and Turner, 1992; Geist and Lambin, 2002). Because there is little overlap in the scales examined between the Walsh study and the others, it is difficult to compare the results. But they demonstrate the phenomenon of scale dependence and some of the research questions it raises. Research that includes local studies in probability samples of a larger spatial units might help explain phenomena of scale dependence, but very little research of this type has been done to date.

Temporal scale dependencies are also being discovered as more and more studies are including a substantial historical component. Many in this volume cover 30 years or more. Studies of the U.S. Great Plains by Gutmann and his colleagues (Chapter 4) covering more than a century since the opening of this frontier to European settlement underscore the importance of decadal and longer cycles of rainfall to human patterns of migration, economic development, and water use. These relationships cannot be seen with shorter temporal coverage because the data do not include sufficient environmental variation. Conversely, analysis at finer temporal scales can reveal aspects of population–environment interactions that do not stand out in, and could not be fully understood from, coarser scale analysis. For example, the dramatic social, economic, and land use changes of the mid-1930s in the U.S. Great Plains resulted from specific environmental events during a brief period that were more extreme than anything else experienced in the twentieth century (Gutmann and Cunfer, 1999) Studies of long temporal scale are often difficult, however, because the farther back one goes, the thinner and more unreliable the records become. Such studies might benefit from collaboration with archeologists or natural scientists, who may be able to retrieve relevant data from artifacts, tree rings, or other nonstandard historical sources.

Phenomena at one scale often influence those at other scales, in cross-scale interactions that may not be evident in research that examines phenomena at only a single social, spatial, or temporal level of analysis. For example, by focusing on households, a researcher accepts the household as the unit of decision making and, unless special provisions are made in the design of the data and analysis, forgoes possibilities to learn about the effects of decisions by other units, such as the family, the firm, or policy-making units from the local to the national level. Nevertheless, choices by large organizations and in the design of social institutions are exceedingly important, are structured differently from individual or household decision making, and have consequences for decision making at lower levels of social aggregation that are unlikely to become visible by studying the lower levels alone. In this cross-scale interaction, higher level social units form part of the context for decisions by lower units. When such phenomena exist, population–land use–environment relationships that hold in a particular site may be conditional on the larger social (and environmental) context and may not generalize to other sites. Matson and her colleagues (Chapter 10) provide an analysis that reveals cross-scale interactions in the environmental and policy domains. They have carefully considered context in their analyses of land use and land cover change in the Yaqui Valley, including the impact of climate (e.g., a recent prolonged drought), the consequences of an earlier white fly infestation, and the implications of policy change in Mexico (e.g., establishment of the *ejido* system of land reform under the Mexican constitution) and internationally (the North American Free Trade Agreement). Social institutions, particularly institutions for governing human–environment interactions, have long been recognized as important mediating factors between individual human behavior and larger scale environmental systems. Their mediating role is partly dependent on the size and dynamics of the human populations using particular environmental systems (e.g., Blaikie and Brookfield, 1987; Wade, 1988; Ostrom, 1990; Baland and Platteau, 1996; National Research Council, 2002).

Issues of scale dependence and cross-scale interaction have been described in other work on human–environment interactions (e.g., Vayda, 1983; Palloni, 1994; Gibson, Ostrom, and Ahn, 1998; Young, 2002; Alcamo et al., 2003). Research on population–land use–environment relationships provides many good test beds for understanding these issues. When key aspects of context change, especially when they change dramatically, there are opportunities to study their impact in a site-based study. When they do not change, however, it is not possible to understand such contextual effects through studies conducted in a single site. Comparisons across studies can begin to reveal them, if the data are sufficiently comparable (examples of comparative analysis can be found in Moran and Ostrom, 2005).

Linking Social and Environmental Data

Research on population–land use–environment relationships depends on integration of social and environmental features at the appropriate social, spatial, and temporal scales, and equally important, appropriate linkages of processes that cross sectoral components of the coupled human–environment system. Such integration has been difficult, although progress has been significant during the past decade (National Research Council, 1998; Fox et al., 2003; Moran and Ostrom, 2005). Much progress has been made possible through the use of GIS tools, in which data on population, land use, and environment can be connected by coding them spatially. However, there is no definitive one-to-one link among population units, land use units, and relevant environmental units.

Over the past decade, analysts have made progress linking population and land units, as well as land units and environmental units, in some contexts. For example, households might be linked to field plots in areas where household impacts on land use are mainly through the plots they farm (Moran et al., Chapter 5; Walsh et al., Chapter 6). Villages can be readily linked to village territories (Walsh et al., Chapter 6; Foster, Chapter 12), as can larger administrative units, such as counties be linked to their territories (Fischer and O'Neill, Chapter 3; Gutmann et al., Chapter 4), although an administratively defined territory may or may not correspond to the land owned, used, or linked in some other way to the individuals and households that live in those units. With effort, pixels can be linked to landscapes, watersheds, or ecosystems, and to political boundaries (Redman, Chapter 7; Seto, Chapter 8; Matson et al., Chapter 10). There is no straightforward cross-step all the way across the population–land use–environment nexus, however. One difficulty arises when multiple units in each domain are relevant to multiple units in other domains, such as when a household includes members who work nearby lands and other members who have temporarily migrated to find work.

The challenge of linking people to land and to environmental conditions is particularly difficult when the populations responsible for changes in land and environment are linked to them through global markets, as with hardwoods, cash crops such as coffee, and the products of aquaculture. It is possible to measure environmental changes at the place where they are visible, as in ecological indicator systems, or to attribute them to the places where consumer or industrial demand acts to bring them about, as is done with indicators like the "ecological footprint" (Wackernagel and Rees, 1996; Wackernagel et al., 2002; Parris and Kates, 2003). So far there is no reliable way to do both at once: to locate the environmental footprint of one country or city on the map of another country. Certain land–environment links are similarly difficult to make when land use changes result in nonlinear responses affecting feedbacks though ecosystems or global environmental systems, such as changes in ecosystem state following fire or flood that affect methane emissions, or community or biodiversity changes that alter pathways of carbon sequestration.

Data Collection

Available data sources do not always provide information at the appropriate resolution for addressing researchers' questions. For example, decadal censuses provide valuable sources of information about population size and structure, but they are limited in important ways relevant to understanding population–land use–environment interactions. One problem is the decadal level of temporal resolution: important population changes occur over much shorter intervals, as pointed out in several papers in this volume (e.g., Seto, Chapter 8; Matson et al., Chapter 10; Weeks et al., Chapter 11). Decadal censuses do a particularly poor job tracking in- and out-migration, focusing instead on net migration (the difference between in-flow and out-flow). Information on net migration is useful, but low levels of net migration may hide substantial rates of turnover: "For every stream, there is a counterstream" is a truism of migration research. Furthermore, censuses are not good sources of information about seasonal, circular, and other forms of short-term migration, nor do they generally include questions about commuting or other forms of local mobility. Because of these problems, researchers are designing and collecting their own data in the form of multilevel, longitudinal, and spatially explicit surveys designed to address an evolving set of specific questions. Surveys have the capability of measuring change at multiple levels of observation, over short as well as longer periods of time.

There are also challenges in measuring land use change and environmental outcomes. For instance, there are fairly well-established methods for measuring land cover from remote observations at the level of major classifications (e.g., forest, agricultural, urban) (Skole et al., 1994; Loveland et al., 1991), but the capability to measure finer differences in land cover (e.g., levels of intensity of agriculture, degrees of urbanization) is still under development. Weeks and colleagues (Chapter 11) propose a satellite-based approach to measuring neighborhood-level variation in urban land cover that combines information about the composition and spatial configuration of pixels within census tracts to describe an urban gradient in Cairo, Egypt. Seto (Chapter 8) describes the inability to find a single model that could classify land cover adequately for several adjacent Landsat scenes in the Red River Delta of Vietnam, as well as the need to analyze each scene individually. Yet through use of intensive field studies, it has been possible to distinguish between stages of secondary succession in the Brazilian Amazon (Moran et al., 1994; Moran and Brondizio, 1998).

Another challenge is to make full use of the historical detail in time series available in remote images, which typically have much higher temporal resolution than censuses, land surveys, or social surveys. By analyzing data from multiple sequential images, much can potentially be learned about social and environmental dynamics following a perturbation to the system. Contributors to this volume describe two possible approaches. One is the application of life course principles (Elder, 1998; Rindfuss, 1991) to an analysis of pixel or plot trajectories (McCracken et al., 1999; Walsh et al., Chapter 6; Redman, Chapter 7). The other is the application of econometric methods designed for the analysis of time series of multidimensional social data to a time series of classified images (Seto, Chapter 8). Both approaches incorporate social science methods into the analysis of satellite-based observations, thus illustrating a potential benefit of cross-fertilization of fields. Historical analysis is also possible by quantifying land surface changes, although it is difficult to link changes in an ecosystem to associated biogeochemical and biodiversity characteristics.

Comparability of Data

Researchers on population–land use–environment relationships typically investigate questions that flow from their interests and the attributes
of their sites. They have usually found their own ways to measure the
variables of interest because coherent global databases on land use or on
the demographic and environmental variables of interest to the research
groups do not exist at the relevant levels of analysis. Thus, ensuring comparability of data on the same variables from different sites is an important
challenge in developing general knowledge from multiple site-based studies
(for an example of an effort to meet these challenges, see National Research
Council, 2001b). In principle, such comparable data might come from
space platforms, but these data must be analyzed in different ways to
address different research questions and to fit the important land use and
land cover changes under way in specific contexts. Moreover, the proper
interpretation of spectral information in terms of phenomena on the ground
is not the same everywhere on Earth (e.g., Seto, Chapter 8; Campbell,
2002). Researchers have been creative in developing their own databases.
The difficulty of this work, and also its value, is illustrated in the papers
included in this volume.

This strategy of data development has advantages and limitations.
It has yielded considerable knowledge about population–land use–
environment processes at a number of sites around the world and, as
projects have evolved over time, the breadth, depth, and detail of the data
have evolved as well. However, what has been learned may not be comparable across sites. The issues of contingency and cross-scale interaction
have already been noted. Population–land use–environment relationships
depend on levels of technology, formal and informal institutions, local,
national, and international markets, policies, and the natural environment.
These relationships are likely to vary from site to site. In addition, there is
no assurance that the same variable, or the same relationship between
variables, has precisely the same meaning from one research site to the next.
Indeed, samples may be very differently constructed. Some studies begin
with land (e.g., Moran et al., 1994, 2003, Chapter 5; Messina and Walsh,
2001), whereas others begin with administrative or social units, such as
villages or households (Walsh et al., Chapter 6; Foster, Chapter 12). Starting point matters. If one draws a sample of land units, for example field
plots, except under unusual circumstances the owners of those plots will
yield a biased sample of households associated with those plots. Landless
households will be excluded, as will absentee landlords. Samples based on
land units can be generalized to populations of land units but not necessarily to populations of households or other social units. The reverse is also
true. If one draws a sample of, for example, villages, land associated with

these villages is likely to be a biased sample of all land. Thus, an estimate of forested land based only on land located in and around villages would probably be inaccurate. Places where people have chosen not to settle would be excluded.

Methods for sampling land and people simultaneously are under development (e.g., Moran et al., Chapter 5), but until these are in widespread use, it will be important to keep starting point in mind when generalizing the results of any particular study. This fact creates serious problems for building a knowledge base that holds across sites and for clarifying the role of contextual conditions as explanations of observed population–land use–environment relationships. It also makes difficult any effort to address questions of scale dependence and cross-scale interaction. The growing number of detailed and sustained site-based studies represents an unparalleled collection of resources for better understanding population processes, land use change, and environmental determinants and consequences. The value of these resources will not be maximized if only a small core of investigators use the data.

One effort to share data between the social and biological sciences appears in the framework adopted by the Long-Term Ecological Research (LTER) Network for core social data (Redman et al., 2004), which prescribes six general areas of social and demographic data to parallel the five core areas of ecological data that the network has long espoused. Another effort, used in the Baltimore Ecosystem Study LTER project, developed several categories of data for characterizing the physical, biological, and socioeconomic components of an ecosystem occupied, built, or managed by people. Important features of this framework include attention to institutional structures, different kinds of capital and infrastructure, and the capacity for self-reflection and learning (Grove and Burch, 1997). In addition, data distribution clearinghouses now exist, such as the Consortium for International Earth Science Information Network and the Inter-University Consortium for Political and Social Research, where scientists can deposit their data and other scientists can access them. If data are to be shared, however, great care must be taken to protect the confidentiality of information about human subjects, who may be at risk. Great scientific value derives from the ability to link social survey data to spatial and environmental coverages in a geographic information system, but socio-spatial links reveal respondents' local communities, and sometimes their households, of residence (Rindfuss et al., 2002).

TOWARD CAUSAL UNDERSTANDING

The earlier volume *Population and Land Use in Developing Countries* (National Research Council, 1993) identified the need to conduct case studies that examine population–land use relationships in relation to markets, property rights regimes, and other factors that may affect these relationships. This approach is a useful way to build the needed causal understanding. Since then, three major kinds of research have been advancing the field in the direction of the needed causal understanding: detailed descriptive studies of change at specific sites, regression-based statistical analyses of change processes, and studies that emphasize mathematical modeling. Research has also begun to examine scale dependencies, cross-scale interactions, thresholds, and feedbacks. These complexities are at the heart of the methodological challenges researchers face.[2]

Descriptive Studies

Careful documentation and descriptive analysis have played a key role in the development of the field over the past decade. Studies that break down population, land use, and environment into their more specific component factors have yielded better evidence of the mechanisms that connect change in each of the three subjects with the others, as well as better understanding of the complex interactions between them (see Cadwallader, 1988). For example, Moran and his colleagues were able to distinguish between the land use practices of households in different settlement cohorts in the Altamira site on the Lower Xingu Basin in the Brazilian Amazon. They linked the developmental stages of households to particular land use strategies: young households focused on production for food needs quickly convert forest for the cultivation of staple crops; as households accumulate capital and labor, they expand into other activities, such as cattle ranching and cash crops; as children become adults, households begin to shift toward productive uses that require less labor. These stages are visible in distinctive trajectories of deforestation and land use that the researchers call the colonist footprint (Brondizio et al., 2002; McCracken et al., 1999; Moran et al., Chapter 5). These observations are an important starting point for explanation, which then would need to consider potential age, period, and cohort effects, various combinations of which could account for the observed patterns. Descriptive research has the capability to expose, or unpack, the assumptions and theoretical structures that researchers in each specialty use and has promoted the integration across disciplines necessary to understand the three-way linkage among population, land use, and environment (Pickett et al., 1999).

---

[2]A useful review of methodological issues in determining the causes of land use change (Rindfuss et al., 2004) appeared in print as this book was being completed.

Regression-Based Statistical Analyses

Significant progress has been made over the past decade by using statistical techniques of regression analysis on data sets that integrate satellite-based measures and survey data or that integrate population data into spatial data sets. Almost every chapter contributed to this volume describes an analysis that incorporates both satellite and survey or census-based measurement. None of the studies published in the 1993 volume did this.

Many of the findings reported in this volume are based on statistical regression analysis. For instance, Foster (Chapter 12) describes a study of forest cover in India. Observing a recent increase in the amount of forest cover in the territories around rural villages, Foster and colleagues (2003) evaluated competing explanations for this trend using a regression approach that related changes in agricultural productivity, population, and wages to changes in forest cover. The analysis led the authors to conclude that the growth in forest around villages was largely driven by demand for wood and paper at the national level coupled with trade barriers that discouraged the importation of these products. This is an example of a cross-scale interaction, in which economic demand and policies enacted at the national level affect relationships within and between villages.

Studies based on quantitative statistical analyses have so far stopped short of fully considering population-environment interactions as a complex system, and particularly the feedbacks from environment to population. Virtually always, population has been treated as exogenous to land use change and environmental impact. Yet there is little reason to believe that this assumption is valid. For instance, numerous studies have examined the impact of frontier living on fertility (e.g., Easterlin, 1976; Van-Landingham and Hirschman, 2001) and the size of landholdings on number of children born (*Genus*, 2002; Cain, 1985; Maglad, 1994; Stokes et al., 1986). There is also quite a bit of research on relationships between the environmental characteristics of areas and migration into and out of those areas (e.g., Cruz, 1996; Pichon, 1993, 1997; Amacher et al., 1998; DeWalt and Stonich, 1999), although little of it addresses the effects of environmental factors and degradation on out-migration from origin areas Although not specifically the focus of any of the papers contributed to this volume, population size, structure, and change are consequences as well as causes of land use and environmental attributes. This feedback is incorporated into emerging conceptual models of coupled human-natural systems (e.g., Pickett et al., 1994; Redman et al., 2004; Turner et al., 2003a, 2003b; Parker et al., 2003). The identification problem it poses is a major challenge to the proper specification of statistical models and especially causal inferences based on these models. Identification problems are not unique to statistical analyses (King et al., 1994), as illustrated by the challenge of separating age-period-cohort effects in interpreting trajectories of deforestation and land use described above.

Modeling Studies

Mathematical modeling has been used in population–environment research at least as far back as the world systems model proposed in *The Limits to Growth* (Meadows et al., 1972). Renewed interest in mathematical modeling of population–environment relationships has been spurred in part by the difficulty of reconciling the complexity of population, land use, and environment relationships, even in single-site studies, with the simplifications necessary for statistical modeling. Fischer and O'Neill (Chapter 3) discuss the role of population in current global models of land use change and environment, with particular reference to the models used by the Intergovernmental Panel on Climate Change to produce scenarios of greenhouse gas emissions and those used to produce scenarios of changes in future ecosystem goods and services for the Millennium Ecosystem Assessment. The authors conclude that although the global models use a variety of approaches to simulating land use change, population generally serves as a simple scale factor affecting demand for agricultural products on the consumption side and as a proxy for labor force on the production side. In short, the treatment of population in these models is much less sophisticated than the state of the art in population–environment research, as illustrated by the site-specific studies in this volume. Fischer and O'Neill present a modeling effort at the country level that might serve as a bridge between local studies and global models.

Interest in other approaches to modeling complex relationships among population, land use, and environment is also beginning to emerge in the literature. Messina and Walsh (2001) have used a cellular automata approach to model land cover change in the Ecuadorian Amazon in a spatially explicit way. Cellular automata models are composed of a regular grid of cells each in a finite state that are iteratively updated in discrete time steps according to a set of transition rules (Walsh et al., Chapter 6). The models provide a formal framework for investigating the behavior of complex, extended systems. The rules that drive the Walsh and Messina cellular automata model are derived from formal theories of growth and change and the results of empirical analyses. The models are now being developed to explore deforestation and the extensification of agriculture in relation to human settlement, the extension of roads, and other changes under way in Nang Rong, Thailand (Walsh et al., Chapter 6).

Some researchers are beginning to use agent-based modeling approaches (e.g., Sanders et al., 1997; Parker et al., 2002; Walker, 2003). Agent-based models examine the characteristics and activities of individual agents as they interact and change over time as they adapt (or not) to their environment and learn (or not) from experience. These models are well suited to the study of complexity in land use change (Berry et al., 2002; Parker et al., 2002). For example, Liu and his colleagues have developed an agent-based model that simulates interactions among population, land use, and panda habitat at multiple levels in the Wolong Nature Research in Sichuan Province, China (Liu et al., Chapter 9; An et al., 2003). They have used the model to project the demographic and ecological consequences of policy scenarios in a spatially explicit manner. Individuals and households are the agents in these models. As with any modeling attempt, of course, the projections are only as good as the parameter estimates on which they are based.

Neither cellular automata nor agent-based models test causal relationships directly. Rather, the models are a vehicle to work out the implications of complex interrelationships among population, land use, and environment specified in theory. Interestingly, none of the models just described yet includes feedbacks from land use and the environment to population size, structure, or change, although the potential clearly exists for doing this.

PROGRESS IN MULTIDISCIPLINARY AND INTERDISCIPLINARY RESEARCH

Research on population–land use–environment relationships over the past decade has opened up new research directions, suggested new hypotheses, and produced interesting results. Much of this research has necessarily been multidisciplinary or interdisciplinary, because the disciplines that study human population dynamics, land use change, and environmental change have not usually communicated much with each other. Projects funded by NICHD, other government agencies, and private foundations, focusing mainly on population–land use interactions, have made good progress in eliciting collaboration across the social sciences and between the social sciences and some natural science disciplines, notably those involved in interpreting remote observations of land use and land cover change. Other studies, focused mainly on connections between land use and environment, have generated productive collaborations linking ecologists and social scientists (Gutmann et al., 2004; Moran and Ostrom, 2005).

These collaborations across disciplines have taken a variety of forms. One involves incorporating the methods and materials from one discipline into another. For instance, Foster (Chapter 12) describes a project that uses a satellite-based measure of greenness (the normalized difference vegetation index) in an analysis of property rights institutions and their consequences for forest cover that is fundamentally rooted in the discipline of economics.

Another approach creates a multidisciplinary team with a coordinated approach to an interdisciplinary question and a division of labor that highlights the unique contribution of specific disciplines. Fischer and O'Neill (Chapter 3) describe such an approach to the modeling of land use and land cover change in China. Mathematical modeling provides a common language that can enable researchers from different disciplines to communicate to each other certain aspects of their expertise that are critical to the complex system they are studying, even though they do not share disciplinary paradigms. Still another approach is to fuse two or more disciplines to create an interdisciplinary framework and analysis. Sometimes a single researcher will become trained in more than one discipline, and the synthesizing is at the level of the individual, but more often, interdisciplinarity is achieved through collaboration. Many of the teams contributing to this volume have attempted this kind of synthesis of theory, approach, data, and interpretation.

Many barriers stand in the way of mixing disciplines in research on population, land use, and environment. Differences in the cultures of separate disciplines are one such barrier. The differences may be as fundamental as vocabulary. When social scientists talk about populations, they mean human populations. When ecologists talk about populations, they are equally likely to be referring to plant or animal populations. When social scientists refer to surveys, they mean surveys of individuals, households, or some other socially defined unit. For ecologists, surveys may connote what land surveyors do. Many other examples could be given. Unless special efforts are made to develop common meaning, not just common language, differences in vocabulary can lead to miscommunication and create misunderstandings (Bohm, 1996).

Discipline-specific standards with respect to data, methods of analysis, and interpretation are also a challenge. To be credible, interdisciplinary research may have to meet standards in *all* of the disciplines involved. As all who have tried it have discovered, interdisciplinary research takes extra time and patience. As Matson noted in comments made during the workshop, the researchers as well as the research need to be integrated. Mixing disciplines in research has benefits, too, including an interesting cross-fertilization among members of some of the teams, with demographers now concerned with the resolution of digital elevation models and environmental scientists concerned about issues involving human subjects. A discussion of some lessons learned from a large interdisciplinary research center's effort in this area can be found in Moran and Ostrom (2005: Chapter 14).

Interdisciplinary research is inherently difficult (National Research Council, 2004a), but it is made more so by the balkanized structure of the university, reward systems, and peer networks. Faculty generally hold appointments in departments, and students generally get Ph.D.s in a single discipline. In making judgments about whom to hire, promote, and grant tenure, there may not be an appreciation for the additional time it takes to do top-quality interdisciplinary research, or for the fact that multiple players are involved and, as a result, most publications are multiauthored. At least in social science departments, coauthors of multiauthored works may not be given credit commensurate with their contributions when it comes to promotion and tenure decisions. Publication may also pose problems. The editors of the most prestigious journals in individual disciplines may not be interested in, or competent to review, interdisciplinary research. These difficulties pose particular problems for scientists in their early careers who work in interdisciplinary teams. Efforts must be made to overcome these institutional and cultural barriers.

Finally, these challenges of interdisciplinarity raise questions about how best to train students to contribute to population–environment research. Although there are hundreds of undergraduate programs across the country with names like environmental studies and environmental science, they vary widely in terms of the disciplines included and in rigor. Graduate programs vary less in rigor, but the opportunities for interdisciplinary work by graduate students vary considerably. Systematic in-depth and rigorous training in the full range of social and environmental sciences relevant to population–land use–environment research is comparatively rare at the graduate level, compared with training in multiple disciplines in either the social or natural sciences.

2

Recommended Research Directions

Over the past decade, considerable progress has been made in understanding the environmental effects of demographic change that are mediated by changes in land use and land cover. Much of this progress has been made through studies that have followed population–land use–environment interactions at particular sites over many years. The ability to conduct such studies has been promoted by the existence of targeted funding for such research and by the development of international networks of researchers, aided in part by the organization of the international Land Use/Land Cover Change Project, and its successor, the proposed Global Land Project, under the auspices of the International Human Dimensions Programme on the Human Dimensions of Global Change and the International Geosphere-Biosphere Programme. Methodologically, research has been greatly advanced by the availability and use of observations from space, particularly from Landsat, that were little used to study land use change a decade ago. The rapidity of change in the use of remote observations can be seen by comparing research reported in the appendixes to this volume with the research reported in *Population and Land Use in Developing Countries* (National Research Council, 1993) more than a decade ago.

Site-based studies have yielded substantive advances in understanding, with potential implications for policy. They have shown how the environmental effects of population change depend not only on increases in population numbers but also on other demographic changes, including migration and changes in household size. For example, research based in Wolong, China, indicates that policies that relocate young people out of the panda reserve are not only more socially acceptable than policies that relocate other groups, but also more ecologically effective and economically efficient (Liu et al., Chapter 9). Site-based studies have shown that environmental effects are seen most clearly when broad land use and environmental categories, such as the urban-rural distinction, are unpacked into more focused distinctions. For example, the distinction between primary forest and secondary forest is crucial to understanding the role of migration, land use practices, deforestation, and rates of regrowth in the Brazilian Amazon (Moran et al., Chapter 5). Site-based studies have shown that population–land use–environment relationships are scale dependent, that is, that the relationships that are evident at one level of spatial, social, or temporal analysis are not necessarily found when analysis is conducted at another level. Such findings caution against naïve generalization across scales and have opened the question of how interactions occurring at one scale affect or embed interactions at other scales.

Site-based studies have also led to methodological advances, such as in the design of multithematic longitudinal data sets, the development of methods to link population units to land units and land units to environmental effects, and innovative approaches to modeling. They have also led to improved methods of measuring land use variables by remote observation—a necessary building block for research that can compare larger numbers of sites.

The site-based approach has also clarified the key challenges for future research. One is to move from descriptive to causal understanding of population–land use–environment relationships. A major challenge is to improve comparability of data and analyses across sites in order to build generalizable knowledge. There is also the challenge of developing interdisciplinary collaboration across the wide range of sciences relevant to this topic and developing the capacity for this interdisciplinary research in the next generation of scientists.

After consideration of research developments over the past decade and the state of knowledge on population–land use–environment relationships, the panel makes the following recommendations for the continued development of this field.

1. Research should be increasingly coordinated to promote creation of a body of integrated knowledge. Knowledge about the relationships among demographic, land use, and environmental variables has been substantially enriched in recent years by empirical studies using new multithematic, multilevel, longitudinal, and spatially explicit data sets to describe and analyze these relationships at specific sites around the world. Of course, with respect to the development of general knowledge, there are inherent limitations of such site-specific studies, as noted in Chapter 1. Such general knowledge is critical for anticipating possible scale dependencies and cross-scale interactions, aggregating appropriately from site-specific knowledge, developing forecasts for specific sites, and understanding the likely trajectory of these processes elsewhere. Several actions can help move the field in directions conducive to building general knowledge.

a. *Organizations that support population–land use–environment research should work with researchers to develop minimum reporting standards for data collected and analyzed in site-based studies.* Reporting standards should be developed to describe the data used in these studies to facilitate comparison among them.

Site-specific studies will continue to contribute important knowledge. Their value can be greatly increased, however, by efforts to establish and increase data comparability across sites. When comparing results from two or more sites, one explanation for any differences among them is in the design and analysis of the data on which the results are based. This explanation cannot be evaluated if the information about the design and analysis of the data is incomplete. To obtain generalizable results from existing studies that will contribute to a deep understanding of fundamental aspects of population–land use–environment relationships, it is therefore critical to establish minimum standards with respect to collecting and reporting data. Even though we do not judge it appropriate at this time to standardize measurement techniques, the need to assess the reliability and generalizability of results presumes that studies are explicit about the properties of the data they are using and how key variables are measured. Survey data provide one example. Researchers using such data in population–environment studies should, at a minimum, report on sample design, size, and response rate. The American Association of Public Opinion Research (2004), for example, has published a set of standard definitions for survey response rates that could serve as a useful guide. New surveys should use sample selection and fieldwork procedures that conform to high standards that maximize comparability and generalizability.

b. *Individual projects should provide an inventory of important contextual variables for their study sites.* Results may differ among two or more sites because of differences among places in technologies used; formal and informal institutions; local, national, and international markets; policies; and the natural environment. For example, differences in property rights (e.g., regarding common land), in the existence and spatial scope of product markets, and in the institutions and regulations governing use of resources can have important effects on how population interacts with land and water use. Specification of the differences and similarities in these characteristics across localities is fundamental to interpreting and generalizing from research findings, developing an understanding of contextual effects and cross-scale interactions, and providing insights into possibly efficacious policy interventions.

c. Efforts should be made to coordinate definitions of variables measured and research designs chosen in different site-specific studies to enhance the creation of a body of integrated knowledge in the field. So far efforts to produce generalizations have been limited by the incompatibility of variables and research designs used in the individual studies. While some of these differences are necessary because of site-specific conditions or varying research questions, others may be due to a lack of communication and coordination among study groups. Such communication might be accomplished through funder-sponsored conferences, international research projects such as the Global Land Project project, or at other meetings of the research community.

d. Two substantive areas of research—regions of new settlement ("frontier") areas and regions of rapid urban (including suburban) development—are ripe for producing integrated, general knowledge. These areas have been the focus of multiple recent studies of similar phenomena in different regions and thus hold promise for building knowledge of generic processes of population–land use–environment interaction. Organizations that support population–land use–environment research should encourage efforts that examine the differences and similarities across sites of these kinds, with attention to contextual differences and similarities. Collaboration and organized communication (e.g., research workshops) involving researchers across projects and sites who are looking at similar phenomena in different places may facilitate in important ways the creation of a body of integrated knowledge about population–land use–environment relationships.

2. Research should continue to decompose or unpack the complex, general phenomena of population, land use, and environment and examine causal relationships involving their more specific component factors. Recent research has demonstrated the importance of insights that can come when broad variables, such as population growth and land cover, are further differentiated. For instance, the effects of population growth depend on whether growth is due to natural increase or migration, and if migration, the relative size of streams into and out of a place, whether the migration is temporary or permanent, and on the characteristics of the migrants. Population effects may depend in important ways on changing numbers of households by size and on the age structures of the members of these households over time and on temporary migrations that are not often measured, such as of commuters, tourists, seasonal workers, and illegal migrants. Land cover categories observable with current remote sensing techniques often contain highly heterogeneous land uses, especially in urban areas. Disarticulated analyses of such general factors will continue to yield better understanding of the mechanisms and feedbacks that connect population, land use, and environment. It will also help clarify the assumptions and theoretical structures that researchers in each specialty use and thus facilitate interdisciplinary communication and integration.

Population–environment research on land use should include research with a substantive focus on water. Human land use inevitably affects and is affected by ground and surface waters and habitats defined by waters. Population–environment relationships mediated by water are particularly important because of the importance of water as a resource and a substrate and carrier for nutrients and pollutants, and because most of the world's urbanization and much intensification of food production are occurring in coastal and riparian regions. Although these areas constitute relatively small percentages of the Earth's surface, they are very important to marine productivity, storm and flood impacts, and transformation of wetland habitats. Even in inland and upland areas, watershed function is highly influenced by human population and land use change. Infiltration and ground water recharge, runoff and erosion, riparian zone desiccation, and altered flood regime are among the important environmental processes that link with population and land use.

3. Research should investigate the dynamic interactions involving population *and* land use *and* environmental variables. Until now, most of the studies addressing the relationships of demographic, land use, and environmental issues have focused mainly on population and land use *or* land use and environment. Few have fully coupled all three classes of variables. Although continued research on pairs of these elements remains useful, it is important to expand research efforts to connect all three elements and forge appropriate scientific linkages. Fully integrated studies that incorporate aspects of population, land use, and environment are needed to better understand how human activities are altering the Earth's system and how these activities are affected in turn by environmental changes.

In developing these integrated studies, researchers should be attentive, as noted above, to the specific demographic, land use, and environmental factors involved and to contextual factors that may influence these relationships, including social institutions and geographic location, among others. They should be attentive, as noted below, to the ways in which population–land use–environment relationships may vary depending on the spatial, temporal, and social units used for analysis and to the mechanisms and causal processes involved. The units of analysis and regional scale of a study should typically reflect the scales at which the processes of concern operate and at which decisions are made. Studies should also be explicit in describing the dynamics of change over time in all three elements and in their interactions.

4. **Research should increasingly explore scale dependencies and cross-scale interactions.** Population–land use–environment relationships that appear strong at one spatial, temporal, or social scale of analysis sometimes weaken or disappear when analyzed at other scales. Moreover, phenomena are linked across scales: larger scales may set the context or limitations for relationships at smaller scales, and relationships at smaller scales may aggregate to larger scales in surprising ways that indicate emergent properties. These general issues of human-environment interaction can be studied productively in the context of population–land use–environment relationships. Adding considerations of scale do not necessarily make research problems more difficult or complex. Often, thinking carefully about the spatial, temporal, and social scales of processes allows investigators to choose a scale of analysis that simplifies the problem.

   a. Researchers focused on population–environment relationships should pay explicit attention to spatial, temporal, and social scale in framing their studies and offering explanations. They should be explicit about the scales at which they are working. Future research will advance understanding more effectively by focusing more explicitly on defining the scales of each study and placing studies in relationship to each other on spatial, temporal, and social scales. Researchers should ensure that their data are spatially and temporally explicit with regard to level of analysis and frequency of data collection, and thus amenable to scaling up or down.

   Research funders should use their influence to develop gridded approaches that can place local studies within spatial matrices and to encourage levels of temporal resolution (including of remotely sensed images) adequate to understanding dynamic processes. The field is now ready to respond to the challenge of using the historical detail available from time series of remote images, as indicated by some of the contributions to this volume that employ such methods as analysis of pixel or plot trajectories (Walsh et al., Chapter 6; Redman, Chapter 7) and econometric methods for time-series analysis (Seto, Chapter 8). A gridded approach can help shape the samples of research sites and measurement times to bear an understandable relationship to the larger spatial, temporal, and social scales to which site-specific data will be aggregated.

   b. Researchers should be encouraged to address explicitly the extent to which the population–land use–environment relationships they study vary by scale of analysis, how these scale dependencies may vary by place or time, and how relationships at one scale may influence those at another scale. There are many strategies for examining these scale dependence and scale interaction issues, including the incorporation of multiple scales of analysis within single studies; the linking of research activities that overlap on one dimension (e.g., same place) but differ in scale of analysis; and the use of dynamic modeling approaches, such as cellular automata, agent-based models, artificial intelligence approaches, and nonlinear dynamics. The dynamic modeling approaches may be helpful in examining temporal and social scale interactions, such as the conditions under which complex systems go into periods of rapid restructuring and the ways in which phenomena at small spatial or social scales may aggregate in nonlinear ways.

5. **Organizations that support population–land use–environment research should support and encourage continued development of linked data sets** that include information about population, land use, and environmental variables and that are spatially explicit, multilevel, and longitudinal. The objectives of building integrated knowledge; linking population, land use, and environment; and understanding scale dependencies and cross-scale linkages will all be greatly advanced by the development of data sets that allow for comparisons across variables, research sites, and scales and for analyses of feedbacks from environmental to demographic variables. Investment should be made both in continuing existing linked longitudinal data sets and in developing similar data sets at new sites in under-studied regions and in places that offer unique research opportunities.

Development of linked data sets will also help identify gaps in research by showing unevenness in data availability as a function of world regions; types of demographic and land use change; institutional and environmental contexts; and the availability of integrative studies that explicitly link population, land use, and environment. Such data sets will also help identify the depth of knowledge available for addressing particular important topics, such as urban expansion, "frontier" and coastal development, and critical environmental issues (e.g., desertification, carbon sinks, loss of biodiversity, invasive species expansion).

a. Continued investment is warranted in developing methods for data and process integration. For example, there are numerous challenges in developing geographic information systems (GIS) that can effectively integrate across time space for integrated studies of population–land use–environment relationships. Even with better measurement, problems will remain because there is no one-to-one link between population units, land use units, and environmental units. Moreover, multiple units in any location are relevant to multiple units in other places. The complexity of these linkages poses a significant methodological challenge for researchers and GIS developers.

b. Guidelines must be developed for use of linked data sets and for making data available to researchers beyond the original research team. A major issue is the tension between the value of broadly available multilevel, spatially explicit data and the confidentiality of individuals, households, or villages that might be identified from the data. Given the recommended investments in new and existing data sets, it is important that maximum value be obtained. However, when researchers such as the contributors to this volume follow standard social science procedures, participants receive promises of confidentiality. Identifiers that reveal the name or spatial location of a village or dwelling unit pose the risk that information about individuals can be seen in or deduced from a data set, thus violating the confidentiality promise. The problem increases with data sets that are multilevel, longitudinal, and spatially explicit and that are potentially useful not only to researchers but also to others who might use the information in ways not desired by the people the data describe. Solutions to this problem are urgently needed.

6. **Increased effort should be devoted to modeling and quantifying causal relationships among population, land use, and environment using a variety of approaches, as well as to analyzing uncertainties in models of these complex systems.** Population–land use–environment relationships are embedded in a larger coupled human-natural system. Mathematical models provide a way to recognize this while working out the particular mechanisms involved in these relationships. They provide a means to address dynamic relationships among population, land use, and environment, including endogeneities and feedbacks that are not readily uncovered by analyses of observational data alone. Mathematical models have considerable value for structuring discussion across disciplines, identifying key questions that require empirical research, and providing forecasts for policy analysis.

7. **A research effort should be made to identify more effective mechanisms to facilitate interdisciplinary research.** Scientists who conduct interdisciplinary population–environment research report special difficulties not usually encountered in disciplinary research. Some of these difficulties impede collaboration, even among senior scientists. These include the use of different words for essentially similar concepts and of the same words to mean different things in different disciplines, the presence of bodies of tacit knowledge that remain hidden during most conversations, disagreements over the best way to tackle interesting research questions, invidious distinctions between "hard" and "soft" science, and the challenge of administering large and sometimes spatially and temporally dispersed teams. Senior scientists report that such difficulties result in slower progress toward research results and increased difficulty in publishing interdisciplinary work. In addition, this research is too often discounted by disciplinary peers. Such problems may pose significant barriers to career progress for junior scientists in a number of disciplines.

Such barriers to interdisciplinary research are widely noted, both among population–land use–environment researchers and more broadly among academic researchers. Little systematic knowledge exists, however, about which barriers are most significant for particular lines of research or about which interventions are most effective in reducing impediments to the progress of research or the training of future researchers.

Organizations that support population–environment research should support a systematic assessment of which approaches seem to result in the best and most rigorously trained young scholars in this field and the most productive research collaborations. This assessment should be based on systematic analysis of experience from population-environment research and related interdisciplinary fields. It should address such questions as these: Does strong interdisciplinary training at the undergraduate or graduate levels make young scholars more effective at interdisciplinary collaboration? Are experienced graduate or postdoctoral mentors necessary to motivate and train interdisciplinary collaborators? Are graduate students and junior faculty who participate in interdisciplinary projects hindered in their careers, or is the perception that interdisciplinary participation is risky partially or entirely mythical? What differentiates effective from ineffective leaders of interdisciplinary teams? How do effective interdisciplinary teams recruit and reward participants? Do certain types of administrative structures, such as interdisciplinary research institutes, foster successful interdisciplinary research? What styles of communication and administration favor successful operation of dispersed multiinstitution and international collaborations?

References

Alcamo, J., E.M. Bennett, and the Millennium Ecosystem Assessment Project
  2003   *Ecosystems and Human Well-being: A Framework for Analysis.* (A report of the Conceptual Framework Working Group.) Washington, DC: Island Press.
Allen, M.J., and M.R. Barnes
  1985   The causes of deforestation in developing countries. *Annals of the Association of American Geographers* 75(2):163-184.
Amacher, G.S., W. Cruz, D. Grebner, and W.F. Hyde
  1998   Environmental motivations for migration: Population pressure, poverty, and deforestation in the Philippines. *Land Economics* 74:92-101.
American Association for Public Opinion Research
  2004   Standard Definitions: Final Dispositions of Case Codes and Outcome Rates for Surveys. Available: http://www.aapor.org/pdfs/standarddefs_3.1.pdf [August 12, 2005].
An, L., M. Linderman, A. Shortridge, and J. Liu
  2003   An Integrative Model with Agent-Based Artificial Intelligence and GIS (IMABAIG): Simulating Spatio-Dynamics of Rural Households and the Associated Impacts on Giant Panda Habitats in the Wolong Nature Reserve (China). Paper Presented at the Annual Meeting of the Population Association of America, Minneapolis, MN.
Axinn, W.G., J. Barber, and A. Biddlecom
  2002   Social Change, Household Size, and Environmental Consumption. Paper presented at the Annual Meeting of the Population Association of America, Atlanta, GA.
Baland, J., and J. Platteau
  1996   *Halting Degradation of Natural Resources: Is There a Role for Rural Communities?* Oxford, England: Clarendon Press.
Berry, B.J.L., L.D. Kiel, and E. Elliott
  2002   Adaptive agents, intelligence, and emergent human organization: Capturing complexity through agent-based modeling. *Proceedings of the National Academy of Sciences* 99:187-188.

Bilsborrow, R.E.
1987   Population pressures and agricultural development in developing countries: A conceptual framework and recent evidence. *World Development* 15:183-203.
1994   Population, Development, and Deforestation: Some Recent Evidence. Pp. 117-134 in *Proceedings of the United Nations Expert Group Meeting on Population, Environment, and Development.* New York: United Nations.

Blaikie, P., and H. Brookfield, eds.
1987   *Land Degradation and Society.* New York: Metheun & Company, Ltd.

Bohm, D.
1996   *On Dialogue.* New York: Routledge.

Boserup, E.
1965   *The Conditions of Agricultural Growth: The Economics of Agrarian Change Under Population Pressure.* Chicago, IL: Aldine.

Brondizio, E.S., S.D. McCracken, E.F. Moran, A.D. Siqueira, D.R. Nelson, and C. Rodriguez-Pedraza
2002   The colonist footprint: Toward a conceptual framework of deforestation trajectories among small farmers in frontier Amazonia. Pp. 133-161 in *Deforestation and Land Use in the Amazon,* C. Wood and R. Porro, eds. Gainesville: University Press of Florida.

Cadwallader, M.
1988   Urban geography and social theory. *Urban Geography* 9:227-251.

Cain, M.
1985   On the relationship between landholding and fertility. *Population Studies* 39:5-15.

Campbell, J.B.
2002   *Introduction to Remote Sensing* (3rd ed.). New York: Guilford Press.

Chayanov, A.V.
1966   *The Theory of Peasant Economy.* D. Thorner, B. Kerblay, and R.E.F. Smith, eds. Homewood, IL: Richard D. Irwin.

Chertow, M.
2001   The IPAT equation and its variants: Changing views of technology and environmental impact. *Journal of Industrial Ecology* 4(4):13-29.

Cruz, M.C.
1996   Population growth and land-use changes in the Philippines. Pp. 63-71 in *Population Growth and Environmental Issues,* S. Ramphal and S.W. Sinding, eds. Westport, CT: Praeger.

Curran, S., A. Kumar, W. Lutz, and M. Williams, eds.
2002   *Interactions Between Coastal and Marine Ecosystems and Human Population Systems.* [Special Issue] *Ambio* 31(4):264-268.

Davis, K.
1963   The theory of change and response in modern demographic history. *Population Index* 29(4):345-366.

DeWalt, B.R., and S.C. Stonich
1999   Inequality, population, and forest destruction in Honduras. Pp. 152-174 in *Population and Deforestation in the Humid Tropics,* R.E. Bilsborrow and D. Hogan, eds. Brussels, Belgium: International Union for the Scientific Study of Population.

Dietz, T., and E.A. Rosa
1994   Rethinking the environmental impacts of population, affluence and technology. *Human Ecology Review* 1:277-300.

Easterlin, R.A.
1976   Population change and farm settlement in the northern United States. *Journal of Economic History* 36:45-75.

Ehrlich, P.R., and A.H. Ehrlich
　1970　　*Population, Resources, Environment.* San Francisco, CA: Freeman.
Ehrlich, P.R., and J.P. Holdren
　1971　　The impact of population growth. *Science* 171:1212-1217.
Elder, G.H.
　1998　　The life course as developmental theory. *Child Development* 69(1):1-12.
Entwisle, B., S.J. Walsh, R.R. Rindfuss, and A. Chamratrithirong
　1998　　Landuse/landcover (LULC) and population dynamics, Nang Rong, Thailand. Pp.
　　　　　121-144 in National Research Council, *People and Pixels: Using Remotely Sensed
　　　　　Data in Social Science Research.* Committee on the Human Dimensions of Global
　　　　　Change. D. Liverman, E.F. Morgan, R.R. Rindfuss, and P.C. Stern, eds. Washing-
　　　　　ton, DC: National Academy Press.
Entwisle, B., J. Edmeades, G. Malanson, C. Podhisita, P. Prasartkul, R.R. Rindfuss, and S.J.
Walsh
　2004　　Village Settlement, Deforestation, and the Expansion of Agriculture in a Frontier
　　　　　Region: Nang Rong Thailand. Paper presented at the Annual Meeting of the
　　　　　Population Association of American, Boston, MA.
Foster, A.D., M.R. Rosenzweig, and J.R. Behrman
　2000　　Population Growth, Income Growth and Deforestation: Management of Village
　　　　　Common Land in India. Unpublished manuscript, Brown University.
Fox, J., R.R. Rindfuss, S.J. Walsh, and V. Mishra, eds.
　2003　　*People and the Environment: Approaches for Linking Household and Community
　　　　　Surveys to Remote Sensing and GIS.* Boston, MA: Kluwer.
Galvin, K.A., J. Ellis, R.B. Boone, A.L. Magennis, N.M. Smith, S.J. Lynn, and P. Thornton
　2002　　Compatibility of pastoralism and conservation? A test case using integrated assess-
　　　　　ment in the Ngorongoro Conservation Area, Tanzania. In *Displacement, Forced
　　　　　Settlement and Conservation*, D. Chatty and M. Colester, eds. Oxford, England:
　　　　　Berghahn Books.
Geist, H.J., and E.F. Lambin
　2002　　Proximate causes and underlying forces of tropical deforestation. *BioScience* 52(2):
　　　　　143-150.
Genus
　2002　　Demographic behaviour in a changing environment: The theoretical background of
　　　　　an EU research project. [Special Issue] *Genus* 56:15-120.
Gibson, C., E. Ostrom, and T-K. Ahn
　1998　　IHDP Working Paper No 1: Scaling Issues in the Social Sciences. A Report for the
　　　　　IHDP. Available: http://www.ihdp.uni-bonn.de/html/publications/workpaper.html
Gleick, P.H.
　1999　　The human right to water. *Water Policy* 1(5):487-503.
　2003　　Global freshwater resources: Soft-path solutions for the 21st century. *Science* 302:
　　　　　1524-1528.
Goody, J.
　1958　　*The Development Cycle of Domestic Groups.* New York: Cambridge University
　　　　　Press.
　1976　　*Production and Reproduction: A Comparative Study of the Domestic Domain.*
　　　　　New York: Cambridge University Press.
Graedel, T., and B. Allenby
　1995　　*Industrial Ecology.* Englewood Cliffs, NJ: Prentice-Hall.
Grossman, G., and A. Krueger
　1995　　Economic growth and the environment. *Quarterly Journal of Economics* 110:353-
　　　　　377.

Grove, J.M., and W.R. Burch
1997   A social ecology approach to urban ecosystem and landscape analyses. *Urban Ecosystems* 1:259-275.

Grove, J.M., M.L. Cadenasso, W. Burch, S.T.A. Pickett, K. Schwarz, M.A. Wilson, and C.G. Boone
2004   *The Social Ecology of Prestige: Group Identity and Social Status of Ecological Structure and its Implications for Urban Watershed Dynamics in the Baltimore Metropolitan Region.* Baltimore, MD: Society & Natural Resources.

Gutmann, M.P., and G. Cunfer
1999   A new look at the causes of the dust bowl. *The Charles L. Wood Agricultural History Lecture Series* 99(1):1-25.

Gutmann, M.P., S. Pullum-Piñón, S.G. Baker, and I.C. Burke
2004   German-origin settlement and agricultural land use in the twentieth century Great Plains. In *German-American Immigration and Ethnicity in Comparative Perspective*, W. Kamphoefner and W. Helbich, eds. Madison: University of Wisconsin Press.

Holdren, J.P., and P.R. Ehrlich
1974   Human population and the global environment. *American Scientist* 62:282-292.

Jolly, C.L., and B.B. Torrey
1993   Introduction. Pp. 1-14 in National Research Council, *Population and Land Use in Developing Countries: Report of a Workshop.* Committee on Population. C.L. Jolly and B.B. Torrey, eds. Washington, DC: National Academy Press.

Kates, R.W., W.C. Clark, R. Corell, J.M. Hall, C.C. Jaeger, I. Lowe, J.J. McCarthy, H.J. Schellenhuber, B. Bolin, N.M. Dickson, S. Faucheaux, G.C. Gallopin, A. Grübler, B. Huntley, J. Jäger, N.S. Jodha, R.E. Kasperson, A. Mabogunje, P. Matson, H. Mooney, B. Moore, III, T. O'Riordan, and U. Svedin
2001   Sustainability science. *Science* 292:641-642.

Kaufman, M.M., and W.M. Marsh
1997   Hydro-ecological implications of edge cities. *Landscape and Urban Planning* 36: 277-290.

King, G., R.O. Keohane, and S. Verba
1994   *Designing Social Inquiry: Scientific Inference in Qualitative Research.* Princeton, NJ: Princeton University Press.

Lambin, E.F., X. Baulies, N. Bockstael, G. Fischer, T. Krug, R. Leemans, E.F. Moran, R.R. Rindfuss, Y. Sato, D. Skole, B.L. Turner II, and C. Vogel
1999   *Land-Use and Land-Cover Change Implementation Strategy.* Stockholm, Sweden: IGBP Secretariat, Royal Swedish Academy of Sciences.

Laney, R.M.
2002   Disaggregating induced intensification for land-change analysis: A case study from Madagascar. *Annals of the Association of American Geographers* 92(4):702.

Liu, J., G. Daily, P. Ehrlich, and G. Luck
2003   Effects of household dynamics on resource consumption and biodiversity. *Nature* 421:530-533.

Lloyd, W.F.
1833   *Two Lectures on the Checks to Population.* Oxford, England: Oxford University Press.

Loveland, T.R., J.W. Merchant, D.O. Ohlen, and J.F. Brown
1991   Development of a land-cover characteristics database for the conterminous U.S. *Photogrammatic Engineering and Remote Sensing* 57:1453-1463.

Lutz, W., ed.
1994   *Population-Development-Environment: Understanding Their Interactions in Mauritius.* Berlin, Germany: Springer Verlag.

Lutz, W., A. Prskawetz, and W.C. Sanderson, eds.
    2002   *Population and Environment. Methods of Analysis.* (A Supplement to Vol. 28, 2002, *Population and Development Review.*) New York: The Population Council.
MacKellar, F.L., W. Lutz, C. Prinz, and A. Goujon
    1995   Population, households and carbon dioxide emissions. *Population and Development Review* 21(4):849-865.
Maglad, N.E.
    1994   Fertility in rural Sudan: The effect of landholding and child mortality. *Economic Development and Cultural Change* 42:761-772.
Malthus, T.R.
    1798   *Essay on the Principle of Population as It Affects the Future Improvement of Society.* New York: Kelley.
    1803   *An Essay on the Principle of Population: A View of its Past and Present Effects on Human Happiness; with an Inquiry into Our Prospects Respecting the Future Removal or Mitigation of the Evils which It Occasions* (revised and expanded 2nd ed. of 1798 printing). London, England: John Murray.
McCay, B., and J.M. Acheson, eds.
    1987   *The Question of the Commons: The Culture and Ecology of Communal Resources.* Tucson: University of Arizona Press.
McCracken, S.D., E.S. Brondizio, D. Nelson, E.F. Moran, A.D. Siqueira, and C. Rodriguez-Pedraza
    1999   Remote sensing and GIS at the farm property level: Demography and deforestation in the Brazilian Amazon. *Photogrammetric Engineering and Remote Sensing* 65: 1311-1320.
Meadows, D.H., D. Meadows, J. Randers, and W.W. Behrens III
    1972   *The Limits to Growth*, (3rd ed.). New York: New American Library.
Melillo, J.M., C.B. Field, and B. Moldan
    2002   *Interactions of the Major Biogeochemical Cycles.* Washington, DC: Island Press.
Messina, J.P., and S.J. Walsh
    2001   Simulating Land Use and Land Cover Dynamics in the Ecuadorian Amazon Through Cellular Automata Approaches and an Integrated GIS. Proceedings, Open Meetings of the Human Dimensions of Global Environmental Change Research Community, Rio de Janeiro, Brazil.
Meyer, W.B., and B.L. Turner II
    1992   Human population growth and global land-use/cover change. *Annual Review of Ecology and Systematics* 23:39-61.
Moran, E.F.
    1993   Deforestation and land use in the Brazilian Amazon. *Human Ecology* 21(1):1-22.
Moran, E.F., and E. Brondizio
    1998   Land-use change after deforestation in Amazonia. Pp. 1-27 in National Research Council, *People and Pixels: Linking Remote Sensing and Social Science.* Committee on the Human Dimensions of Global Change. D. Liverman, E.F. Moran, R.R. Rindfuss, and P.C. Stern, eds. Washington, DC: National Academy Press.
Moran, E., and E. Ostrom, eds.
    2005   *Seeing the Forest and the Trees: Human-Environment Interactions in Forest Ecosystems.* Cambridge, MA: MIT Press.
Moran, E., E. Brondizio, P. Mausel, and Y. Wu
    1994   Integrating Amazonian vegetation, land use and satellite data. *BioScience* 44(5): 329-338.

Moran, E., A. Siqueira, and E. Brondizio
  2003   Household demographics structure and its relationship to deforestation in the Amazon Basin. Pp. 61-89 in *People and the Environment: Approaches to Linking Household and Community Surveys to Remote Sensing and GIS*, J. Fox, V. Mishra, R. Rindfuss, and S. Walsh, eds. Dordrecht, The Netherlands: Kluwer Publishers.

Mortimore, M.
  1993   Northern Nigeria: Land transformation under agricultural intensification. Pp. 42-69 in National Research Council, *Population and Land Use in Developing Countries*. Committee on Population, C.L. Jolly and B.B. Torrey, eds. Washington, DC: National Academy Press.

National Academy of Engineering
  1994   *The Greening of Industrial Ecosystems*. Advisory Committee on Industrial Ecology and Environmentally Preferable Technology, B. Allenby and D.J. Richards, eds. Washington, DC: National Academy Press.

National Research Council
  1984   *Energy Use: The Human Dimension*. Committee on Behavioral and Social Aspects of Energy Consumption and Production, P.C. Stern and E. Aronson, eds. New York: Freeman.

  1988   *Toward an Understanding of Global Change: Initial Priorities for U.S. Contributions to the IGBP*. Committee on Global Change (U.S. National Committee for the IGBP), Office of International Affairs. Washington, DC: National Academy Press.

  1990   *Research Strategies for the U.S. Global Change Research Program*. Committee on Global Change. Washington, DC: National Academy Press.

  1992   *Global Environmental Change: Understanding the Human Dimensions*. Committee on the Human Dimensions of Global Change, P.C. Stern, O.R. Young, and D. Druckman, eds. Washington, DC: National Academy Press.

  1993   *Population and Land Use in Developing Countries: Report of a Workshop*. Committee on Population, C.L. Jolly and B.B. Torrey, eds. Washington, DC: National Academy Press.

  1997   *Environmentally Significant Consumption: Research Directions*. Committee on the Human Dimensions of Global Change, P.C. Stern, T. Dietz, V.W. Ruttan, R.H. Socolow, and J.L. Sweeney, eds. Washington, DC: National Academy Press.

  1998   *People and Pixels: Using Remotely Sensed Data in Social Science Research*, Committee on the Human Dimensions of Global Change, D. Liverman, E.F. Moran, R.R. Rindfuss, and P.C. Stern, eds. Washington, DC: National Academy Press.

  1999a   *Global Environmental Change: Research Pathways for the Next Decade*. Committee on Global Change Research. Washington DC: National Academy Press.

  1999b   *Our Common Journey: A Transition Toward Sustainability*. Board on Sustainable Development. Washington, DC: National Academy Press.

  2001a   *Grand Challenges in the Environmental Sciences*. Committee on Grand Challenges in the Environmental Sciences, Oversight Commission for the Committee on Grand Challenges in Environmental Sciences. Washington DC: National Academy Press.

  2001b   *Growing Populations, Changing Landscapes: Studies from India, China, and the United States*. Indian National Science Academy, Chinese Academy of Sciences, U.S. National Academy of Sciences. Washington, DC: National Academy Press.

  2002   *The Drama of the Commons*. Committee on the Human Dimensions of Global Change, E. Ostrom, T. Dietz, N. Dolsak, P. Stern, S. Stonich, and E. Weber, eds. Washington DC: National Academy Press.

2004a *Facilitating Interdisciplinary Research.* Committee on Facilitating Interdisciplinary Research and Committee on Science, Engineering, and Public Policy. National Academy of Sciences, National Academy of Engineering, and Institute of Medicine. Washington, DC: The National Academies Press.

2004b *Materials Count. The Case for Material Flows Analysis.* Committee on Material Flows Accounting of Natural Resources, Products, and Residuals. Board on Earth Sciences and Resources, Division on Earth and Life Studies. Washington, DC: The National Academies Press.

O'Neill, B.C., F.L. MacKellar, and W. Lutz
2001 *Population and Climate Change.* Cambridge, England: Cambridge University Press.

Ostrom, E.
1990 *Governing the Commons: The Evolution of Institutions for Collective Action.* New York: Cambridge University Press.

Palloni, A.
1994 The relation between population and deforestation: Methods for drawing casual inferences from macro and micro studies. Pp. 125-165 in *Population and the Environment: Rethinking the Debate,* L. Arizpe, R. Wilkshire, and P. Stone, eds. Boulder, CO: Westview Press.

Parker, D.C., T. Berger, and S.M. Manson
2002 *Agent-Based Models of Land Use and Land Cover Change: LUCC Report Series 6.* Bloomington, IN: LUCC Focus 1 Office.

Parker, D.C., S.M. Manson, M.A. Janssen, M.J. Hoffmann, and P. Deadman
2003 Multi-agent systems for the simulation of land-use and land-cover change: A review. *Annals of the Association of American Geographers* 93(2):314-337.

Parris, T.M., and R.W. Kates
2003 Characterizing a sustainability transition: Goals, targets, trends, and driving forces. *Annual Review of Environment and Resources* 28(13):1-13, 28.

Paulson, D.D.
1994 Understanding tropical deforestation: The case of Western Samoa. *Environmental Conservation* 21:326-332.

Pebley, A.R.
1998 Demography and the environment. *Demography* 35(4):377-389.

Pichon, F.
1993 Agricultural settlement, land use and deforestation in the Ecuadorian Amazon frontier: A micro-level analysis of colonist land-allocation behavior. Ph.D. dissertation, Department of City and Regional Planning, University of North Carolina at Chapel Hill.

1997 Colonist land allocation decisions, land use and deforestation in the Ecuadorian Amazon frontier. *Economic Development and Cultural Change* 45(4):707-744.

Pichon, F., and R.E. Bilsborrow
1999 Land use system, deforestation and demographic factors in the humid tropics: Farm-level evidence from Ecuador. In *Population and Deforestation in the Humid Tropics,* R. Bilsborrow and D. Hogan, eds. Liege, Belgium: International Union for the Scientific Study of Population.

Pickett, S.T.A., W.R. Burch, and J.M. Grove
1999 Interdisciplinary research: Maintaining the constructive impulse in a culture of criticism. *Ecosystems* 2:302-307.

Pickett, S.T.A., I.C. Burke, V.H. Dale, J.R. Gosz, R.G. Lee, S.W. Pacala, and M. Shachak
1994 Integrated models of forested regions. Pp. 120-141 in *Integrated Regional Models: Interactions Between Humans and Their Environment,* P.M. Groffman and G.E. Likens, eds. New York: Chapman and Hall.

Pickett, S.T.A., M.L. Cadenasso, J.M. Grove, C.H. Nilon, R.V. Pouyat, W.C. Zipperer, and R. Costanza
2001   Urban ecological systems: Linking terrestrial ecological, physical, and socioeconomic components of metropolitan areas. *Annual Review of Ecology and Systematics* 32:127-157.

Redman, C.L., J.M. Grove, and L.H. Kuby
2004   Integrating social science into long-term ecological research network: Social dimensions of ecological change and ecological dimensions of social change. *Ecosystems* 6.

Rindfuss, R.R.
1991   The young adult years: Diversity, structural change, and fertility. *Demography* 28(4):493-512.

Rindfuss, R., B. Entwisle, S.J. Walsh, P. Prasartkul, Y. Sawangdee, T.W. Crawford, and J. Reade
2002   Continuous and discrete: Where they have met in Nang Rong, Thailand. Pp. 7-37 in *Linking People, Place and Policy: A GIScience Approach*, S.J. Walsh and K.A. Crews-Meyer, eds. Norwell, MA: Kluwer Academic Publishers.

Rindfuss, R.R., A. Jampaklay, B. Entwisle, Y. Sawangdee, K. Faust, and P. Prasartkul
2004   The collection and analysis of social network data in Nang Rong, Thailand. In *Network Epidemiology: A Handbook for Survey Design and Data Collection*, M. Morris, ed. Oxford, England: Oxford University Press.

Rosa, E.A., R. York, and T. Dietz
2003   Tracking the anthropogenic drivers of ecological impacts. *Ambio* 33(8):509-512.

Saikia, A.
1998   Shifting cultivation, population and sustainability: The changing context of Northeast India. *Development* 41:97-100.

Sanders, L., D. Pumain, H. Mathian, F. GuerinPace and S. Bura
1997   SIMPOP: A multiagent system for the study of urbanism. *Environment and Planning B* 24:287-305.

Shivakoti, G.P., W.G. Axinn, P. Bhandari, and N.B. Chhetri
1999   The impact of community context on land use in an agricultural society. *Population and Environment* 20(3):191-213.

Skole, D.L., W.H. Chomentowski, W.A. Salas, and A.D. Nobre
1994   Physical and human dimensions of deforesttion in Amazonia. *Bioscience* 44(5):314-322.

Steffen, W., A. Sanderson, P.D. Tyson, J. Jäger, P.A. Matson, B. Moore III, F. Oldfield, K. Richardson, H.-J. Schellnhuber, B.L. Turner II, and R.J. Wasson
2004   *Global Change and the Earth System: A Planet Under Pressure*. Berlin, Germany: Springer-Verlag.

Stokes, C.S., W.A. Schutjer, and R.A. Bulatao
1986   Is this relationship between landholding and fertility spurious? A response to Cain. *Population Studies* 40:305-311.

Thornton, P.K., K.A. Galvin, and R.B. Boone
2003   An agro-pastoral household model for the rangelands of East Africa. *Agricultural Systems* 76:601-622.

Tiffen, M., M. Mortimore, and F. Gichuki
1994   *More People Less Erosion: Environmental Recovery in Kenya*. London, England: John Wiley & Sons.

Turner, B.L., D. Skole, S. Sanderson, G. Fischer, L. Fresco, and R. Leemans
1995   *Land-Use and Land-Cover Change*. (Science/Research Plan. IGBP No 35/HDP Report No. 7.) London, England: John Wiley & Sons.

Turner, B.L. II, W.C. Clark, R.W. Kates, J.F. Richards, J.T. Mathews, and W.B. Meyer
  1990   *The Earth as Transformed by Human Action. Global and Regional Changes in the Biosphere over the Past 300 Years.* Cambridge, England: Cambridge University Press.
Turner, B.L. II, G. Hyden, and R. Kates, eds.
  1993   *Population Growth and Agricultural Change in Africa.* Gainesville: University Press of Florida.
Turner, B.L. II, P.A. Matson, J.J. McCarthy, R.W. Corell, L. Christensen, N. Eckley, G.K. Hovelsrud-Broda, J.X. Kasperson, R.E. Kasperson, A. Luers, M.L. Martello, S. Mathiesen, R. Naylor, C. Polsky, A. Pulsipher, A. Schiller, H. Selin and N. Tyler
  2003a   Illustrating the coupled human-environment system for vulnerability analysis: Three case studies. *Proceedings of the National Academy of Sciences* 100(14):8080-8085.
Turner, B.L. II, R.E. Kasperson, P.A. Matson, J.J. McCarthy, R.W. Corell, L. Christensen, N. Eckley, J.X. Kasperson, A. Luers, M.L. Martello, C. Polsky, A. Pulsipher, and A. Schiller
  2003b   A framework for vulnerability analysis in sustainability science. *Proceedings of the National Academy of Sciences* 100(14):8074-8079.
Turner B.L., II, J.G. Geoghegan, and D.R. Foster, eds.
  2004   *Integrated Land-Change Science and Tropical Deforestation in the Southern Yucatan: Final Frontiers.* Oxford, England: Clarendon Press/Oxford University Press.
Umezaki, M., Y. Kuchikura, T. Yamauchi, and R. Ohtsuka
  2000   Impact of population pressure on food production: An analysis of land use change and subsistence pattern in the Tari Basin in Papua New Guinea Highlands. *Human Ecology* 28:359-381.
United Nations Population Fund
  2001   *State of World Population 2000. Footprints and Milestones: Population and Environmental Change.* New York: United Nations Population Fund.
VanLandingham, M., and C. Hirschman
  2001   Population pressure and fertility in pre-transition Thailand. *Population Studies* 55:233-248.
Vayda, A.P.
  1983   Progressive contextualization: Methods for research in human ecology. *Human Ecology* 11(3):265-281.
Vitousek, P.M., H.A. Mooney, J. Lubchenco, and J.M. Melillo
  1997a   Human domination of earth's ecosystems. *Science* 277(5325):494-499.
Vitousek, P.M., J. Aber, R.W. Howarth, G.E. Likens, P.A. Matson, D.W. Schindler, W.H. Schlesinger, and G.D. Tillman
  1997b   Human alteration of the global nitrogen cycle: Causes and consequences. *Issues in Ecology* 1(spring):1-17.
Wackernagel, M., and W. Rees
  1996   *Our Ecological Footprint: Reducing Human Impact on the Earth.* Babriola Island, British Columbia, Canada: New Society.
Wackernagel, M., N.B. Schultz, D. Deumling, A. Callejas Linares, M. Jenkins, V. Kapos, C. Monfreda, J. Loh, N. Myers, R. Norgaard, and J. Randers
  2002   Tracking the ecological overshoot of the human economy. *Proceedings of the National Academy of Sciences* 99(14):9266-9271.
Wade, R.
  1988   *Village Republics: Economic Conditions for Collective Action in South India.* San Francisco, CA: ICS Press.
Walker, R.T.
  2003   Mapping process to pattern in the landscape change of the Amazonian frontier. *Annals of the Association of American Geographers* 93:376-398.

Walsh, S.J., T.P. Evans, W.F. Welsh, B. Entwisle, and R.R. Rindfuss
  1999   Scale dependent relationships between population and environment in Northeast Thailand. *Photogrammetric Engineering and Remote Sensing* 65:97-105.
Walsh, S.J., T.W. Crawford, W.F. Welsh, and K.A. Crews-Mayer
  2001   A multiscale analysis of LULC and NDVI variation in Nang Rong District, Northeast Thailand. *Agriculture Ecosystems and Environment* 85(1-3):47-64.
Williams, R.H., E.D. Larson, and M.H. Ross
  1987   Materials, affluence, and industrial energy use. *Annual Review of Energy and Environment* 12:99-149.
York, R., E.A. Rosa, and T. Dietz
  2003   Footprints on the Earth: The environmental consequences of modernity. *American Sociological Review* 68:279-300.
Young, O.R.
  2002   Institutional interplay: The environmental consequences of cross-scale interactions. Pp. 263-291 in National Research Council, *The Drama of the Commons*. Committee on the Human Dimensions of Global Change. E. Ostrom, T. Dietz, N. Dolsak, P.C. Stern, S. Stonich, and E.U. Weber, eds. Washington. DC: National Academy Press.

PART II

PAPERS

3

Global and Case-Based Modeling of Population and Land Use Change

Günther Fischer and Brian C. O'Neill

INTRODUCTION

Much of the recent literature on interactions between population and land use has focused on case studies at subnational geographic scales, from individual villages and districts (Walsh et al., Chapter 6) to larger regions, such as the Brazilian Amazon (Moran, Brondizio and VanWey, Chapter 5) and the U.S. Great Plains (Gutmann et al., Chapter 4). There is also an ongoing stream of research addressing questions at the global level, particularly as applied to assessments of biodiversity loss, climate change, and outlooks for agriculture and water. This chapter asks whether and how such global analyses can be informed and improved by recent case study research. Following this introduction, we review prominent global models of land use change, with a particular focus on the role of population. We conclude that the best way to bridge the gap between such models and case study research is through spatially explicit analysis at the level of large regions. We then describe one such research project, the CHINAGRO project at the International Institute for Applied Systems Analysis (IIASA), which is aimed at analyzing the potential impacts of trade liberalization and increasing incomes on the agricultural sector and on the livelihoods of the rural population that depends on agriculture in China.

GLOBAL MODELING OF LAND USE

Global models of environmental change simulate links among demography, economic growth, technological development, policy, and environmental outcomes to assess the state of current knowledge, help set research priorities, explore possible alternative futures, and test the potential effect of policies. Early, well-known attempts at global modeling—most prominently the World3 model from the Limits to Growth study (Meadows et al., 1972)—were heavily criticized for being too aggregated to be meaningful, thin on empirical or theoretical support for presumed quantitative relationships among variables, lacking in representation of price-mediated adjustment mechanisms, and insufficiently accounting for the role of technological change (O'Neill, 2001). A new generation of global models was developed in the late 1980s and early 1990s under the label of *integrated assessment*, primarily to assess the climate change issue and future scenarios for food and agriculture. These models rest on a much more rigorous framework than the earlier work, owing in part to a separate heritage in energy-economic models, which were then combined with simplified versions of well-developed disciplinary models of other components of global issues (Parsons and Fisher-Vanden, 1997). They have played prominent roles in recent assessments by the Intergovernmental Panel on Climate Change (e.g., Nakicenovic et al., 2000; McCarthy et al., 2001), the United Nations Environment Programme's Global Environmental Outlook (United Nations Environment Programme, 2002), and scenarios for future ecological changes being produced for the Millennium Ecosystem Assessment. They have also figured prominently in prospective agricultural studies, including those carried out for the International Food Policy Research Institute (Rosegrant, Cai, and Cline, 2002a, 2002b) and the United Nations (Fischer, Shah, and van Valthuizen, 2002).

Questions Addressed by Global Models

Global models are used to address a number of types of questions (e.g., Alcamo, Leemans, and Kreileman, 1998):

- What is the outlook for global environment, or for some aspect of it?
- What might the costs be of achieving particular environmental goals?
- What is the relationship between long-term environmental outcomes and short-term action to reduce degradation?
- What is the relative importance of different linkages in the society-economy-environment system?
- What are the relative strengths of different feedbacks in this system?
- What are the most important sources of uncertainty in the system?
- What gaps in knowledge about the system exist, and how might new research fill these gaps?

For example, in the climate change field, global integrated assessment models have played an influential role in both the science and policy communities (Toth et al., 2001). These models typically consist of linked subcomponents representing population; economic activity leading to demand for energy, agricultural products, and wood products; technological and other factors that determine how these products are supplied; emissions of radiatively active gases associated with this production; resulting change in atmospheric composition and climate; and impacts of climate change on ecosystems and society. Not all models include all of these components, and the level of detail with which any single component is represented varies widely, but this scheme represents the overarching framework in which all integrated assessment models of climate change either explicitly or implicitly operate. These models are the primary tools informing estimates of how much greenhouse gas emissions from human activity might increase, and therefore how much climate might change, in the absence of emissions reduction policies (Nakicenovic et al., 2000). They have also been used extensively to estimate the costs of various types of climate change policy (Weyant and Hill, 1999) and the potential damages from the impacts of future climate change (Ahmad et al., 2001).

While global model analyses are not typically aimed at investigating land use per se, land use change can play an important role in analyses of climate change, biodiversity loss, and agricultural production. For example, land use and land use change are estimated to account for about 30 percent of total greenhouse gas emissions, primarily carbon dioxide (CO_2) from deforestation, nitrous oxide (N_2O) from the application of fertilizers, and methane (CH_4) from livestock and rice production. Global model analyses have addressed such land use–related questions as:

- What is the potential for commercial biomass as a fuel source— especially if there are future constraints on carbon emissions—and how might it compete for land use with production of food and feed crops?
- What might future greenhouse gas emissions be from land use change, and how important might they be relative to emissions from energy production and use?
- What options for reducing greenhouse gas emissions from land use are there, and how large a role could they play in greenhouse gas reduction strategies?
- How much land might have to be devoted to agriculture in order to meet future demand?
- How might climate change affect future agricultural productivity, and which regions appear to be most vulnerable to these effects?

Role of Population in Global Models of Land Use

For this chapter we reviewed nine global models (Table 3-1) that simulate land use change to varying degrees:

1. AgLU: Agriculture and Land Use
2. AIM: Asian-Pacific Integrated Model
3. ASF: Atmospheric Stabilization Framework
4. BLS/AEZ: Basic Linked System/Agro-ecological Zones
5. EPPA: Emissions Prediction and Policy Analysis
6. FARM: Future Agricultural Resources Model
7. IMAGE: Integrated Model to Assess the Greenhouse Effect
8. IMPACT: International Model for Policy Analysis of Agricultural Commodities and Trade
9. MARIA: Multi-regional Approach for Resource and Industry Allocation

These models include all of those used to produce long-term scenarios of greenhouse gas emissions for the Intergovernmental Panel on Climate Change (IPCC; models are AgLU, AIM, ASF, IMAGE, MARIA), as well as those used to produce scenarios of changes in future ecosystem goods and services for the forthcoming Millennium Ecosystem Assessment (MA; models are AIM, IMAGE, and IMPACT). In addition, we reviewed three models (BLS/AEZ, FARM, IMPACT) that have been used extensively to explore scenarios of future agricultural demand and supply, and one prominent model (EPPA/IGSM) used in climate change analyses with a highly simplified land use component that is representative of a much larger number of models in which land use is not a primary focus. Table 3-1 lists these models along with key references, the modeling approach each one takes, and the level of regional disaggregation they employ. Population enters these models principally as a determinant of the demand for goods that may require land for production and as a factor of production.

In these models land use change is typically driven by demand for agricultural products, commercial wood products, and biofuels (traditional or modern or both). Land is used to produce these products, and some of the models simulate the allocation of land to different uses and the consequences for the environment. The models vary in their approach to projecting demand and supply and in geographical and commodity detail. For example, the EPPA model (Babiker et al., 2001) is representative of a relatively simple approach to land use within integrated assessments (although it has a relatively detailed representation of the energy sector). It is a 12-region, 8-sector general equilibrium model in which crops, livestock, and forest products are represented by a single composite good. Production

TABLE 3-1 Global Models

Model	Institution	Key References	Approach[a]	Geographic Regions
AgLU (Agriculture and Land Use)	Joint Global Change Research Institute (JGCRI), Pacific Northwest National Laboratory, USA	Sands and Leimbach, 2003	PE	11
AIM (Asian-Pacific Integrated Model)	National Institute for Environment Studies (NIES), Japan	Masui et al., 2001; Jiang et al., 2000	S	17
ASF (Atmospheric Stabilization Framework)	U.S. Environmental Protection Agency	Lashof and Tirpak, 1990	GE[b]	34
BLS/AEZ (Basic Linked System/ Agro-ecological Zones)	International Institute for Applied Systems Analysis (IIASA), Austria	Fischer et al., 1988, 2002b	GE	34
EPPA (Emissions Prediction and Policy Analysis)	Massachusetts Institute of Technology (MIT), USA	Babiker et al., 2001	GE	12
FARM (Future Agricultural Resources Model)	U.S. Department of Agriculture	Darwin et al., 1995	GE	8
IMAGE (Integrated Model to Assess the Greenhouse Effect)	National Institute of Public Health and the Environment (RIVM), the Netherlands	Alcamo et al., 1998	S[b]	17
IMPACT (International Model for Policy Analysis of Agricultural Commodities and Trade)	International Food Policy Research Institute (IFPRI), USA	Rosegrant et al., 2002b	PE	36
MARIA (Multi-regional Approach for Resource and Industry Allocation)	Science University of Tokyo, Japan	Mori and Takahashi, 1998	S	8

[a]GE = general equilibrium; PE = partial equilibrium; S = simulation.
[b]Based on the 1990 version of the Basic Linked System model; simulation approach is taken beyond 2050.

of this good treats land as a fixed factor. The current version of the model is not aimed at producing realistic scenarios of land use change or shifts in use of land among various categories, but rather at reasonable scenarios of emissions resulting from the production of goods requiring land as an input. The relation between emissions and production of these goods is treated exogenously, capturing the potential effects of shifts in land use only implicitly.

In contrast, the IMAGE model (Alcamo et al., 1998) has the most detailed simulation of spatially explicit land use. Production of agricultural and forest goods uses land based on assumptions about changes in the productivity of land over time. Spatially explicit land use is simulated using a global grid of 0.5 × 0.5 degree geographic cells. Grid cells are ranked according to suitability for a particular land use based on specified rule set, and demand is satisfied using the cells with highest suitability first. Thus IMAGE produces scenarios not only of the total amount of land devoted to alternative uses (and calculates the emissions associated with these uses), but also of *where* land is being put to each use.

The three models that have been used primarily in agricultural studies (BLS/AEZ, FARM, and IMPACT) are, not surprisingly, the models with the greatest commodity detail in sectors that use land as an input. IMPACT, for example, is a 36-region partial equilibrium model with 16 agricultural commodities. FARM and BLS/AEZ include an explicit accounting of available land within each region, using spatially explicit biophysical information in calculating potential yields. FARM defines a baseline allocation of land to six different classes that implicitly captures variations in soil types and climate conditions, and climate change scenarios from general circulation models can be used to revise this allocation based on changed temperature and precipitation patterns. BLS/AEZ combines a spatially explicit biophysical model of potential productivity of global land resources with a 34-region, 10-sector general equilibrium model. The spatial component allows a more detailed and realistic accounting for available land, its potential productivity, and the effect of future climate change on productivity.

While a variety of approaches are taken by these global models to land use change in general, the role of population is conceptually similar across all models. On the demand side (Table 3-2), population size acts as a simple scale factor for demand for food, wood products, and energy (which can be satisfied in part by traditional or modern biomass or both). Demand for these goods and services in turn drives land use. Demand is typically a function of population size, income, and prices (although see Table 3-2 for exceptions). Higher income leads to a shift in demand toward more animal products, a shift that is modeled either with commodity-specific income elasticities of demand, by exogenous scenario assumption, or both.

On the supply side (Table 3-3), population enters through labor force as a factor of production. Only BLS/AEZ takes age structure into account in specifying labor force. Demographic factors generally do not affect the allocation of land across uses. Most of the models use a general or partial equilibrium framework, so that market-clearing prices allocate land among competing uses. IMAGE is a notable exception. Its rule set for spatially explicit land allocation uses population density as one factor among several others in decisions to convert uncultivated land in particular grid cells to agriculture. Population density itself is projected based on current spatially explicit population data sets (Center for International Earth Science Information Network, 2000) scaled up by projected future population growth.

Global models use exogenous population projections, typically scenarios produced by the United Nations, IIASA, or the World Bank. A few global models incorporate their own cohort component population projection modules, enabling modelers to produce their own population projections if desired. Typically there are no explicit feedbacks onto demographic processes in these models; future fertility, mortality, and migration are specified exogenously. However, demographic assumptions are often chosen to be consistent (in the modeler's judgment) with assumptions about other socioeconomic trends, such as economic growth rates.

In addition to the direct effects of population on land use, population size can have an indirect effect on land use through price feedbacks. A larger population size will, all else being equal, raise the price for agricultural goods due to greater demand and the consequent need for increased production. These price changes may lead to a shift in demand for commodities with a lower land use intensity of production.

The simple manner in which population affects land use in global models, and the high level of aggregation at which actors affect consumption or production, imply that the gulf between such modeling and research on population and land use at the subnational level is wide. Insights gained from case studies of small, subnational areas have typically emphasized the importance of context rather than possibilities for the kind of generalization of relationships to large spatial scales and longer time horizons necessary for use in global modeling. For example, lessons drawn from analysis of land use at the village level (Walsh et al., Chapter 6), or in the context of particular land reserves (Liu et al., Chapter 9) are difficult to scale up to the level of countries or larger world regions, which are used in global modeling, given their dependence on context. Some attempts have been made to draw more general conclusions by carrying out meta-analyses of the large number of case studies at the national or subnational level. While this work has led to insights and caveats about the complexity and context-dependence of the relationship between demography and land use change (Lambin et al., 2001), putting

TABLE 3-2 Summary of Demand for Commodities Requiring Land Use in Global Models

Model	Total Commodities	Agriculture[a]		Forest Products			Demand Methodology
		Crops	Animal Products	Industrial Wood	Comm. Biomass	Trad. Biomass	
AgLU (Agriculture and Land Use)	5	1	1	1	1	1	Calculate market clearing prices; demand a function of own price and income, scaled with population; agricultural products also include exogenous path of per capita calorie consumption
AIM (Asian-Pacific Integrated Model)	6	2	2	1	1	N/A	Exogenous demand[b]
ASF (Atmospheric Stabilization Framework)	12	6	3	1	1	1	For agriculture, similar to Basic Linked System through 2050[c]
BLS/AEZ (Basic Linked System/Agro-ecological Zones)	9	6	3	N/A	N/A	N/A	Maximize per capita utility based on prices, income; scale with population. Shift diet from staples to vegetable and livestock products according to calorie intake limitations
EPPA (Emissions Prediction and Policy Analysis)	1 (composite agriculture and forest products)						Maximize per capita utility based on prices, income; scale with population
FARM (Future Agricultural Resources Model)	7	4	2	1	N/A	1[d]	Maximize per capita utility based on prices, income; scale with population

Model							Demand
IMAGE (Integrated Model to Assess the Greenhouse Effect)	13	12	1	2^e	1^e	1^e	Maximize utility based on exogenously preferred consumption pattern for composite crops and composite animal products, land availability, and land requirements. Demand disaggregated to 13 commodities based on exogenous specifications
IMPACT (International Model for Policy Analysis of Agricultural Commodities and Trade)	16	10	6	N/A	N/A	N/A	Calculate market clearing prices; demand a function of prices and income, scaled with population
MARIA (Multi-regional Approach for Resource and Industry Allocation)	6	1	3	N/A	2	N/A	Calculate income scenario with multiregion GE model; demand a region-specific function of income^f

[a]Agricultural commodities include sectors with indirect land use requirements, such as processed foods and dairy products.

[b]Demand appears to be defined exogenously by scenarios, but documentation obtained to date is insufficient to confirm this characterization.

[c]Regions representing the United States, China, the former Soviet Union, and India differ from the basic general equilibrium structure of other regions. The U.S. model contains an econometric supply model; in China, demand is specified exogenously, the former Soviet Union model reflects centrally planned policies rather than being based on balanced supply and demand; and the India model uses a different aggregation scheme. A simulation approach is taken for forest products.

[d]Fuelwood is part of a single composite forestry good.

[e]Demand for industrial wood products is calculated separately based on income and available forest land; demand for commercial and traditional biomass is calculated separately in the IMAGE energy module.

[f]Relationship between food consumption and income is bidirectional; thus scenarios that encounter food production constraints due to land scarcity also suffer losses in income.

TABLE 3-3 Supply Side Summary of Global Models

Model	Land Use Categories	Geographic Resolution	Land Allocation Methodology	Population Role
AgLU (Agriculture and Land Use)	3 (crops, pasture, forest products)	11 regions, implicit subregional potential yield distributions	Maximize return based on joint probability distribution over yields for alternative land uses, prices, and nonland production costs	None
AIM (Asian-Pacific Integrated Model)	4 (crops, pasture, forests, biomass)	17 regions	Minimize costs of production given available labor, land, capital and exogenous yield assumptions	Total population a factor of production
ASF (Atmospheric Stabilization Framework)	Same as BLS	34 regions	Same as BLS through 2050, but production potential exogenous	Same as BLS to 2050, none beyond 2050
BLS/AEZ (Basic Linked System/Agro-ecological Zones)	BLS: 6 crop sectors, 3 livestock sectors AEZ: 154 (crop, fodder, pasture types)	BLS: 34 regions AEZ: 5 minute latitude/longitude grid	Maximize return given prices, calculated yields, and available land, labor, and capital	Working age population a factor of production
EPPA (Emissions Prediction and Policy Analysis)	1	12 regions	None	Total population a factor of production

Model	Land categories	Spatial resolution	Production/land use determination	Role of population
FARM (Future Agricultural Resources Model)	6 (by crop types/pasture)	0.5 × 0.5 degree grid	Maximize return given prices, calculated production potential, and available land, water, labor, and capital	Total population a factor of production
IMAGE (Integrated Model to Assess the Greenhouse Effect)	4 (agriculture [12 types], natural vegetation, forests, regrowth forests)	0.5 × 0.5 degree grid	Regional production is equal to regional demand minus exogenously specified trade. Spatial allocation of land based on ranking of grid cells according to suitability based on specified rule set	Population distribution affects land use suitability ranking of grid cells
IMPACT (International Model for Policy Analysis of Agricultural Commodities and Trade)	1 (agriculture [10 types])	36 regions	Land use a function of prices and exogenously specified trend in harvested area	Population an implicit determinant of exogenous trend in harvested area
MARIA (Multi-regional Approach for Resource and Industry Allocation)	7 (cropland, commercial biomass, natural forest, afforested, grassland, urban, oth. non-productive)	8 regions	Land use a function of demand multiplied by exogenous yield assumptions	None

these lessons to use in global quantitative analyses is another matter. For example, Geist and Lambin (2002) conclude that under some conditions, and in some regions, in-migration of frontier settlers has been an important factor driving deforestation, while under other conditions and in other regions economic factors, such as market failures, growth of timber markets, or price increases for cash crops, have been dominant. These findings could be used to support the development of alternative scenarios for a range of possible land use changes, but they are harder to interpret in more quantitative terms.

A more promising bridge between the two types of studies is spatially explicit analysis carried out at the level of large world regions (countries or groups of countries). Such analyses trade global coverage for more spatial detail and heterogeneity within the region. This detail offers the possibility that results from studies on a local scale could meaningfully inform the regional analysis, while the regional models can in turn inform global modeling. We illustrate this possibility by describing a detailed model of China developed by the Land Use Change (LUC) project at IIASA, discussing several key issues and opportunities it raises.

THE IIASA-LUC MODEL OF CHINA

Following accession to the World Trade Organization (WTO), Chinese policy makers are facing the challenge of defining transition strategies that maintain a socially sustainable level of rural incomes and employment, meet the needs of rapidly growing urban populations, are environmentally sustainable, and meet international commitments. The IIASA-LUC project, together with partners in Europe and China, has been developing new methodologies and modeling tools for a detailed case study of China (the CHINAGRO project) to help inform these policy choices. This study focuses attention on two themes central to projecting land use changes: (1) cross-sectoral linkages, including such important land use drivers as urbanization, infrastructure development, water supply, bioenergy production, and international trade and (2) spatial and social diversity, that is, the overarching question of what constitutes an adequate treatment of real world heterogeneity, aggregation issues, and scaling.

Need for Spatially and Socially Explicit Analysis of China's Development

The CHINAGRO project takes into account two prominent trends: China's increasing international trade relations as a result of its accession to the WTO and the change of dietary patterns due to rapid per capita income increases and fast urbanization. The project analyzes the impacts of these trends on the agricultural sector and on the livelihoods of the rural population that depends on agriculture.

Specifically, one of the issues under study is whether, in light of the fast-rising demand for animal proteins by Chinese consumers and the sustained rural to urban migration, the country should aim at (1) self-sufficiency in cereals, protein feeds, and meat, including animal feed; (2) importing feed; or (3) importing meat. A second issue under investigation is, not surprisingly, how the WTO accession, the Doha Round, and more generally China's opening to world trade will affect the agricultural economy of the country, and what feedbacks to the world market and hence to consumers and producers in other regions can be expected. A third issue is to assess the implications of major ongoing infrastructural projects, in particular those aiming at redirecting water flows.

Although this particular set of issues is specific to Chinese conditions, one might expect that they are not unique, and that well established methods of economics, for example computable general equilibrium models, can readily be applied, by incorporating the major specificities of the country in the demand and supply functions of such a model. Our experience suggests that such an aggregate national-level macro approach would not be fruitful for analyzing the relevant population-economy-environment relationships, as it would not capture the critical linkages between and within China's diverse regions.

Recognition of the basic fact that the scale of a country should be accounted for has taken a prominent place in our research in the past years. We may note in this context that the usual practice in macro modeling, including in computable general equilibrium models, is to apply a model structure independent of scale. In these models, the scale of a country or region enters through large numbers, for example, the population number or the size of the land area, and possibly through the magnitude of some model coefficients, but nowhere appears in the structure of these models. For instance, the model structure for a small country, for example The Netherlands, would typically be the same as the one used for Brazil or China.

To study these issues, CHINAGRO conducts its analysis within a modeling framework that (1) represents the consumer, producer, and government decisions in the various regions, with farmers represented at county level; (2) builds the supply response on spatially explicit assessment of the resource base and its biophysical characteristics; (3) describes agricultural processing and supply of farm inputs; and (4) accounts for transportation costs in the economy.

The model provides a representation of different social agents in different regions, their income levels, preferences, resource constraints, and certain environmental implications of their activities and covers interactions on regional markets between supply, demand, and prices, both in the absence of, as well as in response to policy changes while allowing for interregional as well as international trade.

A distinctive feature of the CHINAGRO project is that we seek to pay due attention to the enormous spatial and social diversity of the country. We realize this aim by conducting our analysis at the county level, distinguishing over 2,400 of these administrative units. This detail is essential in the analysis of Chinese agriculture and its scope for transformation, because the country is so diverse and, through its fast economic growth, becoming ever more so. Population densities differ tremendously throughout China; consumers have different lifestyles across the country; crop growing conditions, cropping patterns, and yields vary widely; and distances are large, implying that a policy change, for example at the border, will affect consumers and producers very differently, depending on their location.

With improved computer technology and software, it has become ever easier to maintain large databases, and to visualize the contents of these databases through maps and other representations of distributions. These visual statistical techniques enable us to present a massive set of data in a tractable form and to investigate the nature of the joint distribution of production, population, natural resources, consumption, etc., in physical space and along social dimensions.

However, the mere description of correlations is not sufficient. To go from analysis based on a geographic information system (GIS), which can provide some spatially detailed descriptive understanding of China's land use conditions and history, to a prescriptive understanding of future land use changes, a highly structured modeling approach is required.

Fundamentals of the CHINAGRO Modeling Approach

Land use represents a critical intersection of the environment and the economy, of which population as a factor in supply and demand is an important element. Land use changes are often directly linked with economic decisions. This recognition has led LUC to choose an economic framework as the organizing principle in the analysis with a broad set of activities geared toward providing a biophysical and geographical underpinning to the representation of land-based economic sectors in modeling land and water use decisions.

In the current CHINAGRO framework, population characteristics enter in an exogenous manner, albeit with a fair amount of detail regarding geographical distribution, income level, and occupation. Population projections employ cohort methods, with fertility and mortality reflecting geographical features as well as a distinction between rural and urban cohorts. Although internal migration across provinces is currently dealt with in a scenario approach, the model includes sufficient geographical, demographic, and economic detail that could allow an endogenous treatment of various pull and push factors of migration such as, for example, age structure, income differences among regions, rural and urban income differences, and off-farm employment opportunities in the nonagricultural sector.

Such considerations have defined our approach in four ways. First, we have made significant efforts to assess the regionally varying land use potentials of the country, for example, in terms of crop production and areas suitable for crop cultivation, with and without irrigation, and for pastures. The spatially explicit representation of potentials, on a raster of grid cells of 5 by 5 kilometers (km), offers an opportunity to incorporate detailed land cover and topographic information from remote sensing and basic knowledge from crop and soil sciences on current limitations and expected technological developments, as well as from water engineers and irrigation experts. This agro-ecological assessment (for details of the agro-ecological zones method, see Fischer et al., 2002b) defines the agronomic/technological option space of (rural/agricultural) actors in the system.

Second, at the spatially detailed level of counties, we maintain the key physical balances for land, labor, fertilizer, and animal feeds, and also balances and flows between the farm sector and the rest of the economy. This enables us to reflect the diversity of farms across China and to represent key features and constraints of farm management regarding crop cultivation, animal husbandry, and the interaction between both.

Third, we relate these balances through transport flows to the local, regional, and international markets to match consumer demand and industrial use with domestic supply and net foreign trade. This step links a location to the province and national economic context.

Fourth, we adopt for the model as a whole a welfare approach, whereby consumers and producer interests are represented explicitly, through utility and profit maximizing behavior, and the budgets of every agent can be made explicit and kept consistent, while markets clear and transport flows are routed optimally through the country. In addition, the framework is sufficiently flexible to accommodate government policies and economic distortions at various levels, ranging from tariffs at the national border, income transfers among rural and urban actors and across regions, to agricultural taxes or subsidies at the county level.

The CHINAGRO welfare model is based on detailed geographical and statistical databases to make analysis and simulations with the CHINAGRO model adequate for the policy questions under consideration.

CHINAGRO Welfare Model

The CHINAGRO model divides China into 8 economic regions comprising of some 2,432 administrative units, mostly counties. It distinguishes 17 commodities (16 agricultural and 1 nonagricultural) and 6 socioeconomic classes (3 rural and 3 urban income classes). For each commodity the model has regional markets connected to the international market. Consumer preferences, geographical distribution of supply, and costs of trade and transportation jointly determine the resulting endogenous trade flows. The nonagricultural production and consumption of tradable commodities are modeled at the level of the 8 economic regions. The economy is opened up to the rest of the world; imports and exports can occur endogenously. Trade between regions and the international market is modeled bilaterally (Keyzer, 2004).

China's agriculture and economy are characterized by a considerable spatial diversity. Distances between producing and consuming areas are sometimes substantial and cannot be neglected. China's direction toward a more market-oriented economy creates price differences across the country. Transport and handling costs play a major role in this. From the start of the project, a key issue was how to incorporate the price transmission between the international harbors and China's vast hinterland.

Spatial Representation of Agricultural Supply

For these reasons, the administrative unit of the county was introduced to represent agricultural activities (14 aggregate cropping activities, 9 livestock supply activities, 5 farm inputs supply activities). It is also the market level for certain rather immobile commodities (e.g., organic fertilizer) and factors (e.g., labor and grassland) used in agricultural production; they are traded only locally. As a consequence of this spatial refinement, the model needs information on trade and transportation costs to connect county-level and regional markets. As mentioned before, a separate transport flow model supplies the necessary coefficients.

The model includes a detailed component for agricultural production operating at the level of the approximately 2,400 counties to achieve a proper multicommodity, multiagent representation, which reflects the diversity of the resource basis and cropping patterns of farms and the nontradability of some of the commodities and inputs between them.

The basic structure of the agricultural production relations consists of an output function and an input response function, linked by means of an agricultural output index. This output index is a quantity aggregation of crops produced. It is based on a standard aggregation rule used in economics, namely a constant elasticity of transformation function. As a starting point for supply estimation, we derived a database of rain-fed and irrigated crop production in 1997 and 2000. The compilation was based on county-level statistical information of crop production and agricultural inputs, land survey data, and spatially detailed (i.e., mapped on a 5 km grid) distribution of cultivated land.

Production is codetermined by the biophysical potential of land and by the level of factor inputs per unit of land. Potential output is based on results generated by an enhanced agro-ecological zones assessment model (Fischer et al., 2002b). The input response function is specified as a generalization of a complex but popular yield function in agronomic literature, called the Mitscherlich-Baule yield function. The rationale behind this specification is that the observed actual crop output level represents a certain fraction of the biophysical potential and is determined by the factor input levels per unit of land, as well as by the technology employed (Albersen et al., 2002).

Spatial Structure of Commodity Markets and Trade

The model emphasizes the central role of commodity markets and prices in the coordination of actor decisions. It distinguishes regional markets and a world market for each commodity. Price differences between regional markets and the international market are explained from trade and transportation costs and, possibly, government-imposed margins (taxes, subsidies, trade quota). Model simulations cover the period 1997-2030. The model is initialized on the basis of detailed benchmark data for the years 1992 and 1997.

The market structure is one of the key features of the welfare program. Below, we outline its representation. Three types of commodities may be distinguished: local commodities, which do not leave the county, regional commodities, which are traded intraregionally, and widely tradable commodities, which are traded intraregionally, interregionally, and, in principle, internationally (Figure 3-1). The arrows indicate the (possible) directions of the trade flows.

Each trade flow implies at the same time a price margin, due to transportation, trade services, and possibly physical transformation of the commodity (e.g., from grain to flour), as well as taxation. In each region, price margins are distinguished between the producer and the regional market, with additional margins to bring the product to the rural and urban consumer, respectively. Furthermore, two-way price margins are specified between regional markets and the world market, with the actual margin dependent on the direction of the trade flow (Figure 3-2). Transportation margins depend partly on such geographic features as topography and transportation infrastructure availability.

Model Calibration Procedures

Modular calibration procedures were established through which it can be ensured that the base year (i.e., for 1997) equilibrium solution of the full

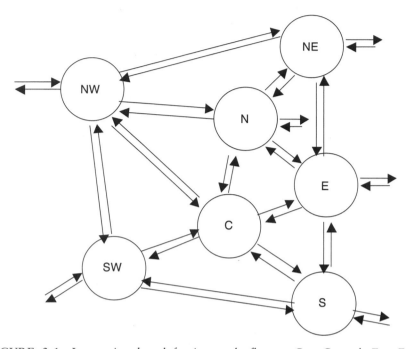

FIGURE 3-1   Interregional and foreign trade flows.   C = Central, E = East, N = North, NE = Northeast, NW = Northwest, S = South, SW = Southwest.

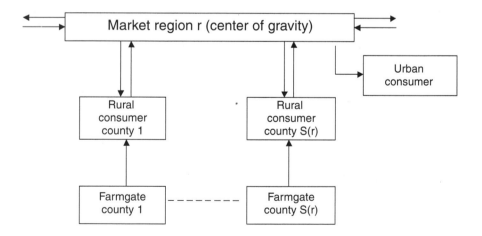

FIGURE 3-2   Trade flows inside a region.

welfare program exactly replicates the base year data (Keyzer and van Veen, 2004). For consumption, we allow for a smooth transition between different linear expenditure systems, under changes in incomes and prices, and specify a separate regression program for its calibration. For interregional trade, we present a new dual programming technique to calibrate flows so as to meet given net export positions of each region at prices that are sufficiently close to the observed ones and cover the associated transportation costs. Nonagricultural inputs are treated as closing items to fit the balance of payments. We note that such a modular decomposition of the calibration process is essential for the future maintenance of this rather large model, as it makes it possible to keep database operations fully separate from the modeling work, while improvements in the database are in a transparent way transmitted to the model outcome and future replacements in specific model components can be implemented without requiring a complete new calibration. Moreover, initialization at a fully calibrated base year solution provides a large number of checks and clues for detecting data inconsistencies and programming errors during the debugging phase of model building and also speeds up model computations and solution finding (Keyzer and van Veen, 2004).

Theoretical Background on Aggregation: Micro-Macro Debates

We have argued in the previous section that China is far too large and diverse to be dealt with as a single agent or as an economy with only few income groups and producers, for example, in an aggregate computable general equilibrium framework. A crucial question is what to do then and how to represent the behavior of individuals spread over a spatial and social continuum by means of a tractable number of representative agents and markets, which can be processed in larger models.

These reasons motivated further investigations in the China study on the subject of aggregation. New theoretical results are now available (Keyzer, 2003b), obtained by our CHINAGRO collaborators at Free University Amsterdam (SOW-VU), with regard to four aspects of model specification and diversity: (1) aggregation over (profit maximizing) producers and individuals with comparable utilities; aggregation over technologies; (2) aggregation over heterogeneous consumers who maximize utilities subject to budget constraints; (3) spatial aggregation over markets; (4) aggregation over commodities.

A main finding is that the mathematical technique of mollification or function averaging, which dates back to the 1930s, provides a basis for many of the fundamental assumptions in economics. If we take payoffs, outputs, or utilities to be comparable, that is, measurable in a common unit across the individuals in the continuum, *exact* aggregation is possible. The aim of exact aggregation is to represent exactly the behavior of many, that is, a continuum, of individuals by a single (representative) agent.

If we stipulate, first, that individuals live in a multidimensional space characterized by a smooth joint distribution that describes the fixed characteristics of their environment (a space with a finite number of physical, social, quality, and possibly even stochastic and temporal dimensions), and, second, that they choose optimally from the options they face, given a finite number of economic signals they receive (prices, taxes, quotas), then it can be shown that discrete choices of actors combined with smooth densities lead to aggregate properties that are usually postulated in microeconomic models: strict concavity/convexity; additive separability; differentiability; risk aversion; and monotonicity of demand. This makes it possible to represent profit-maximizing farmers in a spatial and social continuum, yet to obtain relatively standard micro models of agricultural production, with strictly concave and differentiable production functions (Keyzer, 2003b).

Noncomparability of payoffs/utilities creates a form of individuality that only becomes more intractable in a continuum, essentially because the micro structure becomes too rich to be represented by parametric forms at the aggregate level. No exact solution is possible any longer. The idea then is to consider aggregation as a problem of optimal rather than exact representation. We seek to find out (a) how many income groups are necessary to represent the underlying functions, (b) how the population weights on these groups should be determined, and (c) how the group demand functions should be specified. The kernel learning technique of support-vector regression provides a suitable tool to determine optimal weights of representative agents and optimal levels of aggregation (Keyzer, 2003b).

The spatial aggregation over markets can be regarded as a special case of aggregation over commodities. It aggregates over commodities that are homogeneous physically and differ only by location and can be converted into one another through transportation. As for commodities, there is no clean theoretical aggregation solution over markets. Hence, in CHINAGRO, we operate two models in parallel: (1) a general equilibrium welfare model, in which intraregional trade is subject to fixed transportation costs for all net purchases and net sales of a county and (2) a (set of) single commodity partial equilibrium model(s) on a 10 by 10 kilometer grid.

Projections and the Role of Population in the China Model

Given the size and the regional diversity of China, any sensible analysis must consider the regional differences in climate, soil, and water resource endowments, population density, and social and economic development. Multiregional assessments require regionally detailed scenarios. A key component of such scenarios is the evolution of the population in the different regions (Toth, Cao, and Hizsnyik, 2003). Such regionally disaggregated population projections are needed for estimating regional food demand and regional labor supply. They can also serve as background information for modeling development-induced migration, if migration processes are to be explicitly modeled.

Province-Level Population Projections

With a view to the above circumstances, our modeling strategy for producing province-level population projections entails the incorporation of relevant data from various sources, their harmonization to ensure consistency, and the preparation of detailed projections by using the maximum amount of information available about the relevant features of the Chinese population. The core building blocks of the projection model are the national-level projections of urban and rural populations by age groups prepared by Cao (2003) and the population distribution across provinces in rural and urban areas by age groups reported by the 2000 census (National Bureau of Statistics of the People's Republic of China, 2002). Additional information sources include provincial projections of birth rates and death rates; projections of provincial urbanization rates; and the magnitude, direction, and age structure of interprovincial migration.

Cao (2000, 2003) prepared a series of multistate population projections for China at the national level by distinguishing demographic patterns (fertility, mortality, migration) in the future according to education achievement and the place of residence (rural or urban) in addition to the usual male-female and age differentiation. Cao clustered her assumptions in a scenario matrix along two groups of attributes: fertility, mortality, educational achievements, and migration on one hand, and convergence of fertility levels in educational categories and in the urban and rural regions on the other.

For the national total, the population projections start from a level of 1.275 billion in 2000. There is relatively little variation among projections of total population for 2010 (about 1.36 billion) and 2020 (1.41-1.43 billion), the range becoming somewhat wider thereafter; in year 2030 a projected range of 1.43-1.47 billion people is estimated. The range of scenarios in CHINAGRO is somewhat narrower than population levels projected by the United Nations. The IIASA projections used here are based on a carefully defined range of fertility assumptions: a total fertility rate in 2030 of between 1.42 and 1.64 in urban areas (total fertility rate estimated to be 1.58 in 2000) and between 1.85 and 2.11 for rural areas (estimated at 1.98 in 2000). It may be noted that the very low total fertility rates reported by the Chinese State Statistical Bureau in the statistical data of the 2000 census (total fertility rate of 1.27 in urban areas and 1.43 in rural areas) deviate from findings of Chinese and international demographers and after thorough discussion were not adopted in CHINAGRO as being unrealistically low (Toth et al., 2003).

The modeling procedure for regional decomposition is based on the following assumptions: the future evolution of the population in China is properly depicted by Cao's national projections, while the best source of the provincial distribution is the 2000 census. From this longitudinal (national population over time) and cross-sectional (provincial distribution in 2000) information, an appropriate decomposition procedure can be developed that provides the evolution of the provincial population over the next 30 to 50 years (Toth et al., 2003). The decomposition procedure can be enhanced and the precision of the results can be increased by drawing on information from supplementary models like statistics-based projections of regional birth rates, death rates, urbanization rates, and interprovincial migration.

Urbanization

The Chinese society has been going through various phases of fast urbanization and antiurbanization over the past half-century. For the CHINAGRO scenario development, Liu, Li, and Zhang (2003) present an in-depth analysis of the characteristics and trends of China's urbanization. They conclude that the urbanization process in China has been heavily regulated and has always been under strict government control. The result of these tight policies is a relatively underurbanized Chinese society in comparison to other developing countries at a similar stage of socioeconomic development and also in comparison to the level of industrialization in China. An important component of the government policy has been rural urbanization adopted to limit rural-urban migration to cities.

There are several important implications of the strong government influence on the urbanization process and on rural-urban migration in the past. First, it has suppressed at least part of the intended migration that would have taken place in the absence of government control. Second, due to the regulation, the complex permit scheme and the difficulties of obtaining permits to change place of residence (*hukou*) has resulted in illegal or tolerated migration, a large part of which remained unregistered. The combined implication is that statistical models trying to establish key historical patterns and relationships for use in projecting possible future trends may be somewhat misleading.

Liu et al. (2003) conducted a thorough statistical analysis of the urbanization process at the national and the provincial level. They transformed the historical data series according to the 2000 definition and applied suitable assumptions about the shares of population with *hukou* (i.e., with registration) and urban immigrants without *hukou* (i.e., without registration).

A series of market-oriented institutional reforms has been or is expected to be launched in China to actively promote the urbanization process, because the Chinese government has realized the serious adverse consequences on urbanization and economic growth resulting from the former urban-rural segmented institutional regulations and therefore defined active promotion of the urbanization process as one of the five strategic priorities of China's economic development during the 10th Five Year Plan period. It includes (1) a reform of the *hukou* system, which will gradually relax the restrictions on farmers' residences in cities and eventually establish a free rural-urban migration system; (2) a reform of the employment system. China's urban and rural labor markets are still separated up to now, which means that rural laborers are still subjected to various discriminative constraints and restrictions; and (3) a reform of the rural land tenure and transfer system and improvement of the social security system in urban and rural areas.

In general, land is state-owned in cities and towns and collective-owned in rural areas. Each farmer is usually allocated by contract the land use rights on a certain amount of collective-owned land in the village or has a share of benefits from leasing or selling collective-owned land. However, in the current situation, the farmer will automatically lose his rights on collective-owned land after he migrates and resides in a city or town. By law, his land use rights on his former collective-owned land are not transferable and cannot be sold. To make things worse, the employment in cities and towns is not stable and the social security system is still backward, particularly in small cities and towns. Thus, plenty of farmers, especially those in suburban or rapidly developing areas, do not want to become urban residents at the cost of losing their land use rights on collective-owned rural land. Liu et al. (2003) conclude that the rural land tenure system has to be reformed to increase its mobility and that the social security system needs to be improved to provide basic life security for both urban and rural residents.

The process of urbanization is being considered as a mighty potential for economic development in the next phase. It is anticipated that urbanization will accelerate in the next decades, thus making significant contributions to economic growth.

Starting from 36 percent urban population estimated by the 5th Census for 2000 and based on different assumptions on the prospects of China's market-orientated institutional reforms, we project that China's urbanization level will reach 42 to 45 percent in 2010, some 48 to 55 percent in 2020, and will fall in the range of 54 to 64 percent in 2030 (Liu et al., 2003).

Having many more and wealthier consumers in urban conditions will have profound impacts on demand. Total direct food consumption of cereals and other staple grains changes modestly in the CHINAGRO Baserun simulations, an increase of only 3 percent during 2003 to 2030. The explanation lies in two factors: first, the food consumption level in China is already high, and there is a low or even negative propensity to spend extra income on food grains, especially for urban consumers. Second, there are significant differences between rural and urban consumption patterns, with lower per capita consumption of cereals by urban residents compared with rural diets. As a consequence, there is a 10 percent decline in average per capita consumption of cereals, even though per capita incomes are much higher in 2030 than in the base year.

While urbanization is slowing down cereal consumption, it is likely to accelerate increases in meat consumption. Urban diets include higher consumption of meat, and per capita meat consumption is responding strongly to income growth. An important change is a rise in meat consumption per capita, from 49 kg per capita in 2003 to 86 kg in 2030, which still falls a few kilograms below the present-day average of industrialized countries and almost 30 kg below the figures for United States. In the Baserun simulations, these factors combine to result in a doubling of total meat consumption between 2003 and 2030.

Transport Flow Model

For the analysis of an economy, specifically also for the agricultural sector and land use change, accounting for transportation is important because people have to commute between home and work, and goods have to be shipped from producers to markets to consumers. In the case of a small country, considering transport as a special type of service may be a reasonable abstraction. For a large country like China, however, the very difficult additional aspect comes to the fore that transport deeply affects price transmission and market structure, as the abstraction becomes untenable of all goods being traded on a single market with one transport cost irrespective of distance and weight and disregarding availability and quality of transportation infrastructure.

It is clear that for the project, and more generally for the line of research that seeks to embed Chinese agriculture in an economy-wide setting, the challenge is to find a level of representation that on one hand is sufficiently detailed to reflect underlying densities of resources and farm characteristics, and on the other hand distinguishes sufficient market nodes, to provide a realistic picture of trade flows and price transmission mechanisms.

The transport flow model builds on work of Ermoliev, Keyzer, and Norkin (2001) and Keyzer and Ermoliev (1999) on aggregation in a spatial continuum. The transport flow model is a partial equilibrium welfare model, which maximizes money metric consumer utility minus transport costs and is subject to site-specific commodity balances.

It uses the formal infrastructure of highways, railways, and waterways (applying statistically recorded expenditures at the provincial level on transport in each category per ton-kilometer) and the less formal infrastructure of secondary roads and pathways, which provide the link between the farmer's field and the main transport infrastructure. The combined cost of the formal and informal infrastructure is shown in Plate 1.

To solve this problem, Keyzer (2003a) has formulated a new algorithm. Its basic idea is that of imposing a gravity ordering inspired by hydrological modeling. At given prices, optimal transport flows never run from a destination with a high price to one with a lower price, just as gravity ensures that water never flows to a higher location. This makes it possible to develop a computational scheme that runs recursively from one site to the next, solving the local welfare problem (for a given price ordering) and proceeding with adjusting the price ordering (i.e., the price landscape) to reflect marginal values of the commodity inflows. The algorithm is monotonically converging for any initial price ordering, improving from one price ordering to the next. Consequently, it ends after a finite number of orderings.

To illustrate the operation of the algorithm, we present an application for rice, based on a population database and a production and consumption representation on a 10 by 10 km grid for some 94,000 markets, coupled through flow possibilities in 8 so-called union jack directions. Commodity flows can leave and enter the country at a limited number of seaports and inland border crossings. The introduction of these rest-of-the-world units makes it possible to deal with a model of the entire world, in which only China is represented in full detail and the other regions in a stylized way. Spatial data for this model were collected (most data sources were for 1997) for transport cost, and for production, consumption, and prices of rice and wheat.

The combined maps of consumption, production, flows, and price are quite informative (Plate 2), highlighting a few well-known points. For rice consumption, which obviously is largest in regions with high population density, it appears that consumption is generally not located far from production. The production and the consumption map do not differ too much. Prices are lower in supply zones, especially in distant ones, and flows are largely domestic. International trade plays only a limited role, and the country is so large that local production is reasonably well protected against foreign imports, which can enter at seaports.

Sequential Downscaling Methods for Spatial Estimation of Production Values and Flows

The analysis of global change processes requires the development of methods that deal in a consistent manner with data on a multitude of spatial and temporal scales. Although GIS provides detailed geophysical information, the socioeconomic data often exist only at aggregate levels. Therefore, the adequate treatment and assessment of spatial heterogeneity calls for the development of appropriate downscaling procedures. In particular, this brings up a number of new estimation problems for recovering information on uncertain partially observable or even unobservable variables.

For example, although we can estimate total departures or arrivals of passengers in transportation systems, the estimation of passenger flows between different locations requires expensive origin-destination surveys, and in many cases the data do not exist. Similar situations occur with projections of migration flows, estimation of flows in communication systems, and trade flows. The main idea of estimation in these new problems is to rely on using an appropriate optimization principle, such as cross-entropy maximization, subject to a variety of constraints connecting observable and unobservable dependent variables.

The estimation of global processes consistent with local data challenges the traditional statistical estimation methods. These methods are based on the ability to obtain observations from unknown true probability distributions. In fact, the justification of these methods, such as their consistency and efficiency, rely on asymptotic analysis requiring an infinite number of observations. For the new estimation problems, referred to as downscaling problems, we often have only very restricted samples of real observations. Additional experiments to achieve more observations may be expensive, time-consuming, dangerous, or simply impossible.

The aim is to develop sequential downscaling methods, which can be used in a variety of practical situations. A main motivation initially was the spatial estimation of agricultural production values. Agricultural production and land data are available at national scale from the Food and Agriculture Organization of the United Nations and other sources, but these data give no clue as to the spatial heterogeneity of agricultural production within country boundaries. A downscaling method in this case has to achieve plausible allocation of aggregate national production values to individual spatial units, for example, pixels, by using all available evidence from observed or inferred geospatial information, such as remotely sensed land cover, soil, climate and vegetation distribution, population density and distribution, etc. These methods are especially interesting and valuable for integrating in a consistent manner geographical data with statistical sources and to provide information and fill data gaps for spatially explicit modeling approaches, such as the transport flow model and the spatially explicit agricultural production relations used in the CHINAGRO project.

As a theoretical underpinning, we establish connections between the fundamental maximum likelihood principle of statistical estimation theory and a maximum entropy principle used for the downscaling. We show that the maximum entropy principle can be viewed as an extension of maximum likelihood, the so-called minimax log likelihood principle. In this sense, the convergence of downscaling methods to solutions maximizing an entropy function can be considered as an analog of the asymptotic consistency analysis in traditional statistical estimation theory.

CONCLUDING REMARKS

Land use change plays a key role in global environmental change, as well as in the future availability of food and water. Modeling land use and land cover change presents new scientific challenges, particularly in integrating biophysical and socioeconomic data and processes and in capturing heterogeneity in both components. Global models take a range of approaches to modeling land use change, including general and partial equilibrium economic frameworks, as well as rule-based simulation modeling, and operate at a range of spatial scales, from only a few large world regions to models operating on a raster of several thousand grid cells. The treatment of demographics in these models is more uniform, generally limited to population size acting as a scale factor on demand for agricultural and forest products and as a measure of available labor force on the production side. Spatially explicit integrated assessment models of large world regions, such as the CHINAGRO project, are developing new methodologies for addressing the key challenges of integration and heterogeneity. For example, although GIS provides rich geophysical information, the socioeconomic data often exist only at aggregate levels. The estimation of aggregate processes consistent with spatially explicit data and, conversely, local implications of aggregate trends call for the development of appropriate aggregation and downscaling procedures, respectively. The approaches of sequential downscaling, and optimal aggregation, being developed and tested as part of the CHINAGRO project, represent promising possibilities for addressing these issues.

Experiences in the China project also suggest two priorities for improving the treatment of demographic factors in integrated assessment models that can be informed by case study research on population-environment interactions. First, migration—in the case of China, internal rural-urban migration in particular—plays a key role in outcomes. A better understanding of the determinants of migration and its relationship to, and effect on, spatially heterogeneous socioeconomic conditions would strengthen this key model component. Second, experience suggests that decisions at the farm level in China are strongly affected by returns to labor and off-farm income-earning opportunities. This indicates that cross-sectoral linkages and a spatially explicit context should be considered when modeling production, consumption, and investment decisions of rural households.

While spatially detailed modeling undoubtedly increases the burdens associated with data collection, checking and compilation, model estimation, and analysis, our experience has been that spatial richness facilitates and fosters interdisciplinary collaboration among diverse disciplines and can provide a mutually beneficial basis for linking case studies and regional analyses.

ACKNOWLEDGMENTS

The research of the IIASA-LUC project is a multidisciplinary and collaborative effort. It has involved researchers at IIASA and in various collaborating institutions in China, Europe, Japan, Russia, and United States. For the work presented in this chapter, the authors are particularly grateful to the researchers who have developed and significantly contributed to the various themes: Michiel A. Keyzer, Peter Albersen, and Wim C.M. van Veen (Free University, SOW-VU, Amsterdam, The Netherlands) designed and greatly contributed to implementing the welfare optimum and transportation models applied in the land use study of China, the CHINAGRO project on "Policy Decision Support for Sustainable Adaptation of China's Agriculture to Globalization." This research has been supported with funds of the European Union (INCO-DEV ICA-2000-20039), the Chinese and Dutch governments, and IIASA's national member organizations. The authors are solely responsible for the results and conclusions and do not express in any way the opinion of the European Commission. The discussion of aggregation issues uses materials and relies on recent research findings of Michiel A. Keyzer, presented at a recent CHINAGRO training course in Beijing (September 2003). The downscaling methodologies discussed in the chapter have been developed jointly with Yuri Ermoliev, Tatiana Ermolieva, and Harrij van Velthuizen (researcher scholars at IIASA) and have benefited from discussions with colleagues at FAO (Ergin Ataman and Barbara Huddleston) and IFPRI (Stanley Wood and You Liang).

REFERENCES

Ahmad, Q.K., T.E. Downing, S. Nishioka, K.S. Parikh, C. Parmesan, S.H. Schneider, F. Toth, G. Yohe, A.U. Ahmed, P. Ayton, B.B. Fitzharris, J.E. Hay, R.N. Jones, G. Morgan, R. Moss, W. North, G. Petschel-Held, and R. Richels
  2001   Methods and tools. In *Climate Change 2001: Impacts, Adaptation, and Vulnerability, A Report of Working Group II of the Intergovernmental Panel on Climate Change.* Cambridge, England: Cambridge University Press.
Albersen, P.J., G. Fischer, M.A. Keyzer, and L. Sun
  2002   *Estimation of Agricultural Production Relations in the LUC Model for China.* (IIASA Research Report RR-02-03.) Laxenberg, Austria: International Institute for Applied Systems Analysis.

Alcamo, J., R. Leemans, and E. Kreileman, eds.
1998   *Global Change Scenarios of the 21st Century: Results from the IMAGE 2.1 Model.*
        Oxford, England: Elsevier Science Ltd.
Babiker, M.H., J.M. Reilly, M. Mayer, R.S. Eckaus, I. Sue Wing , and R.C. Hyman
2001   *The MIT Emissions Prediction and Policy Analysis (EPPA) Model: Revisions, Sen-*
        sitivities, and Comparisons of Results. (Report Series No. 71.) Cambridge, MA:
        MIT Joint Program on the Science and Policy of Global Change.
Cao, G.-Y.
2000   *The Future Population of China: Prospects to 2045 by Place of Residence and by*
        Level of Education. (Report No. IR-00-026.) Laxenburg, Austria: International
        Institute for Applied Systems Analysis.
2003   *The Future Population of China: New Projections. Model Runs.* Laxenburg, Aus-
        tria: International Institute for Applied Systems Analysis.
Center for International Earth Science Information Network (CIESIN), Columbia University;
International Food Policy Research Institute (IFPRI); and World Resources Institute (WRI)
2000   Gridded Population of the World (GPW), Version 2. Palisades, NY: CIESIN, Co-
        lumbia University. Available: http://sedac.ciesin.columbia.edu/plue/gpw [2/23/05].
Darwin, R., M. Tsigas, J. Lewandrowski, and A. Raneses
1995   *World Agriculture and Climate Change: Economic Adaptations.* (Natural Re-
        sources and Environment Division, Economic Research Service, Agricultural Eco-
        nomic Report No. 703.) Washington, DC: U.S. Department of Agriculture.
Ermoliev, Y., M.A. Keyzer, and V. Norkin
2001   *General Equilibrium and Welfare Modeling in Spatial Continuum: A Practical*
        Framework for Land Use Planning. (Report No. WP-01-07.) Amsterdam, The
        Netherlands: Centre for World Food Studies.
Fischer, G., K. Frohberg, M.A. Keyzer, and K.S. Parikh
1988   *Linked National Models: A Tool for International Policy Analysis.* Amsterdam,
        The Netherlands: Kluwer Academic Publishers.
Fischer, G., M. Shah, and H. van Valthuizen
2002a   *Climate Change and Agricultural Vulnerability.* (Special Report.) Laxenberg, Aus-
        tria: International Institute for Applied Systems Analysis.
Fischer, G., H. van Velthuizen, M. Shah, and F.O. Nachtergaele
2002b   *Global Agro-Ecological Assessment for Agriculture in the 21st Century: Methodol-*
        ogy and Results. (Research Report RR-02-02.) Laxenburg, Austria: International
        Institute for Applied Systems Analysis.
Geist, H.J., and E.F. Lambin
2002   Proximate causes and underlying driving forces of tropical deforestation. *BioScience*
        52(2):143-150.
Ginsburgh, V., and M.A. Keyzer
1997   *The Structure of Applied General Equilibrium Models.* Cambridge, MA: MIT Press.
Jiang, K., T. Morita, T. Masui, and Y. Matsuoka
2000   Long-term GHG emission scenarios for Asia-Pacific and the world. *Technological*
        Forecasting and Social Change 63:207-229.
Keyzer, M.A.
2003a   *Using Gravity Constraints to Optimize Transport Flows in a Spatially Explicit*
        Equilibrium Model. (Working Paper.) Amsterdam, The Netherlands: Free Uni-
        versity, SOW-VU.
2003b   Theoretical Background on Aggregation: Micro-Macro Debates. Notes, Lecture 2.
        Second CHINAGRO Training Course, Policy Decision Support for Sustainable
        Adaptation of China's Agriculture to Globalization, September 23-24, Beijing.
        Available: http://www.sow.econ.vu.nl/downloadables.htm.

2004   *Towards a Spatially and Socially Explicit Agricultural Policy Analysis for China: Specification of the CHINAGRO Models.* (Working Paper.) Amsterdam, The Netherlands: Free University, SOW-VU.

Keyzer, M.A., and Y. Ermoliev
1999   Modeling producer decisions in a spatial continuum. In *Theory of Markets and Their Functioning,* J. Herings, G. van der Laan, and A.J.J. Talman, eds. Amsterdam, The Netherlands: Elsevier Science.

Keyzer, M.A., and W. van Veen
2004   *A Summary Description of the CHINAGRO Welfare Model.* (Working Paper.) Amsterdam, The Netherlands: Free University, SOW-VU.

Lashof, D.A., and D. Tirpak, eds.
1990   *Policy Options for Stabilizing Global Climate.* Washington, DC: Hemisphere Publishing Corp.

Lambin, E.F., B.L. Turner II, H. Geist, S. Agbola, A. Angelsen, J.W. Bruce, O. Coomes, R. Dirzo, G. Fischer, C. Folke, P.S. George, K. Homewood, J. Imbernon, R. Leemans, X. Li, E.F. Moran, M. Mortimore, P.S. Ramakrishnan, J.F. Richards, H. Skånes, W. Steffen, G.D. Stone, U. Svedin, T. Veldkamp, C. Vogel, and J. Xu
2001   The causes of land use and land cover change: Moving beyond the myths. *Global Environmental Change* 11:261-269.

Liu, S., X. Li, and M. Zhang
2003   *Scenario Analysis on Urbanization and Rural-Urban Migration in China.* (IIASA Land Use Change Report IR-03-036.) Laxenburg, Austria: International Institute for Applied Systems Analysis.

Masui, T., Y. Matsuoka, T. Morita, M. Kainuma, and K. Takahashi
2001   Development of land use model for IPCC new emission scenarios (SRES). Pp. 441-448 in *Present and Future of Modeling Global Environmental Change: Toward Integrated Modeling,* T. Matsuno and H. Kida, eds. Tokyo, Japan: Terrapub.

McCarthy, J.J., O.F. Canziani, N.A. Leary, D.J. Dokken, and K.S. White, eds.
2001   *Climate Change 2001: Impacts, Adaptation, and Vulnerability.* (Intergovernmental Panel on Climate Change.) Cambridge, England: Cambridge University Press.

Meadows, D.H., D.L. Meadows, J. Randers, and W.W. Behrens III
1972   *The Limits to Growth.* New York: Universe Books.

Mori, S., and M. Takahashi
1998   An integrated assessment model for the new energy technologies and food production—and extension of the MARIA model. *International Journal of Global Energy Issues* 11:1-16.

Nakicenovic, N., O. Davidson, G. Davis, A. Grübler, T. Kram, E. Lebre La Rovere, B. Metz, T. Morita, W. Pepper, H. Pitcher, A. Sankovski, P. Shukla, R. Swart, R. Watson, and Z. Dadi
2000   *Emissions Scenarios. A Special Report of the Intergovernmental Panel on Climate Change.* Cambridge, England: Cambridge University Press.

National Bureau of Statistics of the People's Republic of China
2002   *China Census 2000, Detailed Data Tables.* [CD-ROM.] Ann Arbor: Michigan State University and China Data Center.

O'Neill, B.C.
2001   Cassandra/cornucopian debate. Pp. 1525-1529 in *International Encyclopedia of the Social and Behavioral Sciences,* vol. 3, N.J. Smelser and P.B. Baltes, eds. Oxford, England: Pergamon Press.

Parson, E.A., and K. Fisher-Vanden
1997   Integrated assessment models of global climate change. *Annual Review of Energy and the Environment* 22:589-629.

Rosegrant, M.W., X. Cai, and S.A. Cline
  2002a *World Water and Food to 2025: Dealing with Scarcity.* Washington, DC: International Food Policy Research Institute.
Rosegrant, M.W., S. Meijer, and S.A. Cline
  2002b *International Model for Policy Analysis of Agricultural Commodities and Trade (IMPACT): Model Description.* Washington, DC: International Food Policy Research Institute.
Sands, R.D., and M. Leimbach
  2003 Modeling agriculture and land use in an integrated assessment framework. *Climatic Change* 56:185-210.
Toth, F., M. Mwandosya, C. Carraro, J. Christensen, J. Edmonds, B. Flannery, C. Gay-Garcia, H. Lee, K. M. Meyer-Abich, E. Nikitina, A. Rahman, R. Richels, Y. Ruqiu, A. Villavicencio, Y. Wake, J. Weyan, J. Byrne, R. Lempert, I. Meyer, and A. Underdal
  2001 Decision-making frameworks. In *Climate Change 2001: Mitigation, A Report of Working Group III of the Intergovernmental Panel on Climate Change.* Cambridge, England: University Press.
Toth, F.L., G.Y. Cao, and E. Hizsnyik
  2003 *Regional Population Projections for China.* (IIASA Land Use Change Report, IR-03-042.) Laxenburg, Austria: International Institute for Applied Systems Analysis.
United Nations Environment Programme
  2002 *GEO: Global Environmental Outlook 3.* London, England: Earthscan.
Weyant, J.P., and J. Hill
  1999 Introduction and overview, costs of the Kyoto Protocol: A multimodel evaluation. *Energy Journal* (Kyoto Special Issue): 7-44.

4

Population and Environment in the U.S. Great Plains

Myron P. Gutmann, William J. Parton,
Geoff Cunfer, and Ingrid C. Burke

INTRODUCTION

In the known histories of the impact of human intervention on the landscape, that of the Great Plains of the United States is among the most frequently described. In the 1930s, clouds of dust rose off the recently plowed land to catch the attention of media and politicians as far away as Washington, DC. The Dust Bowl permanently focused attention on the ways that human interaction with the environment could have consequences for both people and the environment (Worster, 1979; Hurt, 1981; Gutmann and Cunfer, 1999; Cunfer, 2002).

The Great Plains of North America is a large region spanning the area from the end of the Midwest mesophytic forests to the front range of the Rocky Mountains (east to west), and from northern Canada to Central Texas (north to south) (Riebsame, 1990). The climate of the Great Plains is one of dry winters and wet summers. It is shaped by three air masses, each leading to its own seasonal dynamics (Lauenroth and Burke, 1995). A Pacific air mass originating in the Gulf of Alaska is dominant in the winter, its air dried by crossing several mountain ranges. An additional polar air mass also shapes winter weather, creating a strong north-south gradient in air temperature and snow cover. In summer, the westerly flow weakens and polar air retreats to the north, allowing an air mass that comes from the subtropical Atlantic Ocean to bring moisture into the region.

The distribution of both natural ecosystems and land use management is controlled in large part by two major climatic gradients: an east-west gradient of increasing precipitation and a north-south gradient of increasing temperature (Figures 4-1 and 4-2). Mean annual precipitation ranges from more than 1,200 mm/yr to less than 300 mm/yr, and mean annual temperature from less than 0°C to greater than 20°C. Plant species composition varies from tallgrass prairie to shortgrass steppe, with decreasing precipitation. In addition to influencing ecosystem type, these gradients have large influences on net primary production and soil organic carbon (Sala et al., 1988; Burke et al., 1989).

There is a conventional storytelling of the development of the Great Plains.[1] Originally lightly settled by native people, the region was colonized by the European-origin population of the United States in the decades following the Civil War (Powell, 1878; Webb, 1931). This settlement was encouraged by the institutional context of the United States in the nineteenth century. At that time a combination of economic, social, and political processes made land and transportation available for individuals and families who wanted to move out of more densely populated parts of the country (Opie, 1987). These settlers discovered a semiarid grassland landscape with agricultural possibilities that ranged from consistent arable cropping in the east to limited cropping and steady pasturing in the west. Some of the implications of aridity (lack of wood for building and unfamiliar prospects for agriculture, for example) delayed settlement, but demographic pressure in the more eastern United States pushed people west. With what seemed like good years of rainfall and with increasing agricultural prices in the 1910s and 1920s, an aggressive stream of would-be farmers and ranchers acquired land and attempted to farm it (Gutmann and Sample, 1995; Worster, 1992). In this conventional history, the plowing up of the grasslands for wheat, combined with the drought of the 1930s, provoked disastrous dust storms and social dislocation. While we may not agree that those were the only causes, or that the greatest areas of wheat farming suffered the worst drought and dust storms, there was a causal relationship. Plowed land is a much greater source of blowing dust than uncultivated grassland.

Despite the social and economic disruptions of the 1930s, land use changed little as a result of the Dust Bowl. Acreage planted in crops dipped during the worst of the 1930s drought, but by 1945 had recovered fully to predrought levels. The balance between cropland and pasture remained virtually stable from the 1920s through the 1990s in most plains counties (Cunfer, 2005). People responded to the problems of the 1930s by changing some of their cultivation practices (Hargreaves, 1992). Some of them migrated out of the region, although there may have been less out-

---

[1]For our interpretation of this history, see Gutmann and Cunfer (1999) and Cunfer (2002, 2005). For aspects of the conventionally written history of the Great Plains narrative, see Webb (1931), Bonnifield (1979), Hurt (1981), Malin (1946), Riney-Kehrberg (1994), and Worster (1979).

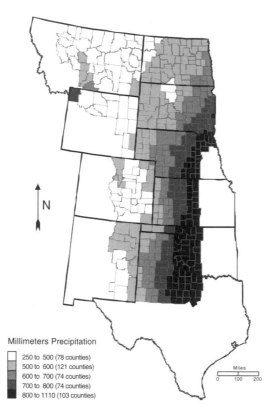

Millimeters Precipitation

☐ 250 to 500 (78 counties)
▨ 500 to 600 (121 counties)
▨ 600 to 700 (74 counties)
▨ 700 to 800 (74 counties)
■ 800 to 1110 (103 counties)

FIGURE 4-1   Average annual precipitation, Great Plains counties, 1961-1990.

migration during the drought of the 1930s than during the drought of the 1950s, when postwar economic development in the United States provided places to go (Gutmann et al., 2002). Those who remained changed their farming practices between the 1930s and 1970s, by introducing techniques that reduced the risk of erosion and made better use of soil moisture, implementing improved crop varieties, enhancing nutrients through fertilization and by increasing the use of irrigation where groundwater was available (Green, 1973). The drought of the 1950s did not last as long as that of the 1930s, and improved agricultural practices made the impact of the later drought less severe. Nonetheless, the adoption of more intense irrigation since the 1940s has led to groundwater depletion and other land use changes that provoked further damage by the 1980s. The Ogallala aquifer has been the largest source of groundwater for irrigation, and it has suffered steady declines in level since the 1970s and 1980s (Opie, 1993; Riebsame, 1991; Cunfer, 2005).

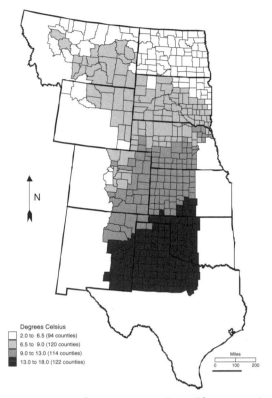

FIGURE 4-2   Average annual temperature, Great Plains counties, 1961-1990.

Whether consistently provoked by environmental conditions or spurred by broader social change, the Great Plains region has experienced significant demographic changes since its colonization by people of European descent beginning in the mid-nineteenth century. The region has grown in population overall, but that growth masks two defining population patterns. The first pattern applies to rural areas, where population grew with settlement until the 1930s and has declined since. While the story is more complex than that told by the media to general audiences, the overall rural pattern since the 1930s has been one of a declining and aging population, with less and less agricultural employment and growing poverty.[2] In the second pattern, most of the long-term growth occurred in a small number of metropolitan areas, led by Denver, Colorado. Since the 1960s, counties close to the front range of the Rocky Mountains have grown,

[2]See, for example, the *New York Times* stories by Egan (2003) and Kilborn (2003). They are only a few among many.

spurred by the growth of recreation and by industrial development in the same areas.

This history of land use and demographic transformation in a context of environmental change animates our study of population and environment in the Great Plains. Population change has acted through land use to influence the environment. Conversely, environmental conditions have influenced demographic change. All this has taken place over more than a century of rapid economic and social change in the United States. The challenge is to measure changes in population, land use, and environment, as well as to disentangle their impacts from the underlying social changes that would have happened anyway.

CONCEPTUALIZING THE CONNECTIONS AND THINKING ABOUT THE DATA

This project has three main research components, and in this chapter we will emphasize two of them. Those three components are: (1) an analysis of county-scale processes based on historical population, land use, and environmental and other data; (2) a series of historical studies of individual localities, of the experiences of farmers and their families, and of agricultural practices throughout the region; and (3) interviews of about 180 farm families in six different parts of the region. This chapter is primarily about the first component, with some information from the second and only brief references to the third.

The Great Plains region as we define it covers much of 10 states of the United States, comprising nearly one in seven U.S. counties: Colorado, Kansas, Montana, Nebraska, New Mexico, North Dakota, Oklahoma, South Dakota, Texas, and Wyoming. Our goal has been to represent a large portion of that region, and our strategy has been to make use of readily available aggregate data about counties. We recognize that we are unable to analyze the behavior and experiences of individual persons, families, farms, or environmental settings. This emphasis on county-scale processes determines how we conceptualize the connections between population, land use, and environment. It led us to relate population to land use through a set of hypotheses, some brought to the project from the beginning, and others formed as our research evolved. These are the hypotheses that are important to the work reported in this chapter.

1. We began with the hypothesis that the growth of population density through European-origin settlement led to changes in land use—and therefore environment—with a more or less linear relationship: the more people there were, the more land use changed. We also hypothesized that different kinds of

population had differential impacts on land use, with urban impacts greater than rural, and some ethnic groups having different impacts than others.

2. We also began with the hypothesis that population density could itself be a function of the resource attributes of the land, so that population density could become greater in areas with more precipitation than in those with less, or where there was oil or coal, because of greater opportunities for employment. This manifests itself as a limitation on the first hypothesis, so that in areas with fewer resources there would be less population, but also less land use change.

3. A third main hypothesis operates more in the realm of methods than results, asserting that it is possible to gauge the impact of population change on the environment by estimating biogeochemical models linked to accurate historical data about population and land use at the county scale, and then draw conclusions based on the modeled results.

Our approach is thoroughly interdisciplinary but still anchored in disciplinary strengths (Riebsame et al., 1994). Our team has a core of historians, ecologists, and sociologists, plus geographers and anthropologists. As we venture further, we build on the cross-disciplinary tools that enable a historian's deep knowledge of the past and the agricultural practices of the past century, coupled with the demographer's clear understanding of demographic processes to inform the ecosystem modeler's task of model specification and interpretation.

DATA, DESIGN, AND STATISTICAL TECHNIQUES

While we make use of many varieties of data, our primary sources come from county tabulations drawn from the U.S. censuses of population and agriculture. We have collected those data for the decennial population censuses from 1880 through 2000, as well as for the agricultural censuses (which were decennial until 1920 and then more frequent thereafter) from 1880 through 1997.[3] In addition to census-based sources, we have collected other county-level tabulations of social characteristics. We use the population and social indicators data to understand population structure and change, and the agricultural census data to understand agricultural land use. Their consistency, as well as the effectiveness and long-term quality of the U.S. census, have made this part of our project straightforward. Some of

---

[3]Since 1920, the agricultural census was taken every five years until 1950. Beginning in 1954, the censuses were enumerated for 1954, 1959, 1964, 1969, 1974, 1978, 1982, 1987, 1992, 1997, and 2002, usually at the beginning of the next year. The 2002 Agricultural Census forms were due on February 3, 2003.

these data were available to us in digital form, and others we collected in print form and then hand-keyed into our database. All of these data are described in Gutmann et al. (1998). Since that document was published, we have added data from recent censuses (1997 agriculture and 2000 population), while maintaining their content and structure. Although our study area is not coterminous with the 10 states, we have collected data that covered the entire area of the 10 Great Plains states, and often neighboring states, especially Iowa and Minnesota.

While data about population size and structure are remarkably similar from 1880 to 2000, we are well aware of the changes that have occurred in the tabulated record during such a long time. On the population side, only in 1910 and since 1980 are good data about ethnicity available. In another example, population size divided into 5-year age categories was not tabulated from 1880 through 1920. On the agricultural side, the definition of major categories of farmland into cropland, pasture, and other types changed significantly in the 1920s, and the yields of irrigated crops have always been difficult to estimate. One challenge of our research has been to find ways to overcome these limitations.

Environmental data are not as easy to acquire as those about land use and population, because they are not normally tabulated at the scale of the county (Gutmann, 2000). We have sought temperature and precipitation data at reasonable intervals of time and space. We have done this by interpolating VEMAP Project data (http://www.cgd.ucar.edu/vemap/) to historical county boundaries. We have also acquired recent soil structure and elevation data, as well as data giving locations of bodies of water and streams, interpolating them to historical county boundaries. Finally, we have acquired other weather data (dust storms, for example), when possible (see Gutmann and Cunfer, 1999; Deane and Gutmann, 2003).

No single method has worked in all our analyses. Some of what we have done is descriptive, based on examining tabular and graphical series of results that display change over time or variation through space. Yet we have consistently attempted to make use of statistical approaches that are appropriate for the data and the hypotheses involved. One challenge has been to take account of the role of time and space in our analysis, with appropriate study of temporal and spatial autocorrelation. We have also pursued innovative ideas about the role of causality (Deane and Gutmann, 2003). Finally, one of our important goals has been to integrate what we can learn from the historical data with ecosystem modeling techniques.

Despite the widespread recognition that the Great Plains represent a perfect test case for the study of population and environment in grassland settings, no earlier study has been able to amass the large body of systematic, quantitative, and region-wide data that we have brought to bear on the problem. These data allow us to start from the beginning, first describing the impact of settlement by European-origin populations, and then systematically analyzing elements of that impact. In this chapter we highlight our findings thus far and point to new directions of research to follow.

MAJOR FINDINGS

In writing about our major findings, we begin with the broadest view of what we have learned about the impact of population on environment over the last 100 years, and then turn to two additional questions. Our presentation echoes the major hypotheses stated earlier, with one major section reporting on our exploration of each hypothesis. From this wide-angle view, we show that a growing European-origin population has massively changed the environment of about a third of the Great Plains region, both through the replacement of open grasslands with fenced and heavily managed croplands and through the creation of significant areas of urban and suburban development. While we cannot always directly measure *environmental* outcomes, this analysis, based largely on land use change, is dramatic. The other two-thirds of the Great Plains, used primarily for extensive livestock grazing, has seen only limited environmental change, as cattle mimicked the ecological impacts of the native bison they replaced. This finding is important, because, while it confirms that settlement changed land use, it demonstrates that there was less land use change than previous researchers have believed.

Our second main point shows the complexity of gauging the relative importance of population and the environment in shaping land use decisions. Paradoxically, although population change has shaped the environment through land use change, we also see that the environment limits human action. Humans can decide to plant crops, for example, but they will not succeed in raising crops in most of the Great Plains. This conclusion is a necessary antidote to the thinking that asserts that human domination of environmental systems is always complete and without limits.

Our final discussion highlights the progress we have made in finding new ways to measure the environmental impact of population on the environment of the Great Plains. In our most recent research, we have run the century ecosystem model with parameters based on historical land uses in a small number of Great Plains counties. The century ecosystem model is a generalized ecosystem model that simulates the dynamics of carbon, nitrogen, and phosphorus in grassland, forest, savanna, and crop systems (Parton et al., 1993; Metherell et al., 1993, 1995; Kelly et al., 1997; Paustian, Parton, and Persson, 1992). The results of these model runs allow us to begin the process of estimating historical and current soil composition and greenhouse gas scenarios for the region. This detailed modeling of environmental outcomes based on accurate historical data is the most precise effort yet undertaken to gauge the impact of human agricultural activity on the grassland environment.

HOW POPULATION CHANGED THE GREAT PLAINS

Our first hypothesis asserts that, as the population of the Great Plains grew due to the influx of the European-origin population, environmental impacts through agricultural (and later urban) land uses accelerated, closely coupling demographic change with land use and environmental change. The exploration of that process has informed much of our work, with conclusions that show that the process is very generally as we expected, but with a number of interesting complications. While it is important to see the broad generalization confirmed, the most valuable findings may come from the complications and the insights they give us for future research.

The Great Plains, by our definition, consist of approximately 390 million acres of land. In 1880, U.S. farmers reported tht they had about 19 million of those acres in farms (see Figure 4-3). By 1910 they had 10 times as much, and by 1930 they reported 288 million acres of farms, nearly three-fourths of the region's land area. At its peak in 1959, nearly eight out of every nine acres of land in the region was reportedly in a farm. For census purposes, pasture and ranch land is included in farmland, so a considerable majority of this farmland was not plowed. The conversion of native grassland to cropland happened somewhat later. Although farmers began plowing out sod in the 1870s, it was a Herculean effort, and as late as 1900 only 8 percent of the region, some 31 million acres, were used for crops. Most of the plowing up of the Great Plains happened in the first three decades of the twentieth century, when farmers brought about 88 million additional acres into crop production, peaking at 31 percent of total land area in 1935 (Cunfer, 2005).

The demographic change that accompanied the transformation of land use is just as dramatic. The region experienced steady population growth as land use changed through 1930, followed by a rapid transformation from overall population growth to urban population growth. The region's rural population has been shrinking since the 1930s, in some decades quite rapidly. We follow the U.S. Census Bureau's definition of an urban place as one having a population of 2,500 inhabitants, a relatively low threshold that moves small towns with populations over 2,500 into the urban category.

The comparisons between population and land use trends displayed in Figure 4-3 show that the growth in farmland generally increased with overall population size, but it continued to increase long after the rural population stopped growing in 1930. Cropland, however, stopped increasing after 1940, only a decade after the rural population peak. Put another way, the link between rural population change and land use change that led

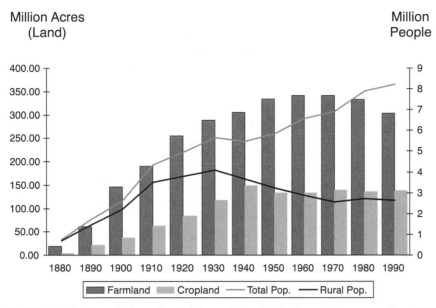

FIGURE 4-3 Population, farmland, and cropland, Great Plains counties, 1880-1990. The figures for cropland represent the sum of cropland harvested for major crops from 1880 through 1920, and the reported total cropland from 1930 through 1992. About one-tenth of the reported total cropland is cropland used for pasture, which may or may not be land that has been plowed and regularly managed.

to conversion to cropland was tighter than that between rural population and overall conversion of land to farm uses, or between the overall population change and either farmland or cropland conversions. The reverse process was not true, however. As rural population declined after 1930, the amount of land in crops remained stable. Depopulation did not equate to land abandonment in the second half of the twentieth century, as remaining farmers continued to plant acreage relinquished by emigrant neighbors.

Figure 4-3 shows that most of the direct impact of rural population change on land use and consequently on the environment took place during the era of rapid settlement from 1880 through 1930 and then diminished. This is true in other areas as well (Moran, Brondizio, and VanWey, Chapter 5). Yet the demographic impact on an agricultural region such as the U.S. Great Plains is not limited to the direct results of local population growth and decline. Environmental changes are as much the result of large-scale shifts in the market for agricultural products (driven by populations and tastes elsewhere) as they are the result of local or regional population change (Cronon, 1991). Local demographic change is usually the symptom that spurs immediate changes in land use, for example, because one needs farmers to make the change from native grassland to crops. That is what we can measure. We can also measure the role of local population changes in the conversion of land from agricultural to urban and suburban uses. This is a topic not dealt with directly in this chapter, but it is part of our research agenda for the future.

Not all the conversion to farmland produced dramatic change in land character with environmental consequences. The amount of cropland reported, however, is a strong indication of the intensity of environmental change that took place in the Great Plains between 1880 and 1992. At its peak in the late 1930s, between 31 and 38 percent of the total land in the region had been converted from native grassland to cropland.[4] The geographical distribution of that cropland varies from subregion to subregion because the eastern Great Plains has more rainfall than the west and is better suited for cropping.

Figure 4-4 shows the growth of total area cropped in the Great Plains from 1880 through 1992, dividing the region into an eastern tier of states (North Dakota, South Dakota, Nebraska, Kansas, Oklahoma, and Texas) and a western tier of states (Montana, Wyoming, Colorado, and New Mexico). Figure 4-5 shows the spatial distribution of cropping in the Great Plains in 1930; a few counties in the east had as much as three-fourths of their land in cropland, while those in the west had 10 percent or less. While not displayed in the figures, there was also a significant increase in the amount of land that is irrigated in small parts of the Great Plains, reaching a peak of more than 17 million acres in the late 1970s. While this represents only about 4 percent of the entire Great Plains, the increase in irrigation has had environmental consequences of local importance. Putting all these findings another way, we see little support for a simple linear relationship between population growth and land use change.

The conversion from native grassland to cropland and other farm uses is as dramatic over the long term as that reported by others in this volume (see Chapters 5, 6, and 8) for regions—such as the Amazon—where deforestation and other kinds of land use conversion has taken place. While it can be difficult to measure the environmental consequences of this change at the large scale that we have chosen to study, we know in general terms what happens when native grasses are plowed and replaced with crops:

- Soil texture changes and topsoil may be lost to wind and water erosion.

---

[4]The difference between the 31 and 38 percent depends on the interpretation of land that farmers classified as "cropland used as pasture." The sources are not clear (and probably not uniform in their classification) about the extent to which that land was transformed through plowing and planting of nonnative species.

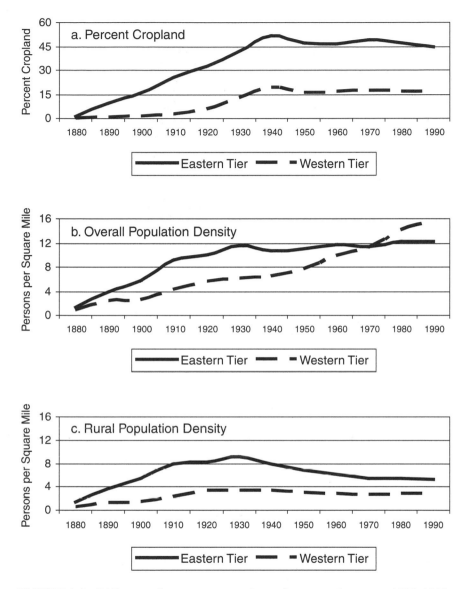

FIGURE 4-4   Differences between eastern tier and western tier states, 1880-1990.

•   Carbon, nitrogen, and other minerals change composition as plowing and cropping alter soil chemistry.
   •   Natural processes related to fire are suppressed.
   •   Hydrological systems are disrupted or altered.

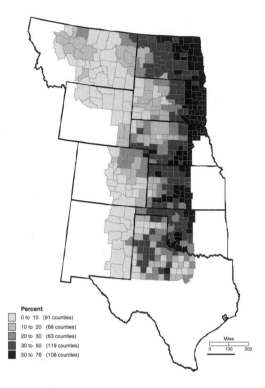

FIGURE 4-5   Percentage of county area in crops, 1930.

•   Species diversity diminishes as introduced crop species replace native plants.
•   Wildlife distribution patterns change as farmers replace habitat and build roads, fences, and other barriers to migration.

In the two-thirds of the grassland that farmers could not successfully plow for crops, environmental change has been much less dramatic. While nearly all of that land has been used for extensive grazing by cattle, and in much smaller proportions by sheep and horses, most of it remains in native vegetative cover. Grazing livestock can have the following environmental impacts on grasslands:

•   Interference with wildlife, especially competing large grazers (bison, pronghorn) and predators (wolves, grizzly bears).
•   Changes in plant diversity, species composition, and ground cover, especially increases in invasive species.
•   Disruption of riparian and aquatic habitats along rivers and streams.

Yet unlike with cropping, grazing has little impact on soil texture and depth or on carbon or nitrogen systems, and it is less disruptive of plant and animal biodiversity (Lauenroth et al., 1994; Cunfer, 2005). Whereas nearly all forest ecosystems in the continental United States have been logged in the past 400 years, nearly two-thirds of the Great Plains remains in unplowed native vegetation. These consequences are by no means all that has happened to the environment of the Great Plains as a consequence of the region's growing population and its long-term conversion from native grassland to cropland, managed rangeland, and later urban and suburban development. While we have only partially quantified them, their impact is important and they constitute the starting point for our understanding.

THE PARADOX OF POPULATION AND ENVIRONMENT

The message in the previous section is clear: the change in population that took place in the Great Plains when the European-origin population grew transformed the environment in ways that have had local consequences and global consequences. They range from the local disruption of faunal wildlife to the global alteration of the carbon cycle, and probably every scale in between.

Despite this simplicity and certainty, our results show that environmental constraints limit the impact of the human population on the environment. These constraints may be in keeping with our second hypothesis, and they are worthy of note. They operate by limiting the flexibility that farmers had to choose how they used the land. Put simply, farmers on the Great Plains were unable to convert all their land to cropland—or to any other single use that they desired—because the land was not environmentally suited to every possible use. In a straightforward way, we see this limitation through the range of variation in cropland in Figures 4-4 and 4-5, and in the parallel knowledge that few Great Plains farms or counties were ever transformed into a single-crop monoculture. This is one important finding in the research of Cunfer (2005).

While change in population is the most important determinant of the overall likelihood of *any* change in land use in the historical time period, a limited group of environmental characteristics are the most important determinants of the *specific kind* of agricultural land use adopted by farmers. If we measure variation in land use as the choice to use the land for cropping or pasture, almost all the variation in agricultural land use in the Great Plains is explained by environmental variables, especially precipitation, temperature, soil texture, and slope (Burke et al., 1994; Burke, Lauenroth, and Parton, 1997; Gutmann et al., 2004; Lauenroth, Burke, and Paruelo, 2000; Sala et al., 1988; Cunfer, 2005). Not much room is left for human intervention beyond deciding whether to irrigate and which crops to plant, and,

even then, irrigation and cropping choices are themselves largely determined by a mix of environmental and market factors over which the farmer
has relatively little control. This is the result we report in Gutmann et al.
(2004) and Cunfer (2005), confirming earlier work by others and making
clear that even when there are ethnic and cultural preferences for certain
crops or land uses, the environmental determinants are very strong.

REFINING OUR UNDERSTANDING OF ENVIRONMENTAL IMPACTS

Thus far the story we have told is very simple, limited to the big picture
of the impact of population change on environment and the constraints of
environment on the exact nature of those impacts. Put another way, the
influx of European-origin people to the United States and especially the
Great Plains caused a dramatic change in the way land was used in the
region, driven largely by the introduction of crop-based and livestock-based
agriculture. At the same time, we show that the introduction and continua-
tion of agriculture has limits imposed by the environment.

To refine our measurement of the environmental impact we have undertaken a new series of analyses (Burke et al., 2002; Parton et al., in press;
Cunfer, 2004, 2005) that make use of the history of nineteenth- and
twentieth-century land use change to estimate the impact of population-
induced agricultural land use on soil biogeochemistry. These analyses are
designed to confirm the assertion of our third hypothesis, that model-based
work on environmental outcomes has value. Burke et al. (2002) and Cunfer
(2005) show that, at both the regional scale and at the level of individual
counties, crop farming resulted in significant losses of soil nitrogen. Nitrogen declined most in the northeastern plains, where higher rainfall supported more vegetation and cooler temperatures slowed decomposition of
plant matter. There soils lost an estimated 1,080 kg nitrogen per hectare as
a result of plowing and cultivation over 75 to 100 years. Losses were much
smaller in the western and southern plains because of dryer and warmer
conditions and significantly less cropping. Soil nitrogen in grazing systems
is roughly in balance, so much of the western plains have lost virtually no
nitrogen since the European-origin settlement. Across the entire Great
Plains, soil nitrogen declined by about 20 percent from original levels (Burke
et al., 2002).

Since farmers began using synthetic fertilizer after World War II, nitrogen dynamics have changed. While soil nitrogen is now roughly stable at
about 20 percent below presettlement levels region-wide, farmers annually
apply an average of 35 kg nitrogen fertilizer per hectare of cropland per
year. About half of that goes into crop plants, increasing their growth. The
other half is lost to the system, either leaching into waterways or volatiliz-

ing into the atmosphere, in either case becoming an environmental pollutant. In the eastern parts of the region, some of the excess fertilizer nitrogen may accumulate in soils, restoring some of the soil nitrogen lost due to a century of cropping, but the extent to which this may be happening is unknown.

At the scale of the individual county, Cunfer (2004, 2005) shows that before 1940 Great Plains farm systems produced enough livestock manure to fertilize only about 20 percent of their cropland each year. Traditional, organic, small family farms mined soil fertility, extracting more nitrogen each year than they returned, and crop yields fell during the first 50 years of cultivation. Like many previous American agricultural frontiers, the Great Plains may have been on a path toward widespread land abandonment due to depleted soil fertility, but the development of synthetic fertilizers after 1945 allowed farmers to artificially replenish the nitrogen they removed each year. Crop farming has continued, year in and year out, for more than 130 years in the Great Plains, longer than most other American agricultural regions, mainly because of energy-intensive inputs of synthetic nitrogen. Widespread farming in New England and in the South, for example, lasted only about a century before land abandonment or reversion to forest became widespread. This process has not yet happened in the Great Plains, as crop acreage has remained roughly stable since the 1920s (Cunfer, 2005).

In another approach that showcases carbon as well as nitrogen, Parton et al. (in press) focus their analysis on four counties in the Great Plains (Hamilton, Nebraska; Ramsey, North Dakota; Pawnee, Kansas; and Hockley, Texas) that have different mixes of agriculture involving dryland and irrigation, grains, grasses, and cotton. This analysis makes use of the century ecosystem model. Figure 4-6 summarizes the model results for carbon by reporting a general pattern of large losses (approximately 50 percent) of soil carbon during the first 50 years following the plowing up of native grasslands, with most of the carbon loss occurring during the first 20 to 30 years. Soil nitrogen mineralization followed a general pattern of increased nitrogen mineralization for 10 to 20 years following the plowing up of grassland, and a sharp decrease in nitrogen mineralization 20 to 50 years after plowing up, with nitrogen mineralization rates approaching 20 percent of grassland levels after 50 years of cultivation. These simulated patterns in soil carbon and nitrogen mineralization are consistent with other studies (Schimel et al., 2000) showing that rapid losses of soil carbon following the plowing up of grassland soils, stabilization of soil carbon levels at 50 percent of initial values after 50 years of cultivation, and substantial decreases in soil mineralization after 50 years of dryland cultivation. The high nitrogen mineralization rates following plowing up of grassland soils are consistent with the observation that nitrogen fertilizer responses are minimal for wheat fields after 30 years of

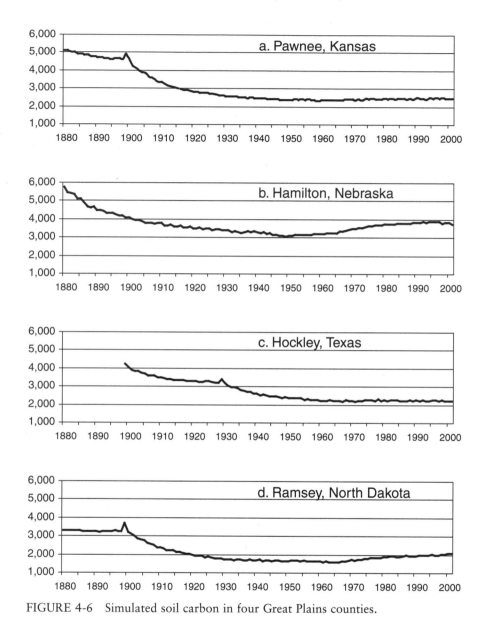

FIGURE 4-6   Simulated soil carbon in four Great Plains counties.

dryland cultivation (Metherell et al., 1995) in the Great Plains, and data showing that wheat yields in response to fertilizer increase with time since cultivation (Greb et al., 1974).

The locally dramatic expansion of irrigated agriculture is one of the major land use changes that has taken place during the past 50 years in some parts of the Great Plains, with corn and alfalfa grown in the northern and central Great Plains, and cotton in the southern Great Plains (Texas and Oklahoma). The land use data suggest that most of the irrigated land in the northern and central Great Plains had previously been cultivated using dryland techniques. Model results from Pawnee and Hamilton counties show that irrigated corn-alfalfa rotations begun in the 1960s produced substantial increases in crop yields, soil carbon levels, and soil nitrogen mineralization rates. Most of the increases in soil carbon and nitrogen mineralization occurred from 1970 to 1990 because of the large increases in the amount of carbon (300 to 400 grams of carbon per square meter per year added as corn stover) and nitrogen (100 to 150 kilograms per hectare per year of fertilizer) added to the system with irrigated agriculture. Model results suggest that soil carbon levels increased by more than 800 grams of carbon per square meter for irrigated land in Pawnee and Hamilton counties from 1970 to 2000. Extrapolating these carbon accumulation rates to the 4 million hectares of irrigated land added from 1960 to 1980 for the central and northern Great Plains would result in 56.0 trillion grams of carbon sequestered in the soil.

CONCLUSIONS

In this chapter we have discussed an approach to the study of population-environment relationships that focuses on changes over a large region that makes use of data at the scale of the U.S. county. Taken to its fullest extent, our approach yields estimates of the consequences for soil chemistry of population-driven changes in land use. As we develop estimates for the specific agricultural practices of more counties, we are able to gauge the large-scale and long-term impact of the transition into and out of agriculture for the region as a whole, which will provide valuable data to everyone studying the past experience and the future prospects of a major northern temperate region, one in which potential carbon storage is a significant question.

The results we have presented do not yet show a tight connection between population change and environmental change. There is a good reason for that, because most of the land use changes that we have signaled are not closely tied to population change, except perhaps during the early years of European-origin settlement. In more recent years, population has changed land use patterns in small parts of the Great Plains by forcing the conversion of land from agricultural uses to residential and other uses. This conversion to residential uses has produced other ecosystem consequences that remain to be studied. Our next approach will be to run century ecosystem model estimates of ecosystem processes for counties that are converting to those uses, measuring the impact of uses, such as lawns, that differ from native grasses, irrigated cropland, and dryland crops. While these land uses are small in the region as a whole (see Parton, Gutmann, and Travis, 2003), recent data suggest that their impacts are large with respect to the region as a whole (Kaye et al., 2004).

Finally, we wish to address the theme of integrating social and natural science. In our experience, the great challenge is to spend enough time working together so that all the parties begin to understand the questions asked by the othr disciplines and begin to understand the range of acceptable answers. Concepts that seem as trivial as "which is the dependent variable in this analysis, population or environment?" can lead to very fruitful insights, and indeed, new scientific questions. In our case, we have developed new perspectives on carbon and nitrogen for the region as a whole, and for a period longer than a century, as they are anchored in a rich historical and demographic record. Perhaps the most difficult challenge is to take our improved understanding of the linkages between human and ecological processes and begin to make predictions for the future of the people and the environment of the Great Plains.

ACKNOWLEDGMENTS

This project has benefited from the hard work of many individuals, too many to be authors of a single chapter. We are especially grateful to Glenn Deane, Lenora Bohren, Denis Ojima, Steve Williams, Mark Easter, Kathleen Galvin, William Travis, Susan H. Leonard, Kenneth Sylvester, and Sara Pullum-Piñón, as well as to a host of others.

REFERENCES

Bonnifield, M.P.
   1979   The Dust Bowl: Men, Dirt, and Depression. Albuquerque: University of New
           Mexico Press.
Burke, I.C., C.M. Yonker, W.J. Parton, C.V. Cole, K. Flach, and D.S. Schimel
   1989   Texture, climate, and cultivation effects on soil organic matter content in U.S.
           grassland soils. Soil Science Society of America Journal 53:800-805.
Burke, I.C., W.K. Lauenroth, W.J. Parton, and C.V. Cole
   1994   Interactions of landuse and ecosystem function: A case study in the central Great
           Plains. Pp. 79-95 in Integrated Regional Models: Interactions Between Humans
           and Their Environment, P.M. Groffman and G.E. Likens, eds. New York: Chapman
           Hall.

Burke, I.C., W.K. Lauenroth, and W.J. Parton
  1997   Regional and temporal variability in aboveground net primary productivity and net
          N mineralization in grasslands. *Ecology* 78:1330-1340.
Burke, I.C., W.K. Lauenroth, G. Cunfer, J.E. Barrett, A. Mosier, and P. Lowe
  2002   Nitrogen in the central grasslands region of the United States. *BioScience* 52: 813-823.
Cronon, W.
  1991   *Nature's Metropolis: Chicago and the Great West.* New York: W.W. Norton and
          Co.
Cunfer, G.
  2002   Causes of the Dust Bowl. Chapter 7 in *Past Time, Past Place: GIS for History,* A.K.
          Knowles, ed. Redlands, CA: ESRI Press.
  2004   Manure matters on the Great Plains frontier. *Journal of Interdisciplinary History*
          34:539-567.
  2005   *On the Great Plains: Agriculture and Environment.* College Station: Texas A&M
          University Press.
Deane, G.D., and M.P. Gutmann
  2003   Blowin' down the road: Investigating bilateral causality between dust storms and
          population change in the Great Plains. *Population Research and Policy Review*
          22:297-331.
Egan, T.
  2003   Amid dying towns of rural plains, one makes a stand. *New York Times,* December 1, Section A1.
Greb, B.W., D.E. Smika, N.P. Woodruff, and C.J. Whitfield
  1974   Summer fallow in the central Great Plains. Pp. 51-85 in *Conservation Research
          Report* 17. Washington, DC: U.S. Department of Agriculture.
Green, D.
  1973   *Land of the Underground Rain: Irrigation on the Texas High Plains, 1910-1970.*
          Austin: University of Texas Press.
Gutmann, M.P.
  2000   Scaling and demographic issues in global change research. *Climatic Change* 44:377-
          391.
Gutmann, M.P., and G. Cunfer
  1999   *A New Look at the Causes of the Dust Bowl.* (Publication 99-1.) Lubbock:
          International Center for Arid and Semiarid Land Studies, Texas Tech University.
Gutmann, M.P., G.D. Deane, N. Lauster, and A. Peri
  2005   Two population-environment regimes in the Great Plains of the United States,
          1930-1990. Submitted to *Population and Environment.*
Gutmann, M.P., and C.G. Sample
  1995   Land, climate, and settlement on the Texas frontier. *Southwestern Historical Quar-
          terly* 99:137-172.
Gutmann, M.P., S. Pullum, G.A. Cunfer, and D. Hagen
  1998   *The Great Plains Population and Environment Database: Sources and User's Guide,
          Version 1.0.* Austin: Texas Population Research Center.
Gutmann, M.P., S. Pullum-Piñón, S.G. Baker, and I.C. Burke
  2004   German-origin settlement and agricultural land use in the twentieth century Great
          Plains. In *German-American Immigration and Ethnicity in Comparative Perspec-
          tive,* W. Kamphoefner and W. Helbich, eds. Madison: University of Wisconsin
          Press.
Hargreaves, M.M.W.
  1992   *Dry Farming in the Northern Great Plains: Years of Readjustment, 1920-1990.*
          Lawrence: University Press of Kansas.

Hurt, R.D.
　1981　　The Dust Bowl: An Agricultural and Social History. Chicago, IL: Nelson-Hall.
Kaye, J.P., I.C. Burke, A.R. Mosier, and J.P. Guerchman
　2004　　Methane and nitrous oxide fluxes from urban soils to the atmosphere. Ecological
　　　　　Applications 14(4):975-981.
Kelly R.H., W.J. Parton, G.J. Crocker, P.R. Grace, J. Klir, M. Körschens, P.R. Poulton, and
D.D. Richter
　1997　　Simulating trends in soil organic carbon in long-term experiments using the century
　　　　　model. Geoderma 81:75-90.
Kilborn, P.T.
　2003　　Bucking trend, they stay on plains, held by family and friends. New York Times,
　　　　　December 2, Section A1.
Lauenroth, W.K., and I.C. Burke
　1995　　Great Plains, climate variability. Pp. 237-249 in Encyclopedia of Environmental
　　　　　Biology, Volume 2. San Diego, CA: Academic Press.
Lauenroth, W.K., D.G. Milchunas, J.L. Dodd, R.H. Hart, R.K. Heitschmidt, and L.R. Rittenhouse
　1994　　Effects of grazing on ecosystems of the Great Plains. Pp. 69-100 in Ecological
　　　　　Implications of Livestock Herbivory in the West, M. Vavra, W.A. Laycock, and
　　　　　R.D. Pieper, eds. Lakewood, CO: Society for Range Management.
Lauenroth, W.K., I.C. Burke, and J.M. Paruelo
　2000　　Patterns of production and precipitation-use efficiency of winter wheat and native
　　　　　grasslands in the central Great Plains of the United States. Ecosystems 3:344-351.
Malin, J.C.
　1946　　Dust storms, 1850-1900. Kansas Historical Quarterly 14:129-144, 265-296, 391-
　　　　　413.
Metherell A.K., L.A. Harding, C.V. Cole, and W.J. Parton
　1993　　CENTURY—Soil Organic Matter Model. (Technical Document, Agroecosystems
　　　　　Version 4.0, Great Plains Systems Research Unit, Technical Report No. 4.)　Ft.
　　　　　Collins, CO:　U.S. Department of Agriculture, Agricultural Research Service.
Metherell A.K., C.A. Cambardella, W.J. Parton, G.A. Peterson, L.A. Harding, and C.V. Cole
　1995　　Simulation of soil organic matter dynamics in dryland wheat-fallow cropping sys-
　　　　　tems. Pp. 259-270 in Soil Management and Greenhouse Effect, R. Lal, J. Kimball,
　　　　　E. Levine, and B.A. Stewart, eds. Boca Raton, FL: CRC Press Inc.
Opie, J.
　1987　　The Law of the Land. Two Hundred Years of American Farmland Policy. Lincoln:
　　　　　University of Nebraska Press.
　1993　　Ogallala: Water for a Dry Land. Lincoln: University of Nebraska Press.
Parton W.J., J.M.O. Scurlock, D.S. Ojima, T.G. Gilmanov, R.J. Scholes, D.S. Schimel, T.
Kirchner, J.-C. Menaut, T. Seastedt, E. Garcia Moya, A. Kamnalrut, and J.L. Kinyamario
　1993　　Observations and modeling of biomass and soil organic matter dynamics for the
　　　　　grassland biome worldwide. Global Biogeochemical Cycles 7:785-809.
Parton, W.J., M.P. Gutmann, and W.R. Travis
　2003　　Historical land use change in eastern Colorado. Great Plains Research 13:97-125.
Parton, W.J., M.P. Gutmann, S.A. Williams, M. Easter, and D. Ojima
　in　　　The Ecological Impact of Historical Land Use Patterns in the Great Plains: A Meth-
　press　odological Assessment. Submitted to Ecological Applications.
Paustian K., W.J. Parton, and J. Persson
　1992　　Modeling soil organic matter in organic-amended and nitrogen-fertilized long-term
　　　　　plots. Soil Science Society of America Journal 56:476-488.
Powell, J.W.
　1878　　Report on the Lands of the Arid Region. (45th Congress, 2nd session, House
　　　　　Executive Document No. 73.) Washington, DC: U.S. Government Printing Office.

Riebsame, W.E.
  1990   The United States Great Plains. Pp. 561-575 in *The Earth as Transformed by Human Action*, B.L. Turner, W.C. Clark, R.W. Kates, J.F. Richards, J.T. Mathews, and W.B. Myers, eds. Cambridge, England: Cambridge University Press.
  1991   Sustainability of the Great Plains in an uncertain climate. *Great Plains Research* 1:132-1150.
Riebsame, W.E., W.J. Parton, K.A. Galvin, I.C. Burke, L. Bohren, R. Young, and E. Knop
  1994   Integrated modeling of land use and cover change: A conceptual scheme for applying an integration strategy to agricultural land use on the U.S. Great Plains. *Bioscience* 44:350-356.
Riney-Kehrberg, R.
  1994   *Rooted in Dust: Surviving Drought and Depression in Southwestern Kansas.* Lawrence: University Press of Kansas.
Sala, O.E., W.J. Parton, L.A. Joyce, and W.K. Lauenroth
  1988   Primary production of the central grassland region of the United States. *Ecology* 69:40-45.
Schimel, D., J. Melillo, H. Tian, A.D. McGuire, D. Kicklighter, T. Kittel, N. Rosenbloom, S. Running, P. Thornton, D. Ojima, W. Parton, R. Kelly, M. Sykes, R. Neilson, and B. Rizzo
  2000   Contribution of increasing CO_2 and climate to carbon storage by ecosystems in the United States. *Science* 287:2004-2006.
Webb, W.P.
  1931   *The Great Plains.* Dallas, TX: Ginn and Company. (Reprint: University of Nebraska Press, 1981.)
Worster, D.
  1979   *Dust Bowl: The Southern Plains in the 1930s.* New York: Oxford University Press.
  1992   New West, true West. Pp. 19-33 in *Under Western Skies: Nature and History in the American West.* New York: Oxford University Press.

5

Population and Environment in Amazônia: Landscape and Household Dynamics

Emilio F. Moran, Eduardo S. Brondízio,
and Leah K. VanWey

INTRODUCTION

Land use decisions by farming families provide a key context for examining the dynamic interactions between people and the environment and are at the core of our research project in the Amazon Basin. Throughout our work in this area, we have focused on the decision-making processes of farm households, how these processes affect land use, and then on how the changes in land use (a social concept) are linked to changes in land cover (an environmental concept). When we began our research in this area, studies examining the causes of deforestation often neglected the dynamic interactions between the human population and the environment, and few studies had paid attention to the role of micro-level decision-making processes, particularly regarding reproductive and migration behavior, underlying regional patterns in population and environmental change. Since then, other teams of researchers, some represented in this volume, have also taken up this challenge. This body of work shows that when only looking at aggregate total population as a cause, the process of deforestation tends to be simplified. To get at the causes of deforestation, we need to examine how households make constrained decisions within their regional context, the land tenure system in place, the opportunities available to households to use their resources, the needs of a given household shaped by age and gender structure, and how members of households understand and make use of their physical environment.

This chapter documents the evolution of a project that has made use of a broad array of theories, methodologies, and conceptualizations linking

traditional household demographic surveys to time-series analysis of remotely sensed data in a spatially explicit framework made possible by
geographic information systems (GIS). The use of multiple theoretical
approaches and methodologies has been key to the past and ongoing success of this project. By asking timely and complex sociodemographic *and*
biophysical questions, this project speaks to diverse audiences and has
attracted researchers from diverse research traditions. The ability of the
project to answer questions about the dynamic interaction of population
and environment is due to the collaboration of these researchers without
the subordination of one particular group of collaborators (i.e., natural or
social science).

Over the more than 30 years of our research project, we have been
guided by theoretical approaches too numerous to adequately describe in
this chapter. We have utilized theoretical approaches that are based in our
disciplines of training (anthropology, sociology, demography) but have also
incorporated the insights of other disciplines. The key to our theoretical
foundations is the dynamic nature of human-environment interactions. The
cultural ecology and ecosystem ecology perspectives that motivated the
early work on this project, as well as the demographic theories of population change that underlie more recent work, focus on the ways in which
human populations adapt to and change their social, cultural, and biophysical environments. At the same time, we utilize theories that allow
agency for individuals and families and discard those that posit structural
determinism. Throughout this chapter we make brief references to the
theoretical perspectives guiding each phase of the project, and we have
given theoretical perspectives a more detailed treatment in VanWey,
Ostrom, and Meretsky (2005).

The integration of methods from various research traditions both allows the research team to speak to all participating disciplines and brings
new insights into each discipline. This project has fruitfully combined data
from soil samples, remote sensing (aerial photos and satellite imagery),
social survey research, and in-depth qualitative data collection (ethnogra-
phy, open-ended interviews). The soils data were originally included in
order to address the concerns raised by Meggers (1954, 1970) that the
humid tropics could not sustain agriculture above the slash-and-burn level.
Survey research has been a longstanding tool for collecting household social
and economic data. Qualitative data represented the anthropological focus
of the original study, supplemented with environmental data collection to
study the human-environment interactions from a cultural ecological perspective. The introduction of GIS into the project allowed us to integrate
point data on soils, household location and survey data, and continuous
data on land cover across the landscape. This allowed us to study the ways
in which landscapes embody a historical summary of past land use and are

the consequences of a given demographic trajectory and the changing dynamics of the interaction between a population and its environment (Crumley, 1994). Through the use of remote sensing and archival data, we have made efforts to reconstruct the history of landscape formation in the colonization areas of the Trans-Amazon Highway. Thus, we track the initial occupation of farm-lots and the temporal process of their transformation resulting from land allocation decision making by families arriving from different places and at different periods.

The motivations for this project of 30+ years have always been both social and environmental. We have been guided throughout our research by two basic questions: (1) How do environmental characteristics constrain human action? (2) How does human action modify the environment? Settlement of the Brazilian Amazon entailed the mass migration of families from throughout Brazil into the interior of the country, a region previously occupied primarily by indigenous groups.[1] This dramatic demographic transformation of the Amazon was accompanied by changes in the environment, specifically by the removal of forests in favor of agriculture, and in economic infrastructure providing road access and establishing the presence of government institutions. In the tropics it has been all too common to blame the smallholder for tropical deforestation (Myers, 1984) or to stress the role of a political economy that favors large-scale farmers and ranchers (Schmink and Wood, 1992). We have focused on how small-scale farmers deal with macro-political economic forces within the constraints of specific landscapes, their own age and gender structure, the local community social structure, and the capacity of local institutions to buffer those external political economic forces. For example, we consider how past agricultural experience and migration history have affected the results from management by different households; how labor was shared through kin and religious networks; and how age and gender structure affected labor availability and cash flow in households. Thus, our project has always focused on understanding the linkages between the actions of individual smallholders and broader landscape change.

The Brazilian Amazon is a region of particular significance on both environmental and demographic grounds. The Brazilian portion of the Amazon accounts for two-thirds of the Amazon Basin or 4 million square kilometers (km^2). Moist and rain forests of the tropics cover only 11 percent of the Earth's surface, but they contain 41 percent of the global terrestrial biomass and over 50 percent of the fauna and floral species. The Brazilian Amazon accounts for 26.5 percent of the Earth's moist forests (Whittaker and Likens, 1975; Salati and Vose, 1984; Prance and Lovejoy,

---

[1]Thanks to better legislation and political organization at various levels, two indigenous reserves have been demarcated in areas contiguous to our study area.

1985; Silver, 1990). Contemporary impact on tropical moist forest tends to come from government development planning, resulting in the construction of roads and settlement schemes to bring farmers to the forest to begin agricultural production, as well as from private enterprises claiming forest land for logging and farming ventures. The population of the Brazilian Amazon has been increasing through such development and settlement schemes, with a deforestation rate averaging 0.5 percent or about 30,000 square kilometers per year between 1975 and 1997. Before 1975, only about 30,000 square kilometers appeared to have been deforested. Since then, the average yearly deforestation has been equal to the total deforestation up to 1975. Deforestation rates in settlement schemes, such as this chapter reports on, can vary between 1 and 6 percent per year, as these are "hot spots" of deforestation—at least during the early years of settlement. It is this process that led to the commencement of this project.

To sum up, our research has evolved through phases of theoretical, methodological, and individual interest since 1972. Initial research in the area focused on understanding human adaptation to the frontier using cultural ecology, agronomic and ecosystem ecology approaches (Moran, 1975, 1976, 1979, 1981). During the 1990s we focused on understanding land use–land cover dynamics following deforestation by linking remote sensing, GIS, vegetation and soil inventories, and land use history. Studying the secondary succession dynamics at the level of vegetation stands and landscapes provided a context in which to understand cycles and strategies of land use, such as rates of fallowing, stages of lot formation, the role of soil fertility in the forest regenerative capacity, and the ability of farmers to keep cleared land in production (Moran and Brondizio, 1998; Moran, 1993; Moran et al., 1994, 1996, 2000; Tucker, Brondizio, and Moran, 1998). Since 1997 our research has focused on linking, spatially and temporally, household demographic and land use change (Brondizio et al., 2002; McCracken et al., 1999, 2002; Moran et al., 2002; Siqueira et al., 2003). In its current stage, we are examining the dynamics associated with second and third generations of migrant farmers, as well as the demographic changes occurring not only at the level of households, but in the larger region.

THE FIRST STAGE OF THE PROJECT (1972-1984): ADAPTATION IN A TROPICAL FRONTIER

The research on which this paper is based began 32 years ago and has continued over that entire period at regular intervals. It began in 1972 as a dissertation project (Moran, 1975) using the theoretical framework of cultural ecology (Steward, 1955) and ecosystem ecology (Odum, 1971; Rappapport, 1968) and focused on understanding the ways in which the biophysical environment constrained and influenced human action. The motive for the study was the announcement in 1971 by the Brazilian government that it would undertake the opening of the Amazon forest to development from one end to the other by means of roads of national integration. Settlement schemes were a central part of this plan with the goal of populating the "empty" Amazon with settlers from throughout Brazil as a way of integrating a region that constituted 54 percent of the national territory into the national strategy of economic development (Programa de Integracao Nacional, 1971). The major road at the center of this program was the Trans-Amazon Highway, running east to west across the Brazilian Amazon. In a short period of three years, the military government was able to build this road and to settle thousands of families along the main trunk of the road and on side roads. The central question guiding the research was understanding how the different migrating groups would adapt socially and environmentally to life in a tropical rain forest ecosystem, particularly to farming in a largely unfamiliar habitat and cultivating soils of below-average fertility (Moran, 1975, 1977). Interestingly, the results pointed less to environmental limitations than to failures of institutions to deliver to farmers promised inputs as culprits in the low yields many of them obtained. The methods used were a combination of ethnographic approaches (living in the community for over a year, participant-observation) and environmental approaches (soil sampling, tree measurement, hunting and gathering weightings, agricultural labor input-output measurements using ethological methods).

The study undertaken by the first author of this chapter sought to document the social and environmental impacts of large-scale settlement by focusing on a showcase site along the road, the Altamira site on the Lower Xingú Basin. This site became a focus of particular attention by government because of the presence of above-average fertile soils (Falesi, 1972). The early advertisements about the project touted the high fertility of the soils and the bumper harvests possible (Ministerio da Agricultura, 1971). Settlement followed a classic "fishbone" pattern (see Figure 5-1), which had been used earlier to settle parts of the state of Paraná, in southern Brazil, and which has become associated with a Brazilian style of settling the Amazon frontier: a main trunk with regularly spaced side roads that create a distinctive pattern visible from satellites (see Figure 5-2).

Before the arrival of the Trans-Amazon Highway and its associated settlement scheme, the Altamira region had been sparsely settled, with a town of less than 1,000 persons along the Xingú River and several posts for trading rubber collected by rubber tappers upriver. In the 1950s the town promoted a small-scale colonization project that brought several dozen people from Piauí, in northeast Brazil, who settled along the first 18 km west of the town of Altamira. As elsewhere in the Amazon, along the rivers,

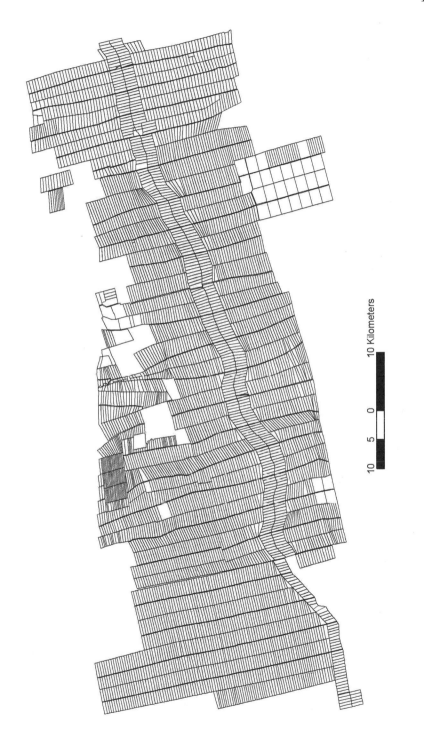

10 Kilometers

10   5   0

FIGURE 5-1   Property grid of Altamira region.

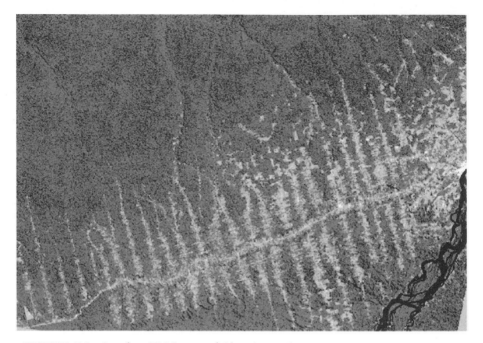

FIGURE 5-2   Landsat TM image of Altamira region.

isolated households of *caboclos* (native non-Indian Amazonians, see Moran, 1974) lived by hunting, gathering, and tending small manioc fields. Many of these *caboclos* moved a short distance from their riverside locations to the highway to make land claims when the highway came. Most of the area was forested in 1971, except along those first 18 km out of town, and the settlement scheme began to divide land holdings from that point west of Altamira into a fishbone pattern. Large patches of fertile soils could be found along those first 20 km, and thus government officials promoted the fertility of the soils of the region as being uniformly high, which proved later not to be the case. There are two types of forest in the area—liana forest and dense humid tropical forest. The former is associated with a dense presence of vines, and it has been suggested by some scholars that this forest type is associated with disturbance by prehistoric Amazonians (Balée, 1989). Indeed, in these areas and their associated fertile alfisols (i.e., moderately leached forest soils), there is an abundance of Tapajoara pottery and patches of anthropogenic black soils, both of which bear testimony to the use of these fertile areas by prehistoric populations associated with, or who traded with, the pre-Columbian chiefdoms along and near the Tapajós River (Smith, 1982).

Between 1971 and 1974 the process of settlement proceeded at a very rapid pace, as the government selected farmers from throughout the country for the project, bringing them by plane, boat, and bus at government expense (and with a guarantee of a return trip if they did not find the area acceptable). Selection criteria used by the government, when examined carefully, were overwhelmingly driven by the size of families. The larger the family, the more likely they were to be selected—a process that resulted in an older than average age for heads of household and a substantial dependency ratio. Agricultural experience was an official criterion, but there was no verification carried out to establish whether statements were true, nor did the criterion distinguish between experience as an owner, a rural wage laborer, or a share-cropper (Moran, 1976, 1979). Upon arrival, settlers were given certificates of occupation, which allowed them to obtain year-to-year loans for agricultural production (but not long-term loans). They were promised land titles, but this process proved to be very slow and difficult for most of them. A few settlers familiar with the process undertook expensive trips to distant towns where they could make their land claim and obtain title, but fewer than 5 percent undertook this process. Even after several years, fewer than 30 percent of the people had received the promised titles. The certificates of occupation could not be passed on through sale. The titles could be reissued to someone who bought a property, but because the process was slow and expensive, most people who bought land from someone simply kept the old title and some rather informal document from the seller to establish ownership. Over time, more complex arrangements have evolved, but the lack of a rigorous titling process has been one of the factors that has prevented a stable land market from emerging, and it may also have influenced the tendency not to fragment properties, as it would be even harder to establish rights to fragments than to entire properties. Inheritance of property has not been seen to be a problem, except in those cases in which several children wish to have land, and resolution of these cases is usually informal rather than legalized through titling.

Adaptation in the frontier was shaped by the intervention of the government in the selection of households and by their intervention through credit programs, extension, and the quality of roads that were constructed to market the produce. As a result of government selection criteria, the demographic age-gender pyramid for the settlers in the study area was quite peculiar—it did not have as the broadest segment the 0-4 age group, which is common for fast-growing populations, and was almost even for the 0-4, 5-9, and 10-14 cohorts, who accounted for 55 percent of the population. It had very few persons above age 50 (2.4 percent) and was remarkably thin in the 20-24 and 25-29 cohorts—usually the most common age cohorts in frontier and migrant populations for a bulge in the heads of household (Moran, 1981:88-89). In this area during the first three years of settlement, the largest cohort of heads of household were in the 40-44 and 45-49 cohorts. Mean household size was 6.2, consistent with the national mean (Moran, 1981). Thus, rather than reflecting a classic migrant population of very young migrants, the migrants to this frontier in the early years were about 10 years older on average and had a larger dependency ratio than is normal (but also more available labor to cut more forest). The low rate of interest provided by the *Banco do Brasil* (Bank of Brazil), upon orders from the president, accelerated the rate of deforestation and, when combined with larger and older households, resulted in higher deforestation rates than might have been expected.

Although a host of institutions were present, they were understaffed and poorly informed about the environmental conditions of the area, contributing to many decisions that exacerbated the propensity to fail in these critical early years—particularly the failure to maintain roads, provide adequate health care, and take into account the high rates of rainfall and the importance of drainage to prevent malaria outbreaks. It must be noted that the process was a classic case of a top-down command economy undertaking. At the time it was touted as "the equivalent of placing a man on the moon." There was an effort to make available the entire set of national institutions in the frontier all at once, but, because of the difficulties of life in the region, few members of those bureaucracies wished to go there. To encourage acceptance of positions in the frontier, double salaries were paid. This attracted largely young people wishing to save for their starting professional careers, but they lacked experience in managing something as complex as this in an unfamiliar environment. The speed with which immigrants were brought to the area by the government contributed to the difficulties of delivering services, as did the poor quality of the roads, particularly in the rainy season.

The settlement scheme very clearly laid out that settlers could clear only the front 50 percent of their properties, with the notion that the 50 percent of the back of lots would remain forest, thereby constituting a fairly uninterrupted expanse of forest for conservation. However, this was interpreted creatively by some settlers to mean 50 percent of whatever forest they had upon buying a property, and thus as land turnover occurred, the new owners would encroach on the forested 50 percent. Moreover, there was no capacity to monitor whether farmers were abiding by the 50 percent rule or not. As satellite imagery began to be used, it became clear that there was enormous variability in how farmers behaved with regard to the 50 hectares to remain in forest out of the total 100 hectares of each property, with some properties having deforested virtually the entire property, while others were well within the 50 percent established area.

The conclusions of this first phase of the study were reported in several monographs (Moran, 1975, 1976, 1981) and in many articles (among them

Moran, 1977, 1979, 1982, 1984, 1988, 1989). In short, Amazonian natives outperformed migrants in yield per hectare, in use of technology, and in overall well-being—contradicting government expectations. Soils proved to be highly variable—not invariably acid and nutrient-poor, and Amazonian natives were more often able to identify better soils, thereby obtaining higher yields per hectare than newcomers. The role of soils in shaping the path of land use has proven to be very important in subsequent research, with farms on good soils being more resistant to turnover of ownership than those on poor soils, and they tend to have a more diversified production portfolio. Previous agricultural experience as managers of a farm property resulted in rapid success in the Amazon frontier and in capital accumulation, both in use of credit and in acquiring local knowledge and applying it to production goals—and these management skills were not geographically concentrated in migrants from the south and southeast, as stated in planning documents. Those who were landless before coming were very likely to become landless again after a short time through farm failure and inability to pay bank loans, and previous high rates of migration were associated with low incomes and farm failure in the new frontier. Those who were most dependent on government institutions were most prone to fail, given the difficulty for state institutions of reliably delivering services in a timely fashion and with a technology appropriate for the local environmental conditions.

THE SECOND STAGE OF THE PROJECT (1991-1996): SECONDARY SUCCESSION AND LAND COVER CHANGE DYNAMICS

Beginning in 1991, we moved from examining social outcomes for farm families to examining the environmental outcomes of human action in the region. This work involved analyses examining both the lot- and landscape-level outcomes of farm-household decisions over time. The focus of this work was on understanding what factors explained the differential rate of secondary succession forest regrowth following deforestation. Until this date, there had been a tendency even among scientists to ignore the fact of secondary forest regrowth and to consider deforestation only (often followed by what was sometimes called "desertification" or degraded pasture development). Our work sought to correct this oversight, while developing methods to integrate ecological and spatial aspects of land clearing and fallow cycles necessary to understand land use change and agricultural choices of colonist farmers. This insight came from the farmers themselves who, when queried with the question "What factor most limits your ability to succeed in farming in this region?" responded most often by saying that it was the vigor of the regrowth—with the pioneer species in the secondary vegetation often being several feet high before they could even plant their crop after burning. Studying regrowth and fallow cycles provided us with tools to understand the demands for labor and technology faced by farmers in the area.

The project took new directions by linking techniques of satellite remote sensing and GIS that permit scaling up from local communities to a much larger landscape captured by Landsat Thematic Mapper (TM) images (185 by 185 kilometers). We used a combination of remote sensing, GIS, forestry, and social survey research, which included components on ethnoecology, demography, land tenure, land use history, production and consumption, marketing of production, credit used, and aspirations for the future. Moran and Brondizio worked together in this stage with several colleagues, developing new methods for linking the behavior of farming households to their use of soils and land use practices and to the pixel data from the satellites (Mausel et al., 1993; Brondizio et al., 1994, 1996; Brondizio and Siqueira, 1997; Moran and Brondizio, 1998; Moran et al., 1994, 1996).

During this period, a great deal of effort was spent on collecting land use histories using interviews and remote sensing data in preparation for vegetation and soil surveys. The goal of this intensive environmental data collection, besides improving the classification of remotely sensed data, was the linkage of detailed environmental information to farm-lot and regional trajectories of land cover change. Consequently, by combining the ability to discriminate deforestation events and stages of secondary succession with a property grid defining farm-lots, we were able to query and understand variation in land use and cover change at the levels of the farm and the larger landscape. In this way, questions such as "What is the rate of deforestation in the area?" could be answered at different levels, time periods, and, most importantly, in terms of variability within the region. Over 100 sites (2,000+ vegetation plots) were sampled across several study areas using standard vegetation survey methods (genus and species identification of all plants in plots selected, diameter at breast height, total height, height to first branch of tree species); soil samples associated with each site were taken with a soil auger to one meter depth. This resulted in a very large data set linking vegetation inventories, soils data, land use history, and spectral data from Landsat TM images from 1985, 1988, 1991, and 1996.

During this phase of the study we expanded from the Altamira site to include an estuary site (Marajó), and two eastern Amazon sites characterized by relatively poor soils to contrast with Altamira and with longer histories of settlement (Igarapé-Açú—in the Bragantina region near Belém, and Tomé-Açú—an area settled by Japanese immigrants in the 1930s). In addition, we were able to do brief fieldwork in the northwestern Amazon in the Vaupés River region of Colombia among Tukanoan native Amazonians in an area characterized by extreme infertility of soils and by native strate-gies of resource use largely disconnected from external markets. The goal was to examine what explained the differential rates of forest regrowth following deforestation under a variety of soil fertility conditions, agricul-tural technologies, and densities. As it turns out, Altamira stood out well above all the other sites in soil fertility and had the fastest rates of second-ary growth (Moran and Brondizio, 1998).

A considerable body of publications report on this part of the research (see http://www.indiana.edu/~act/pubs.htm). We found that land use by farmers explained most of the difference in rates of regrowth when compar-ing sites in a given region, but when comparing different regions of the Amazon that we have studied, soils proved to be a more robust factor in explaining differences. This finding suggests a more general conclusion, also supported by the work of Gutmann et al. (Chapter 4) and Walsh et al. (Chapter 6), that biophysical characteristics may stand out as limiting fac-tors when considering large geographic units/extents, whereas human char-acteristics drive variation at the property or community level. Interestingly, rates of regrowth did not differ significantly between oxisols (highly weath-ered soils), ultisols (strongly leached, acid forest soils), and spodosols (acid soils with a subsurface accumulation of humus)—but regrowth on the fer-tile alfisols was considerably more rapid, and this difference accelerated over time (Moran and Brondizio, 1998). We found confirmation that initial soil selection played a key role in farmer stability, with very little turnover for farmers with substantial areas of the fertile alfisols (with very few plots with these soils entering the land market), whereas on the others soils, turnover was high. Moreover, we found that crop choice after 20 years of settlement had been profoundly affected by the soils present on the farm; we found a significant relationship between the percentage of fertile soils on properties and the diversity of the portfolio of the farm household, with over 80 percent of the area in pasture on the poor soils and a steady shift toward cash crops and tree crops with increases in the proportion of alfisols on the property (see Figure 5-3). This is affected by the predominance of cocoa and sugar cane in the Altamira area, both of which require fertile soils for good results.

Despite its many advantages, remote sensing data when used alone present a number of limitations to accomplishing land use assessment tasks, including limitations in temporal resolution in order to capture interannual land use changes and limitations in spatial and spectral resolution that would allow a distinction to be made between subtle land cover classes that are crucial to land use interpretation at the farm level (e.g., types of agricul-ture and agroforestry). Often, the growing period of most Amazonian crops coincides with high cloud cover, thus limiting image availability. The inclusion of detailed fieldwork and vegetation and soil inventories has been

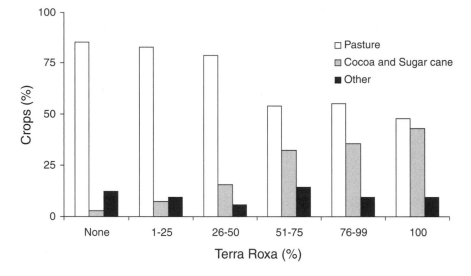

FIGURE 5-3   Crops and Terra Roxa. Terra Roxa is an alfisol, a soil of dark red-brown color, nutrient rich, and of basaltic origin. It is very fertile with excellent drainage. As the proportion of terra roxa increases so does a farm's crop diversity. Adapted from Moran et al. (2002).

important to overcome some of these limitations. Baseline research on vegetation inventories and interviews about the use of fallow areas has provided guidance for image analysis and in understanding land cover change. These include estimating rates of regrowth across areas of different land use histories, mapping of different stages of secondary vegetation to characterize fallow cycles across different land use systems, assessing the occurrence of economic species in fallow areas, and estimating above-ground biomass in landscapes characterized by different land cover complexities (Tucker, Brondizio, and Moran, 1998; Brondizio et al., 1996; Moran et al., 1996, among others). Still, this work needs to be combined with survey instruments aimed at capturing the farmers' perspective on the sequence of crops planted, the arrangements of crops, and their location on the farm lot. As part of this process we developed several methods for using remote sensing images during land use interviews and survey techniques to capture the farmers' perspectives on environmental management and land allocation. While still not ideal, the combination of this suite of methods and approaches helps us to understand the dynamics of land use and land cover change in the region, as well as how to best overcome the trade-offs and limitations of each tool and research instrument.

Important outcomes of this research include discriminating, mapping, and understanding of biomass accumulation in different stages of forest regrowth, species dominance, and structural characteristics of mature forest and secondary forests in the region; and also finding that structural characteristics of the vegetation directly influence spectral data and are key features used during image classification. Using this approach, we have been able to differentiate up to three stages of secondary succession, which has in turn allowed for a more detailed estimation of above-ground biomass and cycles of land use (Mausel et al., 1993; Brondizio et al., 1996; Moran et al., 2000). As our work links to the larger literature on global environmental change, these variables on vegetation and soil and their relationship to spatially explicit spectral data have allowed us to contribute to debates about the estimation of carbon sequestered in secondary forests, nutrient cycling, and trajectories of forest recovery. Important issues include testing a selection of suitable variables and allometric equations for developing estimation of above-ground biomass to support biomass modeling at local and regional levels (Lu et al., 2002). Most important, perhaps, it allowed us to continuously test new methods of image classification (e.g., combining textural and spectral data) and achieve finer land cover discrimination. Deforestation is only one component of land cover change; as colonization areas age, secondary succession tends to dominate not only in areal extent, but in the decision making of farmers. In our Altamira study area, for instance, we found a total deforestation of 40 percent from 1970 to 1996; however, we found that deforestation rates vary widely both regionally (settlement level) and locally (farm level). We observed that, at the settlement level, half of the deforested area stayed in production, while the other half appeared in different stages of secondary succession (Brondizio et al., 2002). Our efforts at detailed land cover classification have been a fundamental step towards moving beyond the typical "forest and nonforest" distinction and closer to accounting for what farmers actually do on their lots.

The combined use of methods from forestry and ecology with the methods of social survey research provided a sound way to link the decisions of farmers to forest cover and to examine how subsequent land use was influenced by environmental factors (e.g., soils) and by constrained decisions by members of the household. This stage of research laid the foundations for the third phase of the work, which focused more closely on population dynamics as they interact with environmental and economic variables. A substantial database of soils, vegetation characterization and biomass measurements, and remotely sensed images laid the basis for the new phase.[2]

---

[2]We have contributed this spatially explicit database to the ongoing Brazilian-led LBA Program (Large Scale Biosphere-Atmosphere Experiment in Amazônia).

THE THIRD STAGE OF THE PROJECT (1997-PRESENT): POPULATION AND ENVIRONMENT IN AMAZÔNIA

As we worked over the years on this project, we came across many cases that seemed to suggest that households underwent significant shifts in land use strategy as they went from being young households to being older ones. In 1997, with support from the National Institute of Child Health and Human Development (NICHD), we undertook to clarify whether it was growth in population or the shifts in the age and gender structure of households that best explained the changes in deforestation rates that we observed using satellite data. For that study we posited a conceptual model, based on the theory of the developmental cycle of households (Goody, 1958, 1976), suggesting that the typical young household on the frontier has to focus primarily on production for household food needs, which results in rapid conversion of forest into annual staple crop production and the growing needs of a young family. Over time, the household is able to save and accumulate capital and more labor through the steady growth of the family, so that it is capable of expanding into other activities, such as cattle ranching and cash crops. However, as the children approach their late teens, the head of household begins to take into account the upcoming loss of this labor through marriage, and thus begins to reallocate land use toward productive uses that require less labor, such as tree crops (see Figure 5-4 for the conceptual diagram guiding this research).

To undertake this work we had the benefit of a property grid, detailed vegetation and soil data, and 25 years of familiarity with the region and the Altamira study site, its people, and government and nongovernmental organizations (NGOs). One of the powerful elements of this new approach, made possible by the existence of a property grid with considerable regularity, was the ability to link households to specific plots of land in what was mostly a one-to-one relationship. Although the property grid proved to be initially inaccurate, over several years of fieldwork we were able to develop at least 90 percent accuracy in the fit of the grid to observed data. Sources of initial inaccuracy included changes in the design of the planned versus actual road system and lot layout, fragmentation and aggregation of lots, variation in lot format according to topographic conditions, the opening of new roads by farmers, and the beginning of nonplanned settlements toward the end of feeder roads. Our team put a significant investment of time, resources, and personnel into collecting differentially corrected ground control points, systematically visiting each feeder road in the region, collecting ground control points in at least two corners of lots, and interviewing farmers about the shape and dimensions of lots. This corrected property grid allowed the project to make inferences about the impact of individual households on the land cover.

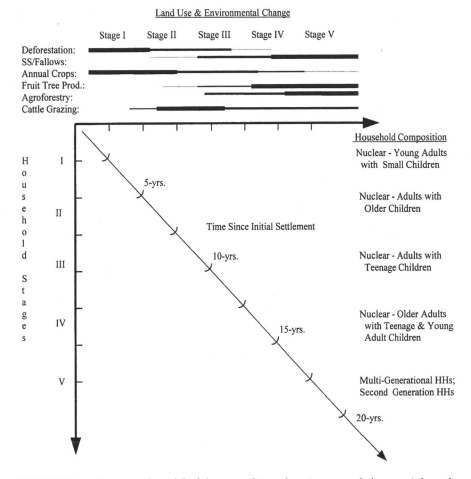

FIGURE 5-4   Conceptual model of demographic and environmental change. Adapted from McCracken et al. (1999).

   While the first stage of this work (1972-1984) had already used multiple methods of data collection, processing, or analysis, each new stage has introduced new methods. The second stage (1991-1996) introduced systematic ecological methods for measuring species diversity, forest cover, remotely sensed data, GIS for integrating data, and spatial analyses. These innovations arose from efforts of Moran to develop remote sensing skills and from the addition of Brondizio to the core research team, as Brondizio came in with substantial skills in remote sensing and botany. Brondizio's concern with studying land use intensification among small farmers and Amazonian ethnobotany helped to link vegetation, land use history, and multitemporal remote sensing analysis. Similarly, his work was focused on developing methods and procedures for using remote sensing data as part of the ethnographic process. Global positioning system (GPS) technology, just emerging during the early 1990s, became an important element to link, for instance, interviews and visits with individual farmers to multitemporal satellite data.

The new methods in this third stage (1997-present) have included methods traditional in demography—large sample (relative to past work) social surveys and regression analysis. Our first NICHD-funded project (1997-2001) collected survey data from 402 households in Altamira and analyzed these data using ordinary least squares regression techniques. The current NICHD-funded project (2003-2006) aims to collect household survey data from just short of 1,000 households and to analyze these data using more sophisticated regression-based methods (e.g., event history analysis, spatial econometric analysis, logistic regression) in two regions—Altamira and Santarém. These innovations largely reflect the addition of traditionally trained demographers to the core research team (Stephen McCracken on the first NICHD project and Leah VanWey on the second NICHD project).

A particular contribution of this project to the population and environment methodologies is the generation of spatially explicit sampling approaches. In our 1998 Altamira survey, sampling was explicitly based on the arrival time on the lots of members of cohorts. We overlaid a property grid of 3,800 properties on the remotely sensed, time-series data, and added hydrography, roads and topography layers. The grid allowed us to focus on the individual property and to use the criterion for assigning membership in a settlement cohort to a household when we could detect in the imagery that five hectares had been cleared (a conservative figure given the average area cleared per year being three hectares and the interval in our time series being of three years). A full description can be found in McCracken et al. (1999). We divided the population into five cohorts and sampled disproportionately from each one so as to have relatively equal sized samples from each cohort. Plate 3 illustrates the distribution of cohorts in the study area. We received extremely good cooperation from sampled households in this phase of our work. Our research team encountered only one household that refused to participate. We completed 402 household surveys that examined demographic and socioeconomic history.

Using these data, we have indeed confirmed that households go through a developmental cycle that is related to the aging of the household and the farm, with distinct trajectories of land use and deforestation (Brondizio et al., 2002; see Plate 3). Most farm labor comes from the household, with very little wage labor used and very few cases of sharecropping.[3] The

---

[3]However, sharecropping is becoming an increasingly common system among cocoa producers.

available household labor changes over the life of the household. More women than men leave their households, and they leave earlier to seek an education or marriage. This loss of women from households is partially made up by their gain of daughters-in-law. The next generation will be relatively small, because the pattern of fertility is very urban—most households are nuclear, rather than extended or multigenerational families, and the total fertility rate is around two children per woman in sampled properties. This low fertility may be related to the low rate of infant mortality in this frontier, with 40 deaths per 1,000 by the mid-1980s. Women use a variety of methods of fertility control, with sterilization being the preferred method and commonly used after the birth of the second child. By ages 25-29, more than 43 percent of women were already sterilized and the proportion continues to increase with age.

Corresponding to this demographic cycle, each of the arriving cohorts of settlers since 1970 followed a similar trajectory of exponential deforestation upon arrival and for about five years, followed by a steady decline in deforestation over the rest of the domestic cycle, except for a short pulse that we have come to call a consolidation phase toward the late stages of that generation before taking off again with the next generation.[4] However, since the Altamira case only provided a single generation to observe, colleagues wondered whether the pulse at the tail end of the cycle represented the beginning of a new domestic cycle or an entirely different set of dynamics. With that in mind, in 2003 we began a new phase of the population and environment project, which added a much older settlement site wherein we might observe whether the cycles repeat themselves in the second and third generations. This new phase also added questions informed by traditional household demography approaches, focusing on the movement of individuals into and out of households and on the allocation of household labor. This project completed one of two planned data collections in summer 2003, and we are now testing our inferences about the domestic cycle across generations.

The new project allows us to examine set of questions generated by the first phase of the project regarding environmental constraints on human action and the environmental impacts of human action, among them:

1. Does the changing availability of household labor over the household life cycle affect the trajectory of deforestation and land use change in the same way for later generations of Amazonian farmers as for first generation in-migrants?

---

[4]It is important to note the variability of deforestation levels among farm-lots within and across cohorts.

2. What are the determinants of changing household labor supply? Specifically, what are the biophysical and socioeconomic determinants of entries into and exits from the household through fertility, migration, and marriage?

3. How are the decisions of households regarding land use and labor allocation constrained by soil quality, access to water supplies, interannual drought events (e.g., El Niño–type events), and other resource scarcities?

4. Are there notable differences in land use choices made by landholders who live in an urban area (away from the piece of land owned in the rural area) in contrast to the decisions made by those who live on their rural properties?

5. What are the bases for the precipitous decline in female fertility in these frontier regions, especially the use of sterilization after two pregnancies?

We are able to explore these new questions through entry into a new study site—the agricultural areas around the city of Santarém. This region has a long history of human settlement and has different biophysical and institutional characteristics. The region has soils of middling fertility, a more marked dry season lasting at least four but sometimes six months, and large areas of secondary succession and of anthropogenic savanna. The terrain is flatter in most areas and has lower overall rainfall than Altamira. It is a much older area, having not only been an important pre-Columbian chiefdom, but also having served as a key trading center for the middle and lower Amazon, with a tradition of cattle ranching along the floodplain. The Santarém region presents significant differences in relation to soil types, distribution of water, and topography when compared to the Altamira region. While the fertile alfisols are not present in this region, one may find sparse patches of "black soil" (*Terra Preta de Indío*) and large stretches of floodplain soils along the Amazon River. The latter is subject to seasonal flooding. Water availability is one of the biggest constraints for farming and ranching in the region. With a low water table and sparse distribution of streams in most of the region, farmers often depend on strategies for saving rainwater and support from municipalities to provide in-farm water delivery. Rainfall is also characterized by a marked period of drought, ranging from three to five months (August to November). Land titling is relatively secure, and there is an active land market in the area. Large farmers from the south and the center west of Brazil have been entering the Santarém region to buy land for mechanized rice and soybean production in the past four years (to such an extent that national newspapers and international media, including the *New York Times* and *The Economist*, have reported on this trend). A large portion of this change has been driven by the construction of a deepwater grain port in Santarém by the local division of the multinational company Cargill. This port can load grain onto ocean-going ships.

At the same time that agriculture is changing, the hinterlands of Santarém have been urbanizing. Small villages are forming on formerly agricultural lands, while many past villages are growing in size. In turn, many villages are also disappearing due to land acquisition by large landowners aiming at producing soybeans. Federal, state, and municipal governments operate health centers and schools in the area. Santarém has a system of agricultural extension similar to many other Amazonian areas. Government agencies such as Empresa Brasileira de Pesquisa Agropecuária (EMBRAPA) and Empresa de Assistencêcia Técnica e Extensão Rural (EMATER) are present in the region and provide some level of support to farmers despite their lack of infrastructure and personnel. The area has been the site of NGO activity and research by Brazilian and foreign scientists for years. Actually, the region is popularly known in Amazônia as "the Mecca of NGOs" for its large number of NGOs working on issues of health, environment, land use, fisheries, and economic development. Dozens of NGOs provide social assistance, economic support, and educational campaigns to local communities. The combination of the higher levels of development (meaning more people were working off-farm or owning land but living in the city) and past study in this area led us to have more difficulty with participant cooperation. We have not processed the data sufficiently to calculate response rates, but we encountered a small number of refusals and a small number of nonresponses due to a failure to encounter a landowner on repeated visits. Because of the rapid rate of land acquisitions by outsiders, there is a high level of suspicion by local small farmers toward outside visitors coming to ask questions about their farms.

In this current NICHD-funded work, we have also built on past work on spatially explicit sampling procedures. We use a multistage cluster sampling approach to account for the reality of a new research site and to select a more appropriate sample for our new research questions. This approach is designed to generate a sample that is representative both of the landscape and of the population. In earlier work, survey data collection sampled lots and focused on the household in which the owner of the lot resided. This generated a sample of lots that is generalizable to the landscape and to households making decisions about lots. This sampling approach allowed us to appropriately generalize analyses about the interactions of households and lots to the population of lots. However, in the most recent work, we are making sample modifications based on two developments. First, we are working in a new study area (around the city of Santarém) with a long settlement history, meaning that we cannot identify the time of settlement for lots through the use of remotely sensed data (available only since 1972). Second, we strive to answer questions about household demographic and socioeconomic processes (e.g., out-migration of children, division of property through inheritance, allocation of labor on- and off-farm). To answer these questions, as well as ongoing questions about land use and land cover change on lots, we need a sample that is generalizable to the population of lots (to the landscape) and to the population of households.

To address these issues we have modified our sampling approach in two ways. First, we have identified four broad regions with distinct settlement histories, based on the location of roads that were built at different times. The sample is stratified by these regions rather than by the cohort of settlement identified at the lot level. In each of these four regions we select a random sample of 20 3 by 3 km squares, and then a random sample of lots (according to our property grid) within these squares (see Figure 5-5). Second, once we have this sample of lots, we interview all the households living on each selected lot. This gives us a sample of lots that is representative of the landscape, a sample of landowning households (using only the owning household on each lot) that is representative of the population of land use decision makers, and a sample of households (including all households on all lots) that is representative of all households in the region.

The design of this current work allows us to address cross-cutting issues that we have encountered in the past and continue to wrestle with. First, we have encountered the problem of accounting for aggregation or fragmentation of lots in our models of land use decision making. In past work we focused on newer settlements and single lots that conformed closely to the areas deeded to settlers by the government. In the current work, we collected information on all lots resulting from the fragmentation of past lots appearing in our sample and on larger lots that included lots appearing in our sample. Thus, we take the property grid from which we sampled as a representation of reality at some point in the past and are able to study how lot boundaries have changed since then.

We plan additional data collection in 2005 that will increase our ability to link dynamic household changes to dynamic land use–land cover changes. We will undertake two sorts of follow-up. First, we will track households that we interviewed in 1998 in the first NICHD project and follow up with them wherever they are living in 2005 (within a feasible distance from the study area); this will allow us to take a dynamic look at household processes (migration, marriage, fertility) and at the process of farm abandonment. Second, we will follow up with the lots on which we conducted interviews in 1998. We will interview the current owners or users of the lot to get a sense of how uses of land have changed over time, as well as of what sort of new owners replace what types of families on what types of land. These two

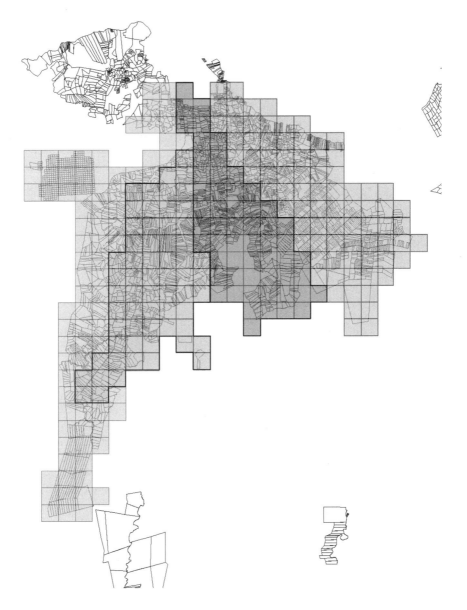

FIGURE 5-5 Property grid of Santarém region, showing sub-regions and sampling grid cells within each of the sub-regions.

follow-ups will give us a picture of land turnover in the region and its place in the regional trajectory of land use and land cover change.

REALITY AND THE FUTURE OF RESEARCH ON POPULATION AND ENVIRONMENT

The 32 years to date of research in Altamira and the four years of work in Santarém provide very different views of the process of population and environment in the Amazon. In Altamira we were able to observe the process of settlement virtually from its start in 1971 to the present and to account for changes in family structure, migration rates, areas of origin, soil fertility, road quality, and available credit. These elements influenced the decisions of household members in a variety of ways that permit reasonably well-informed inferences about the trajectories of change. In the case of Santarém, an area settled for over 300 years, and even longer when we consider the pre-Columbian chiefdoms, it is harder to capture the process of change because initial conditions are not precisely known, the area is far more densely populated, and the multiple influences that act on the decision of heads of household are imperfectly understood. We hope in the coming years, as we work longer in this area, to be able to have a better sense of these complex components of decision making, particularly as the area evolves toward mechanized, export-based agriculture.

The rapid expansion of soybean production in the Santarém study area has been dramatic. The area under soybean production expanded from only a few experimental plots in 2002 to 7,000 hectares in 2003, and it is projected to expand to 30,000 hectares in 2004. The construction of the port combined with the high levels of demand for soybeans in Europe and Asia have been a trigger event for rapid change in land use, as Redman (Chapter 7 in this volume) defines the term. This event fundamentally changed the economic and political environment in which land use (and sale) decisions are made. This event shows the difficulty of predicting change when external forces, such as the aggressive actions of a multinational to reduce its transportation costs, are so important. This is a good example of that category known as "surprises" in global change dynamics. It is only a surprise in that there has been such a persistent assumption in the scholarly literature (since Meggers, 1954, and reaffirmed in 1970) that the Amazon is unfit for intensive agriculture. Whether a similar expansion will occur in Altamira remains to be seen, but it would not be a surprise there. The population has shown considerable alertness to outside markets (e.g., cocoa expansion in the 1980s in response to the rise in world prices) and is characterized by bank managers as far more entrepreneurial than the population of Santarém. Of course, much of the current change is a result of outsiders buying up land from locals, consolidating small properties into large ones, and mechanizing. Because many areas of Altamira have very good soils and have had stable occupation, it is less likely that owners would be eager to sell their better soils to outsiders. However, it would not be surprising if some of the flatter areas west of Altamira and closer to the Cuiabá-Santarém Highway may experience the diffusion of this type of agriculture. The small size of families in this frontier predisposes them to urban living, rather than traditional farming, but also to the use of technology to replace the lack of household labor. Thus, one can expect them to adopt mechanized farming whenever possible. The Altamira study area lost 40 percent of its forest cover in the first 25 years after settlement began. Our models suggest, based on farm-level analysis, that by 2020 it will have about 25-32 percent of forest cover remaining. This projection does not account for the arrival of mechanized soybeans. The impact of soybeans on forest cover is not expected to be large in existing farms, as most farms would have their remaining forests in areas where flat land is less likely, or where wetlands are present, as most good soils on flatter land are already in cultivation.

The reality is that people are interacting with the physical environment in a myriad of ways—from the cognitive act of choosing where to settle, whom to migrate with, whether they pick flat or steep terrain, whether they give priority to proximity to a water supply or not, to soil color or not, whether they interact with natives or keep to themselves, whether they collect germplasm regularly from neighbors or import it from areas of origin, whether they have the knowledge and the means to practice contraception, and how the timing of contraception fits with views they may have of desirable family size and long-term goals for those children and themselves. This complexity of human-environment interactions requires multidisciplinary research involving theoretical flexibility and a multiplicity of data collection tools that can capture the variety of sources of change and the variety of responses by the population. The use of satellite remote sensing and GIS allowed the earlier study to expand geographically more than 30-fold in areal extent. The use of ecosystem ecology and modeling allowed the study to pay attention to both ecosystem and social variables in an integrative modeling framework—an approach that failed, however, to give attention to individual actors. This has now been addressed by use of agent-based modeling approaches (Deadman et al., 2004).

Over the past 32 years, some things remain the same, while others have radically changed. Road quality and episodic agricultural credit have persisted as constraints to the productivity of farming households. Farmers have learned to combine rural and urban employment to make ends meet and to overcome the difficulties of accessing services in the rural areas. Women have taken dramatic action to control their fertility across economic groups, thereby bringing about a fertility transition quickly. This transition in fertility and the resulting small families may have very large implications for the future of small farmers in the region: Will they sell their farms due to lack of available labor whenever economic conditions result in credit tightening? Or will they effectively modernize and mechanize, thereby developing farming in the region toward greater intensification? They have shown, at the level of the farm, that they can conserve forest, but that the quality of soils plays a role in the trajectory of land use and deforestation.

The concerns of the population are multifaceted—social standing and income, how much production they can extract from their soils, how easily they can market their produce, and whether they can have enough to carry them over to next year. They are concerned with their physical and cultural survival, and they understand that this survival depends on how well they manage their natural resources and their social relations and how lucky they may be in making felicitous choices in a globally connected world in which prices may be determined by events far away from their location. Thus, they try to stay informed about events in faraway places that may impact the price of cocoa, sugar, rice, or soybeans. An analysis of the lives of settlers on the Amazon frontier must have a broad social and environmental perspective if it is to capture the complex interactions acting reciprocally on people and environment. The benefits are a more complete understanding of how people and environment interact and shape the next iteration of this mutually reinforcing set of feedbacks. This is dynamic analysis requiring complex alternative scenarios, driven by stochastic processes and by sudden shocks coming from external political, economic, and environmental sources. Our challenge is to explore these dynamic interactions without simplifying them to the point that we deceive ourselves that we understand the system completely. We are likely to be surprised by unexpected shocks, emergent properties, the creativity of the biological world, and the human propensity to be contrarian when we least expect it.

ACKNOWLEDGMENTS

Work over the past 30 years has been funded by the Social Science Research Council; the National Institute of Mental Health; the National Institute of Child Health and Human Development (2R01 HD035811-02 and 04); the National Science Foundation (SBR9100526, SBR9310049, SBR9521918); the National Aeronautics and Space Administration (NCC5-334, NCC5-695); the National Institute for Global Environmental Change; and the National Oceanic and Atmospheric Administration (NA06GP0344). We are grateful for their support that has made this work possible. We also wish to thank the many pioneer families who have given generously of their time to answer our questions over these many years. In the process we have learned about courage, determination, and strength of character. We thank them for their inspiring example. We would like to thank also the LBA office of Santarém for their continuous support during our field campaigns, the EMBRAPA and EMATER offices in Belém, Santarém, and Altamira, and all our colleagues from ACT (Anthropological Center for Training and Research on Global Environmental Change) and CIPEC (Center for the Study of Institutions, Population, and Environmental Change) at Indiana University. The funding agencies above should not be held responsible for the views expressed herein. They are the sole responsibility of the authors.

The order of authorship in the paper reflects the length of time each of the coauthors has been engaged in the project. The three coauthors participated equally in the construction of the manuscript.

REFERENCES

Balée, W.
  1989   The culture of Amazonian forests. *Advances in Economic Botany* 7:1-21.
Brondízio, E.S., and A. Siqueira
  1997   From extractivists to forest farmers: Changing concepts of agricultural intensification and peasantry in the Amazon estuary. *Research in Economic Anthropology* 18:233-279.
Brondízio, E.S., E.F. Moran, P. Mausel, and Y. Wu
  1994   Land use change in the Amazon estuary: Patterns of Caboclo settlement and landscape management. *Human Ecology* 22(3):249-278.
  1996   Changes in land cover in the Amazon estuary: Integration of thematic mapper with botanical and historical data. *Photogrammetric Engineering and Remote Sensing* 62(8):921-929.
Brondízio, E.S., S.D. McCracken, E.F. Moran, A.D. Siqueira, D.R. Nelson, and C. Rodriguez-Pedraza
  2002   The colonist footprint: Toward a conceptual framework of deforestation trajectories among small farmers in frontier Amazônia. Pp. 133-161 in *Deforestation and Land Use in the Amazon*, C. Wood and R. Porro, eds. Gainesville, FL: University of Florida Press.
Crumley, C., ed.
  1994   *Historical Ecology*. Santa Fe, NM: School of American Research Press.
Deadman, P.J., D.T. Robinson, E.F. Moran, and E.S. Brondízio
  2004   Effects of colonist household structure on land use change in the Amazon rainforest: An agent based simulation approach. *Environment and Planning B: Planning and Design* 31:693-709.
Falesi, I.C.
  1972   *Os Solos da Rodovia Transamazonica*. Belém, Brasilia: Empresa Brasileira de Pesquisa Agropecuária do Norte.
Goody, J.
  1958   *The Developmental Cycle of Domestic Groups*. New York: Cambridge University Press.
  1976   *Production and Reproduction: A Comparative Study of the Domestic Domain*. New York: Cambridge University Press.
Lu, D., P. Mausel, E.S. Brondizio, and E.F. Moran
  2002   Aboveground biomass estimation of successional and mature forests using TM images in the Amazon basin. Pp. 183-196 in *Advances in Spatial Data Handling*, D. Richardson and P. van Oosterom, eds. New York: Springer-Verlag.

Mausel, P., Y. Wu., Y. Li, E.F. Moran, and E.S. Brondizio
  1993   Spectral identification of successional stages following deforestation in the Ama-
          zon. *Geocarto International* 8(4):61-81.
McCracken, S., E. Brondizio, D. Nelson, E. Moran, A. Sinqueira, and C. Rodriguez-Pedraza
  1999   Remote sensing and GIS at farm property level: Demography and deforestation in
          the Brazilian Amazon. *Photogrammetric Engineering and Remote Sensing* 65(11):
          1311-1320.
McCracken, S., A. Siqueira, E. Moran, and E. Brondizio
  2002   Land use patterns on an agricultural frontier in Brazil: Insights and examples from
          a demographic perspective. Pp. 162-192 in *Deforestation and Land Use in the
          Amazon*, C. Wood and R. Porro, eds. Gainesville: University of Florida Press.
Meggers, B.
  1954   Environmental limitations on the development of culture. *American Anthropolo-
          gist* 56:801-824.
  1970   *Amazônia: Man and Culture in a Counterfeit Paradise.* Chicago, IL: Aldine.
Ministerio da Agricultura
  1971   *Urbanismo Rural.* Brasilia DF: Ministerio da Agricultura.
Moran, E.F.
  1974   The adaptive system of the Amazonian caboclo. Pp. 136-159 in *Man in the Ama-
          zon*, C. Wagley, ed. Gainesville: University of Florida Press.
  1975   Pioneer Farmers of the Transamazon Highway: Adaptation and Agricultural Pro-
          duction in the Lowland Tropics. PhD Dissertation, Department of Anthropology,
          Gainesville: University of Florida.
  1976   *Agricultural Development along the Transamazon Highway.* (Center for Latin
          American Studies Monograph Series No. 1.) Bloomington: Indiana University.
  1977   Estrategias de sobrevivencia: O uso de recursons ao longo da rodovia Trans-
          amazonica. *Acta Amazonica* 7:363-379.
  1979   Criteria for choosing successful homesteaders in Brazil. *Research in Economic An-
          thropology* 2:339-359.
  1981   *Developing the Amazon.* Bloomington: Indiana University Press.
  1982   Ecological, anthropological and agronomic research in the Amazon basin. *Latin
          American Research Review* 17(1):3-41.
  1984   Colonization in the Transamazon and Rondônia. Pp. 285-303 in *Frontier Expan-
          sion in Amazônia*, M. Schmink and C. Wood, eds. Gainesville: University of Florida
          Press.
  1987   Monitoring fertility degradation of agricultural lands in the lowland tropics. Pp.
          69-91 in *Lands at Risk in the Third World: Local Level Perspectives*, P. Little, M.
          Horowitz, and A.E. Nyerges, eds. Boulder, CO: Westview Press.
  1988   Social reproduction in agricultural frontiers. Pp. 199-212 in *Production and Au-
          tonomy: Anthropological Studies and Critiques of Development*, J. Bennett and J.
          Bowen, eds. Washington, DC: University Press of America/Society for Economic
          Anthropology.
  1989   Models of native and folk adaptation in the Amazon. *Advances in Economic Botany*
          7:22-29.
  1991   Human adaptive strategies in Amazonian blackwater ecosystems. *American An-
          thropologist* 93:361-382.
  1993   Deforestation and land use in the Brazilian Amazon. *Human Ecology* 21:1-21.

Moran, E.F., and E. Brondizio
1998   Land use change after deforestation in Amazônia. Pp. 94-120 in National Research Council, *People and Pixels: Linking Remote Sensing and Social Science.* Committee on the Human Dimensions of Global Change, D. Liverman, E.F. Moran, R. Rindfuss, and P. Stern, eds. Washington, DC: National Academy Press.
Moran, E.F. , E. Brondizio, P. Mausel, and Y. Wu
1994   Integrating Amazonian vegetation, land use and satellite data. *BioScience* 44(5): 329-338.
Moran, E.F., A. Packer, E. Brondizio, and J. Tucker
1996   Restoration of vegetation cover in the eastern Amazon. *Ecological Economics* 18(1):41-54.
Moran, E.F., E.S. Brondizio, J. Tucker, M.C. Silva-Forsberg, I. Falesi, and S. McCracken
2000   Strategies for Amazonian forest restoration: Evidence for afforestation in five regions of the Brazilian Amazon. Pp. 129-149 in *Amazônia at the Crossroads*, A. Hill, ed. London, England: Institute of Latin American Studies.
Moran, E.F., E. Brondizio, and S. McCracken
2002   Trajectories of land use: Soils, succession and crop choice. Pp. 193-217 in *Deforestation and Land Use in the Amazon*, C. Wood and R. Porro, eds. Gainesville: University of Florida Press.
Moran, E.F., A.D. Siqueira, and E.S. Brondizio
2003   Household demographic structure and its relationship to the Amazon Basin. Pp. 1-30 in *People and the Environment: Approaches to Linking Household and Community Surveys to Remote Sensing and GIS*, J. Fox, V. Mishra, R. Rindfuss, and S. Walsh, eds. Boston, MA: Kluwer Academic Press.
Myers, T.
1984   *The Primary Source.* New York: Scribners.
Odum, H.T.
1971   *Energy, Power and Society.* New York: Wiley.
Prance, G., and T. Lovejoy, eds.
1985   *Key Environments: Amazônia.* Oxford, England: Pergamon Press.
Programa de Integracao Nacional (PIN)
1971   *Rodovia Transamazonica.* Brasilia DF: Presidencia da Republica.
Rappaport, R.
1968   *Pigs for the Ancestors.* New Haven, CT: Yale University Press.
Salati, E., and P. Vose
1984   Amazon Basin: A system in equilibrium. *Science* 225:129-138.
Schmink, M., and C. Wood
1992   *Contested Frontiers of Amazonia.* New York: Columbia University Press.
Silver, C.
1990   *One Earth, One Future: Our Changing Global Environment.* Washington, DC: National Academy Press.
Siqueira, A., S. McCracken, E. Brondizio, and E. Moran
2003   Women and work in a Brazilian agricultural frontier. Pp. 243-265 in *Gender at Work in Economic Life*, G. Clark, ed. New York: Altamira Press.
Smith, N.
1982   *Rain Forest Corridors.* Berkeley: University of California Press.
Steward, J.
1955   *The Theory of Cultural Change.* Urbana: University of Illinois Press.

Tucker, J., E.S. Brondizio, and E. Moran
  1998   Rates of forest regrowth in eastern Amazônia: A comparison of Altamira and
          Bragantina regions, Para, Brazil. *Interciencia* 23(2):61-71.
VanWey, L.K., E. Ostrom, and V. Meretsky
  2005   Theories underlying the study of human-environment interactions. In *Seeing the
          Forest and the Trees: Human-Environment Interactions in Forest Ecosystems*, E.F.
          Moran and E. Ostrom, eds. Cambridge, MA: MIT Press.
Whittaker, R.H., and G.E. Likens
  1975   The biosphere and man. Pp. 305-328 in *Primary Productivity of the Biosphere*, H.
          Leith and R.H. Whittaker, eds. Berlin, Germany: Springer-Verlag.

6

Population Change and Landscape Dynamics: The Nang Rong, Thailand, Studies

Stephen J. Walsh, Ronald R. Rindfuss,
Pramote Prasartkul, Barbara Entwisle,
and Aphichat Chamratrithirong

INTRODUCTION

During the past 40 years there have been two major popular and scientific environmental initiatives. The first was in the 1960s and early 1970s, perhaps triggered by the 1962 publication of Rachel Carson's *Silent Spring*. The second focused on global climate change and is perhaps best indexed by the formation of the International Geosphere-Biosphere Program in 1986.

During the first environmental research initiative, population researchers tended to stay on the sidelines. There were several reasons. First, the research questions were not well framed; they were more polemical than scientific. Second, appropriate, high-quality data to address the environmental concerns did not exist. Third, many of the necessary methods had not yet been developed. The research community using remote sensing and geographic information systems (GIS) techniques also was not actively engaged in this first round of environmental concern and research. Again, the reasons were varied. First, satellite (Landsat) data became available only in the early 1970s. Initial research with Landsat data focused on broad mapping issues that only suggested pattern-process relationships, including the human dimensions of land use and land cover and subsequent changes in landscape patterns. Such early studies were without a clear and rigorous link between people and the environment; the exploration of possible feedbacks between human behavior and environmental patterns, processes, and dynamics was yet to come. Also, in these early years of mapping land use and land cover, the remote sensing community was dominated by natural and spatial scientists; therefore, the applications of remote sensing technology tended to emphasize resource assessments and far less on social sciences and its importance in understanding the role of people as agents of environmental change and land use and land cover dynamics.

Population researchers and the remote sensing and GIS research community became active during the second initiative. The Nang Rong projects, which began in the early 1980s, began to focus on land use and land cover change partially in response to questions about global warming, environmental degradation, and human behavior. The links between global warming and land cover change, especially deforestation and reforestation, were in the process of being established (e.g., Meyer and Turner, 1992; Kasperson et al., 1995; Houghton et al., 1999; Lambin et al., 1999). We were primarily a team of sociologist-demographers, adding environment, geography, and GIS science expertise in the early 1990s. The issue of land use and land cover change fit our preexisting theoretical concerns. Global change issues provided additional impetus.

In this chapter, we describe the portion of our ongoing work in Nang Rong, Thailand, relevant to the human dimensions of global environmental change, with an emphasis on mapping and modeling patterns and dynamics of land use and land cover by linking people, place, and environment in fundamental ways to address research questions that extend across the social, natural, and spatial sciences and that require integration of data, methods, and perspectives.

QUESTIONS IN CONTEXT

What are the reciprocal relations between population change and landscape dynamics? How do these relations operate at different social, spatial, environmental, and temporal scales? What are the scale, pattern, and process relationships that extend across social, biophysical, and geographical domains? These are the large questions that motivate our research. We have not tended to begin with substantive environmental questions and then create links to people and place. Rather, we have posed basic questions that seek to understand how social change and environmental change are linked. Adapting the research questions to our research setting, the scales at which we work, and the information and tools that are either available or possible to devise, we have focused on migration and household formation as engines of population change, as well as on deforestation, the expansion of rice production, the resource endowments of sites, geographic connections between places, and the introduction of upland crops as fundamental aspects of land use and land cover change. We have studied these issues at seasonal, annual, and decadal scales and at fine to coarse spatial scales over the past half-century, and we have considered the relationships between people, place, and the environment as well as the feedbacks among human behaviors, geographical settings, and ecological processes.

Nang Rong district, Thailand, is our research setting (Figure 6-1). The district occupies approximately 1,300 square kilometers (km^2) in the northeast region of Thailand. The district and the surrounding region are noted for the undulating landscape. In the lower elevations there is paddy land, and in the higher elevations there is open-canopy forest and uplands for dry field crops (Fukui, 1993). Elevation matters. Relatively small variations in elevation result in major differences in crop suitabilities in this setting. The region is classified as a tropical dry forest characterized by dry dipterocarp forest and woodlands. The environmental setting is one of marginality: low soil fertility, insufficient and unpredictable precipitation, insufficient drainage, and, generally speaking, a limited natural resource base.

Until the middle of the twentieth century, Nang Rong was a frontier area,[1] more similar in this respect to recently settled areas in Latin America than to a typical Southeast Asian setting. Nang Rong was populated through migration combined with high rates of natural increase in the 1950s and 1960s. Even after the frontier closed in the early 1970s, the population continued to grow until the early 1990s. Deforestation has been extensive. Initially, forest was converted to paddy rice in the lowlands. In the late 1960s and through the 1970s, in part because of changed import regulations in Europe, cassava cultivation became profitable, and forest was converted to agriculture in the uplands. At approximately the same time, a paved road linking the district to Korat (a regional city) and ultimately Bangkok was constructed (for military reasons related to the Vietnam War and to communist insurgencies from nearby Cambodia). The interaction of population and environment through forces both within and exogenous to the region has created a dynamic landscape mosaic. Plate 4 shows the district in 1972-1973 and 1997. Changes in the composition and spatial patterns of land use and land cover, principally caused by deforestation of the uplands and the cultivation of cassava or sugar cane or both, are most obvious, but more subtle changes in the lowlands, caused by pond development, loss of isolated trees and small clusters of trees, and the expansion of Nang Rong town, the central market and administrative town (shown in light blue), are also seen in the image comparison.

Most villagers today are farmers, growing rice in the extensive lowlands and such crops as cassava, sugar cane, kenaf, and corn in the uplands. The timing and amount of the yearly monsoon is of particular significance. Most of the year's precipitation in Nang Rong occurs as unevenly distrib-

---

[1]"Frontier" is used to represent the past 500 to 700 years. At the time of the Angkor civilization, roughly 802 to 1432, Nang Rong was part of the Angkor empire.

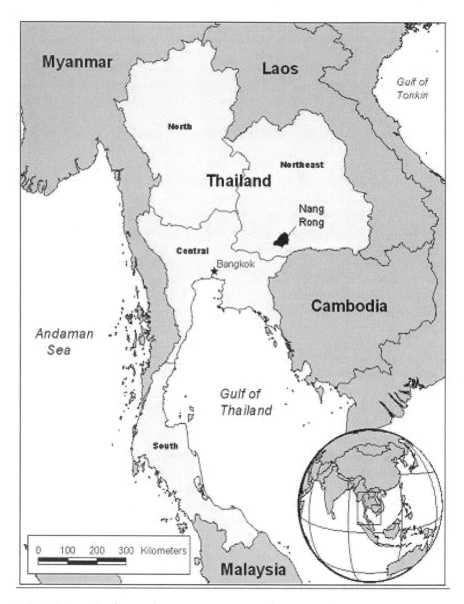

FIGURE 6-1   Study area location: Nang Rong district, northeast Thailand.

uted torrential rains from June to November. Rain almost never falls in December (Konrad, 2000). Rice must be harvested soon after the rain stops and before the fields dry out (Edmeades, 2000). This is a period of peak labor demand in Nang Rong. Migrants tend to leave the district after the rice harvest. It appears that many migrants are seasonal, returning in the summer to help with rice planting. Seasonal pulses in rainfall thus inspire a seasonal pattern in migration. There is substantial interannual variability as well. Annual precipitation totals have decreased over the past 30 years (Konrad, 2000) and there is evidence that this is related to deforestation (Kanae, Oki, and Musiake, 2001). A significant portion of the decrease occurred during the wettest month of the year, October. Monthly precipitation amounts increased slightly during April and May, the period immediately prior to the rice-growing period. June, a critical month for planting rice, experienced a slight decrease in precipitation amounts (although there is a slight increase in the number of days observed for all precipitation thresholds, particularly the number of days having precipitation totals of 1 and 2 inches). There is considerable variability in the annual precipitation totals. Three of the four wettest years occurred prior to 1984 (with 1983 the wettest since records began to be kept in 1965), whereas all four of the driest years occurred between 1989 and 1994 (with 1989 the driest on record). We expect that when the monsoon is late, light, and sporadic, return migration will be less and out-migration greater.

Migration patterns also depend on opportunities elsewhere. Through the 1980s and 1990s, the Thai economy grew at a remarkable rate. This growth was concentrated primarily in Bangkok and the eastern seaboard, as well as in the manufacturing and service sectors. This trend, in combination with the closing of the frontier in the northeast, encouraged young adults from that region to migrate to cities, either temporarily or permanently. There was yearly variability in migration trends (Jampaklay, 2003). In all likelihood, this reflects variability in the demand for labor in the urban areas as well as variability in the monsoon in rural areas. Of particular interest are the potential consequences of the economic crisis of 1997, when the Thai *baht* was devalued.

Social as well as biophysical phenomena are related to pulses observed on the landscape. For instance, circular migration patterns of young adults working in Bangkok, the eastern seaboard, and other urban places are related to the efficacy of monsoonal rains for the cultivation of lowland paddy rice in Nang Rong district and the selected mode of rice cultivation, broadcast or transplant, which have very different labor requirements. Feedbacks between the monsoon, characterized by floods, droughts, delayed rains, or normal to near-normal rainfall conditions, have implications for people and the environment. Also, upland deforestation and the cultivation of cassava or sugar cane in the district are related to population-environment interactions involving globalization and the emergence of a market economy, travel distances from the nuclear village, population density and land competition from nearby villages, and site conditions, including resource endowments. Finally, the economic status of villages and the nature of household assets are also part of the calculus of land use and land cover dynamics, household decision-making processes about the land, and defining the geographic "reach" on the land through use or ownership patterns.

THEORETICAL APPROACHES AND PERSPECTIVES

Questions about population, land use, and environment are inherently multidisciplinary. The theoretical approaches taken in any application tend to reflect the disciplinary background and training of the research team. In our case, we have looked to the disciplines of geography and sociology, as well as the emerging area of complexity theory, for guidance in our research. From geography, we have drawn on three perspectives: landscape ecology (e.g., Forman and Godron, 1986), human ecology (e.g., Johnston, Taylor, and Watts, 1995), and political ecology (e.g., Blaikie and Brookfield, 1987). From sociology and social demography, we have also drawn on three perspectives: the multiphasic theory of change and response (Davis, 1963), models of household decision making (Stark, 1991), and the life course perspective (Elder, 1974, 1998). Complexity theory is not tied specifically to either discipline, but rather is emerging in both (e.g., Malanson, 1999, 2002; Urry, 2001). We use the complexity perspective as the basis for linking people, place, and the environment to study nonlinear relationships, feedback mechanisms, and critical thresholds related to self-organization and complex adaptive systems. Each approach has informed some part of our research and has provided valuable insight. In this chapter, we reflect on two: the life course perspective and the complexity perspective. We choose the life course perspective because, although central in our work, it is relatively new in research on land use and land cover change. The complexity perspective is also relatively new, both to our research and to the field more generally.

Life Course Perspective

Individuals and their personal histories are at the core of the life course perspective. The life course refers to a sequence of socially defined, age-graded events and roles that individuals enact over time (Elder, 1998:941). Core elements are role states, transitions, and trajectories. Each transition combines a role exit and entry (e.g., from nonparent to parent). Transitions vary in their structuredness or degree of external regulation, duration, timing, predictability, and novelty (Elder, 1998:957; also see Rindfuss, 1991). Trajectories are composed of role states and transitions; trajectories, in turn, provide some of the context for particular transitions (e.g., whether early or late). Central to the life course framework is the notion that individual lives are independent, connected through social arrangements including households and families. Also central is the notion that lives are lived in a historical context, which shapes both the opportunities and constraints faced by individuals as they move through their life course. In the life course perspective, concepts of time range from biological age to historical context. Potentially relevant social contexts range from the micro to the macro.

Although myriad role transitions are of interest in the life course perspective, the transition to adulthood is particularly important to an understanding of population and land use. Young people on the threshold of adulthood make decisions about migration, marriage, household formation, and childbearing. In fact, these all-important behaviors from the standpoint of demographic process are relegated to a relatively narrow segment of life, from the teens to the 30s, depending on context (Rindfuss, 1991). In Nang Rong, young people generally finish their schooling at age 12; few go beyond a primary education.[2] Then, they work: cultivating rice and other crops in their home village; as temporary laborers in agriculture and construction in the district and other nearby places; and as factory, service, and construction workers in major urban destinations, such as Bangkok. Often young people rotate among several jobs and locations, on a seasonal or longer term basis. Work and migration experiences during the teen years and early 20s affect whether, when, and where young people marry and form new households. In 1990, the singulate mean age at marriage in Thailand was 23.0 for women, 25.7 for men (Limanonda, 1992; Phananinarai, 1997). Fertility rates are highest for women in their 20s (Hirschman et al., 1994), as they are in most places. It is clear that the behavior of young people is central to relationships between population dynamics and land use. Yet this simple observation is oddly missing from most accounts of these relationships.

A related observation is that environmental impact will depend importantly on the size of this cohort. As Hunter points out, because of the history of mortality decline and lagged fertility decline in most parts of the world, we are now witnessing the largest-ever generation of young people on every continent but Europe (Hunter, 2000:28). The ultimate impact of these large numbers is yet to be understood. To date, the Nang Rong data have featured the 1984-1994 decade, although the addition of another wave of data collected in 2000 has expanded this window of intensive research. Who were the young people most likely to finish school, migrate (out and perhaps back), marry, form households, and have children over the 1984-1994 decade? Roughly speaking, these were people ages 8-25 in

---

[2]It should be noted that this is changing as more secondary schools are opened and as factory employers are requiring workers to have a secondary education.

1984, born between 1960 and 1976, and demographically the most significant cohort in recent Thai history. The large size of this cohort potentially
changes the context of decision making for all of its members. Cohort size
is a key element of historical context that needs to be recognized when
drawing general conclusions, not only from the Nang Rong study but most
studies currently under way in different parts of the world.

Complexity and Hierarchy Perspectives

The goal of complexity is to understand how simple, fundamental
processes can be combined to produce complex holistic systems (Gell-Mann,
1994). Such systems contain more possibilities than can be actualized, and
their descriptions are not constrained by an a priori definition (Luhman,
1985). Nonequilibrium systems with feedbacks can lead to nonlinearity
and may evolve into systems that exhibit criticality, or phase transitions, a
condition in a system in which any outcome is possible, response to perturbation is of any size, and correlations extend across scales (Malanson,
1999). In the Thailand setting, multiple stakeholders interact through
endogenous and exogenous processes to create a dynamic land cover and
land use system that is space and time dependent, in which feedbacks
among human activities, land cover and use change, and ecological dynamics produce nonlinearity. Critical points in the spatial structure of land use
patterns and feedbacks have produced a system with potential alternative
states and dynamics characterized by phase changes. For example, we have
found that as patterns of land use and land cover become more fragmented,
young adults out-migrate to engage in off-farm employment, suggesting
that the landscape has exceeded a real or perceived threshold of land availability or contiguity for use or ownership, or for subsequent household
formation (Rindfuss, Walsh, and Entwisle, 1996). But as a consequence of
off-farm employment, households may accumulate additional assets through
remittances, thereby affecting household decisions about the use or ownership of the land.

Hierarchy theory, developed in general systems theory and incorporated into ecology to describe the structure of ecological systems through
their spatial and temporal organization, is integrated in the context of
complexity theory by considering scale-dependent mechanisms and processes operating at fine and coarse grains and extents that give meaning to
the characteristic space and time scales being studied (Allen and Starr,
1982; Ahl and Allen, 1996). Fundamental questions being examined re-
volve around (1) rates, patterns, and mechanisms of deforestation, agricultural extensification, village settlement patterns, and feedbacks among land
use patterns and social, biophysical, and geographical processes; (2) spatial
and temporal patterns of road development, migration and household for-

mation, land tenure, monsoonal variability, agricultural intensification, co-operative water use, shifts in world markets, and electrification and spread of consumerism as critical thresholds and feedback mechanisms that alter the trajectories of land use patterns; and (3) uncertainties among land use patterns, processes due to system dynamics, and spatial simulations developed through cellular automata and agent-based models. We routinely explore changes in the geographic extent (e.g., size of village territories, regional subsets of Nang Rong district, and the entire district) and grain size (e.g., spatial or temporal resolutions of analysis) for considering population-environment interactions. For example, Walsh et al. (1999, 2001) examined the variations in landscape greenness by linking variables describing people and the environment measured at a range of spatial scales, and Walsh et al. (2003) reported on a similar study in which intraannual, interannual, and decadal scales were examined through variables describing demographic characteristics of villages, terrain settings, and local resource endowments.

MULTIPLE UNITS, SCALES, THEMES, AND PERSPECTIVES

The Nang Rong project database combines and integrates information on many kinds of units, from individuals to households to villages and from pixels to plots, lines, patches, watersheds, and landscapes. It covers a range of spatial, social, and temporal scales of people, place, and environment. It is multithematic, representing social, biophysical, and geographical domains. The design and collection of the relevant data and their integration into a wide-ranging and flexible, spatially explicit GIS database is one of the accomplishments of the Nang Rong projects. Figure 6-2 summarizes the central elements of this database, which are briefly described below.

Social Surveys

The social surveys were the starting point for research in the Nang Rong setting. They consist of three waves of data collection: 1984, 1994, and 2000. Two surveys were conducted in 1984: a community survey in 51 study villages and a complete household census conducted in the study villages, with the census obtaining information on all members of all households. The census design in the context of a highly focused and largely local study laid the groundwork for new insights about demographic behavior (Entwisle et al., 1996, 1998), subsequent innovations in data collection (Rindfuss et al., 2003, 2004), and, importantly, the integration of demographic, biophysical, and land use and land cover data at social, spatial, and temporal scales that played to strength on the social demographic as well as ecological sides (Entwisle et al., 1998).

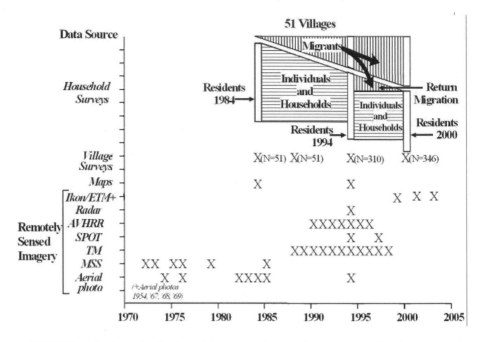

FIGURE 6-2 Longitudinal social survey data and remote sensing imagery collected for the Nang Rong projects.

A second round of surveys were fielded a decade after the baseline, building on and extending the original design and focus. The 1994-1995 data were collected through a community survey administered in all villages in Nang Rong, including but not limited to the original 51; a household survey; a complete census of all households in each of the 51 villages; and a migrant follow-up, which collected data from out-migrants from 22 of the original 51 villages who had gone to one of four urban destinations (metropolitan Bangkok; the eastern seaboard, a focus of rapid growth and development; Korat, a regional city; and Buriram, the provincial city).

The 2000-2001 data collection included a community survey in all villages in Nang Rong; a household survey; a complete census in the 51 study villages; and the collection of locational data for dwelling units and agricultural plots, linked to the household survey, as well as a migrant follow-up that tracked migrants from 22 villages to the four urban destinations and to rural villages in Nang Rong district. Because of administrative subdivisions of villages (villages are generally administratively divided when the total number of households is greater than 100), the original 51 villages expanded to 76 in 1994 and 97 by 2000. Also, because of village subdivisions, the total number of administrative villages in the district expanded from 310 in 1994 to 346 in 2000.

Remote Sensing

An aircraft and satellite image time series has been assembled that extends from 1954 to the present. Panchromatic aerial photography at scales ranging from 1:6,000 to 1:50,000 have been acquired for 1954, 1968, 1969, 1974, 1976, 1982, 1983-1984, 1985, and 1994. Digital air photo mosaics have been derived for selected periods and reformatted into seamless image mosaics that cover the entire district. The digital air photo mosaics are single high spatial resolution images that are easily combined with other digital data contained in the GIS database and integrated as part of overlay analyses and data visualizations. In addition to extending our remote sensing time series to deeper historical periods, the digital mosaics, particularly those that correspond to field or social and demographic surveys, are used to validate classifications of land cover. We are also using the high resolution digital aircraft data to calibrate and validate statistical and spatially explicit models.

Our primary remote sensing platform and sensor system is the Landsat Thematic Mapper (TM). This system "views" the landscape at a 30 m cell resolution for its optical channels, and offers relatively large geographic coverage for each collected image or scene (i.e., 185 by 185 km). Both the grain and extent of Landsat are useful for assessing human imprints on the land indicative, for example, of population settlement patterns, land clearing for the cultivation of crops, and a host of other land transformations that have important population-environment signatures and cause and consequence implications for examining land use and land cover dynamics.

Approximately 35 images have been acquired from the Landsat TM for the period 1973-2003. SPOT (Le Système pour l'Observation de la Terre (Earth Observation System) panchromatic (10 m spatial resolution) and multispectral (20 m spatial resolution) data have been acquired for selected high interest dates approximated to social survey periods. Also, Ikonos data[3] are being used to assess settlement patterns of Nang Rong district migrants who have sought off-farm employment in Bangkok. Using migrant data, destinations of migrants from 22 survey villages (1994 and 2000 surveys) are examined in the context of urban morphology and evolution, including core-periphery concepts, migration streams, and patterns of "new" and "old" migrants and issues related to social networks. The Ikonos data provide both multispectral and panchromatic images with very

---

[3]The Ikonos satellite, launched into orbit on September 24, 1999, is a commercial satellite owned and operated by Space Imaging, Inc.

high spatial resolution: the multispectral imagery has a 4 m spatial resolution, whereas the panchromatic imagery has a 1 m spatial resolution.

Using the deep Landsat TM time series, a number of image change detections are under way. Similar to a panel data set familiar to social scientists, we are tracking the "pixel histories" or trajectories of co-registered, classified images to explore the persistence and dynamics of land use and land cover patterns in both space and time and to associate the social, biophysical, and geographical determinants of patterns of these changes through space and time. Other change detection approaches such as change vector analysis, postclassification change, binary masks, and principal components analysis, are being derived (Walsh et al., 2003).

Geographic Information System

A GIS was also developed that includes a number of base coverages as well as derived coverages for the study area. Most fundamental was the generation of a digital elevation model. Using a 1:50,000 scale 1984 base map from the Thai Ministry of Defense, contour lines and spot elevations were digitized. A 10 m contour interval was used on the 1984 map, and spot elevations were maintained to a 1 m vertical resolution. Using the terrain information and the linear surface drainage patterns (perennial and intermittent rivers and streams and ponds or reservoirs), a digital elevation model was developed along with a number of value-added terrain products (e.g., topographic curvature, topographic convergence or wetness index, and solar radiation potential). Also fundamental to our studies was the development of a road network generated by digitizing road types from the 1984 base maps. Roads were described on the Thai base map (and subsequently digitized) as paved all-weather roads, loose-surface all-weather roads, fair dry-weather roads, and cart paths. Using a derived aerial photo image mosaic for 1954, 1967-1968, and 1994, the road network captured from the 1984 Thai military map has been expanded to examine how changes in geographic accessibility through a dynamic road network may contribute to land use and land cover dynamics throughout the Nang Rong district. The district outline was also captured from the 1984 base map, as well as district villages and regional market towns. In the 1994 and 2000 surveys, villages (and households) were also geographically referenced by using differentially corrected global positioning system coordinates. Discussions with village headmen have yielded important updates to the road network. The hydrographic data layer also is being augmented by satellite views of surface water impoundments to extend the 1984 representation to important antecedent and subsequent periods. Hydrologic flow data at dams and stream gauging stations add to our understanding of rainfall patterns captured at a constellation of climate stations within and surrounding the study district. Climate stations are being used to assess the spatial and temporal patterns of precipitation and droughts and their deviations from long-term normals as an important exogenous shock to population-environment interactions.

MULTIPLE ANALYTIC APPROACHES

Statistical Approaches

Our initial approach to an integrated analysis of population and land use and land cover change was to incorporate measures based on one into a disciplinary framework that already existed for the other. For example, we wondered whether the proximity and relative availability of forest lands would affect whether young people chose to stay or leave the village. Again, in the life course framework, the transition to adulthood is a time when numerous transitions are occurring in both the work and family spheres. In the 1970s and 1980s, land was ambiguously titled in much of Nang Rong, which allowed young people to clear a land parcel, farm it, and claim it as their own. Since for all practical purposes farming was the only viable occupation in Nang Rong, access to land was a crucial issue for young people as they considered their work and family future. We examined the availability of nearby forest cover on the migration patterns of young people. The unit of observation was individuals nested within villages, the outcome of interest was migration between 1984 and 1994, and the statistical set-up a multinomial regression analysis. We incorporated measures of land cover based on satellite data from the 1970s as independent variables at the village level. Specifically, we used measures of forest cover within a set distance from the village (radial buffer) and of land cover fragmentation, and we related them to whether two prospective panels of young persons moved out or stayed in the village. We found that young persons were more likely to stay if they lived in villages close to forest cover and with less land cover fragmentation (Rindfuss et al., 1996). Forest cover is an attractive force with respect to the out-migration of young people.

An example illustrating the incorporation of social variables into a spatially based approach can also be given. We were interested in whether relationships between population variables and measures of land cover were stronger at smaller than larger spatial scales. To answer this question, we had to take measures of population referring to discrete points and distribute them over continuous space (Rindfuss et al., 2002). Although people in Nang Rong live in clusters, their impact on land use extends far beyond their village clusters. Considering relationships between social and biophysical factors explaining plant biomass patterns for a single time period for nine scale steps ranging from 30 to 1,050 square meters, we found that relationships between measures of population (such as number of households) and measures of land cover and land use were stronger at finer than coarser scales, and that relationships between biophysical measures (such as slope) and land use were stronger at coarser than finer scales (Walsh et al., 1999, 2001).

More recent work has focused on land cover *change* assessed for intraannual (i.e., seasonal), interannual (1994-1995), and decadal (1993-2002) intervals (Walsh et al., 2003). In this work, topographic settings, such as the mean elevation and mean slope angle as well as mean distance to water in a prescribed village territory, were significantly and positively correlated with the percentage of land cover change. This is true for all three time intervals, although the strength of the association varied, suggesting some temporal scale dependency. Distance to Nang Rong town, the central market town in the district, was also significantly correlated with the percentage of land cover change for all three time intervals, but, interestingly, the correlation was positive for seasonal and decadal change but negative for annual change. The price of rice land (a proxy for land quality) was statistically and negatively correlated with the percentage change of land cover for the intra- and interannual periods.

The correlations reported so far all involve an assessment of change versus no change, without regard for the direction of change, if it occurs. Turning now to a specific direction of change, from forest to rice (1993-2002), the data show significant and negative relationships between the growth in the number of households between 1994 and 2000, the density of settlement as reflected in the number of villages located within a 3 km buffer surrounding each village, and the distance to Nang Rong town. An interpretation involves a historical context of prior development to support lowland rice production, thereby creating a relatively stable landscape during the decadal study period, and demographic change, primarily the increase in the number of village households and a corresponding increase in the number of villages formed through administrative splits when the number of households exceeded 100. Off-farm employment is also increasing, particularly in villages that border Nang Rong town, the central market and service center of the district.

Mathematical Models: Cellular Automata and Agent-Based Models

Agent-based models examine the basic characteristics and activities of individual agents as the basic building blocks. Agents differ in important characteristics and their interactions are dynamic, in that the characteristics of the agents change over time as the agents adapt to their environment, learn from experiences through feedbacks, or "die" as they fail to alter behavior relative to new conditions or factors. The dynamics that describe how the system changes are generally nonlinear, sometimes even chaotic, and seldom in any long-term equilibrium. Individual agents may be organized into groups or hierarchies that may influence how the underlying system evolves over time. Complex adaptive systems are self-organized systems that combine local processes to produce holistic systems (Bak, 1998). They are emergent in that macro-level behaviors emerge from the actions of individual agents, as they learn through experiences and change and develop feedbacks with finer scale building blocks. Agent-based models capture the building blocks or processes of an emergent hierarchical system.

We have used agent-based models to simulate the development of villages based on elevation, the distance to nearest water, and distance to the nearest preexisting village. Village agents, representing individual agents, simulate the establishment of villages, and geocategory agents manage the geographic categories of information that influence the locations of simulated villages and respond to requests from the village agents (that we have determined to most influence the location of actual villages). A longitudinal survey was used to define village establishment dates for observed villages, an image animation was used to visualize the pattern of observed village establishment on an annual time step, and a GIS was used to represent topography and road and water networks as village attractors.

Cellular automata are used in our research to simulate land use and land cover dynamics. Cellular automata models are composed of a regular grid of cells each in a finite state that are iteratively updated in discrete time steps. The state of a cell is determined by the states of the neighboring cells in the previous time step. Growth or transition rules allow systems to grow from initial conditions, vary their rates of change, or reverse directions in a recursive sequence of iterations. Rules are determined by (1) observing an existing system using an assembled image time series and transition probabilities; (2) theory-based approaches; (3) variable weights and relationships generated through multilevel models and logistic regressions that integrate a longitudinal survey, GIS coverages, and land use and land cover patterns and change trajectories; (4) constructing functions by building and analyzing data distributions; and (5) an expert system informed through qualitative field techniques involving knowledgeable local informants to associate patterns of land cover change to associated processes. The rules embodied in a cellular automata model can be developed to realistically represent the decision making of multiple actors. These decisions are made in the context of an existing pattern of land use and land cover. Each cell in an area represented by the model begins at a known land cover state. In a true cellular automata model, the transition of that cell to another state is determined by the states of surrounding cells. For highly dynamic land cover types, transition probabilities can be developed that depend on the state of the cell and its surrounding cells on its resource endowments (e.g., slope, soils, vegetation, hydrology), demographic characteristics (e.g., population density and number of households), and its geographic proximity (e.g., roads, markets, water, and other villages). These probabilities are generally derived from the satellite image time series, GIS coverages, and the longitudinal household survey (Messina and Walsh, 2001). Once transition probabilities are determined, the model runs stochastically to increase the number of possible outcomes and to better represent dynamic systems. Model convergence and variable sensitivities of the analysis tracks are compared, and analyses of system dynamics and uncertainty are assessed. The results are calibrated and validated by comparing the composition and spatial pattern of simulated land cover to observed patterns represented in a classified satellite data set for the same annual time periods (Messina and Walsh, 2001). Summary correlations and pattern metrics are used to assess differences between observed and expected land cover on the basis of composition and spatial organization.

Complexity theory concepts of critical thresholds, feedback mechanisms, and hierarchy relationships are infused into the cellular automata models for generating simulations to match observed states or for future periods by allowing the model to iterate within the expected bounds of the defined rules. For example, we have developed transition or growth rules to model rice, forest, and upland field crops (cassava and sugar cane). Another example is explicit geographic and biophysical rules that describe the environmental conditions important in the cultivation of rain-fed, lowland paddy rice. Slope angle, elevation, land forms, distance to perennial rivers and streams as well as large reservoirs and ponds, soil suitability, and topographic relative moisture potential are considered. Data distributions, GIS coverages, and satellite maps of land use and land cover are used to define the spatial pattern of each variable, and change functions are developed to indicate the propensity of cells in paddy rice to remain rice or change to another type of land use and land cover in successive time steps in our model runs.

Figure 6-3 is a generalized flow chart showing how rules could be implemented in our cellular automata model to spatially simulate patterns of land use and land cover, primarily lowland paddy rice and upland field crops using initial conditions, stochastic elements, neighborhood conditions, landscape criteria for characterizing cells, and change directions for each model iteration. The model depicted in Figure 6-3 applies interatively across a grid of cells. Initially, the two land classes are modeled separately. Whether a pixel is in rice or in upland field crops depends on a stochastic element (to allow for spontaneous change), the influence of neighboring pixels, and then landscape criteria, such as elevation, slope, soils, access to water, proximity to villages, etc. Because the two land classes are modeled separately, it is possible for a given pixel to be allocated to both. When this

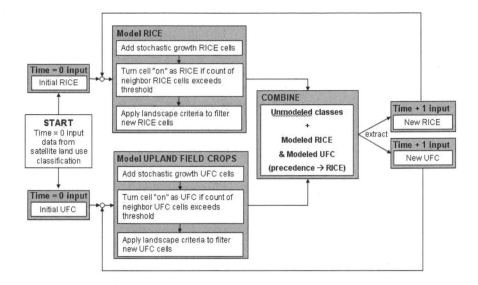

FIGURE 6-3 Generalized schematic of cellular automata rules for modeling changes in rice and upland field crops, Nang Rong district, Thailand.

happens, the pixel is assigned a given land use according to preset rules about crop precedence. The entire grid is then updated, and the model moves to the next iteration. Cellular automata models allow us to spatially simulate patterns of land use and land cover, examine likely future land use and land cover scenarios, and examine how social and demographic factors at the household or community levels, as well as exogenous shocks, have altered trajectories of land use and land cover change, resulting in possible shifts in the composition and spatial structure of the landscape, which has implications for human behavior.

Qualitative Fieldwork

Throughout, we have used qualitative data collected through semi-structured open-ended interviews with focus groups, residents, and key informants. We have used these data to pretest survey items, generate hypotheses, validate observations, and assist with interpretation. We illustrate with an example of each use.

First, following a long tradition in the design of social surveys (Biemer and Lyberg, 2003:363-367), we have conducted small studies using qualitative techniques in the development and pretesting of survey items. When developing questions, we want to ensure that the question wording makes sense to our respondents, and that we and they have a common interpretation of the question. For example, in developing our procedures for the 2000 data collection to link households to the agricultural plots they use, we did extensive qualitative prework to ensure that we used terms that were understandable to the respondents and captured our meaning of agricultural plot (Rindfuss et al., 2003). We selected the Thai term *plang* to represent "plot." Not only does this term appear throughout the Thai questionnaire, it appears as well in the English translation. *Plang* is now part of the team vernacular, used in discussions of data and plans for analysis.

Second, we have used qualitative data to generate hypotheses. For example, recent discussions with people in Nang Rong pointed out the importance of charcoal production in the deforestation pattern that occurred in Nang Rong and in the retention of trees in rice paddy fields for sustained production of charcoal. This is now on our list of topics to investigate with quantitative data.

Third, we see a potential for the use of qualitative methods to ground truth classifications derived from historical remotely sensed images. As noted above, our series of aerial photographs begins in 1954, and our series of satellite images begins in 1972. A challenge we have faced is the validation of classifications of land use and land cover based on these images. The general idea is to find individuals who have lived and farmed in Nang Rong for at least 20 years, preferably longer. Then, taking the respondent to a known place relative to the historical classification and using the insights from social demographic life history data collection methods (e.g., Freedman et al., 1988) to orient a respondent or group of respondents to the time period covered by the remotely sensed image, ask the respondent to recall land cover for particular points in time. This is a variant of a procedure used in Brazil (Moran et al., 1994; Moran and Brondizio, 1998).

Finally, we have used qualitative data collection to help understand and resolve puzzling results that emerge from our models. For example, in recent work using agent-based models to understand the historical pattern of the location and growth of villages, the models were doing poorly in predicting an arc of villages in the southwest corner of Nang Rong. This is an area with little surface water, and the model did not predict the location of villages there. Discussions with older residents of these villages made it very clear that the presence of underground water near the surface led to the founding of villages along this arc. When looking for possible sites to start a village, information about underground springs was obtained by potential settlers from a number of sources. First, the vegetation was distinctively different when water was close to the surface. Second, large mammals would scratch the ground to expose the water for their own drinking. Hunters would discover these places and, in turn, would tell those looking for a village site. There was some timbering occurring in the area, and those looking for an appropriate village site would also learn about subsurface springs from loggers.

INTEGRATING CHALLENGES

Vocabulary

Land change science projects are, by their very nature, interdisciplinary, and ours was no exception, bringing together sociologists, environmental geographers, spatial scientists, and social demographers. Scientific disciplines develop their own language or jargon to facilitate communication among members, but this, in turn, makes it difficult to communicate across disciplines. In our case, this happened with the term "network" or "network analysis." In sociology, the term implies a social network which links social actors (individuals, households, organizations, and so forth) to one another by links generated through kin relations, friendship, neighborhood proximity, or other generators. For those steeped in GIS science, network analysis refers to travel from one point to another along routes that have assigned travel times, often within a location/allocation context.

Long Distance Collaboration

Since the mid-1980s, researchers at the Institute for Population and Social Research, Mahidol University, Bangkok, and at the Carolina Population Center, University of North Carolina, Chapel Hill, have been collaborating on the ever-evolving Nang Rong studies. Bangkok and Chapel Hill are separated by 12 time zones. This means that there is no overlap in the normal working hours at the two sites, making telephone discussion problematic. In recent years, email connectivity has been excellent, but email is a poor substitute for face-to-face discussions when project research questions, techniques, and analyses are rapidly evolving, and especially when more than one discipline is involved. And the roughly 36-40 hours travel time required for a round trip between Chapel Hill and Bangkok, not to mention the required time zone adjustments, make it daunting to frequently get together for collaborative meetings. These problems can clearly be surmounted by visits and extended stays, but our progress undoubtedly would have been faster if we were all at the same university and the study site was right next door.

Locating Collaborators

As the goals of our projects have become more complex, we have found ourselves needing additional collaborators who have the required expertise

that goes beyond our own. Three areas have been important: social network analysis, cellular automata modeling, and agent-based modeling.
Relying on a network among our own colleagues, we were able to locate
appropriate collaborators at the University of California, Irvine; the University of Iowa; and Michigan State University. These collaborations are
working well, but face-to-face meetings have been limited by travel and
time costs.

Develop New Data Collection Techniques

At a number of points in our research we found that standard techniques in demography, geography, and sociology did not meet our needs
(Rindfuss et al., 2002, 2003, 2004). Nowhere was this more the case than
in linking people to the land units over which they have decision-making
power. Early in our research on land cover and use change, we linked at the
village level, but this had numerous problems in a district in which people
lived in nucleated villages, households had multiple agricultural plots, and
land was frequently ambiguously titled (Entwisle et al., 1998; Evans, 1998;
Rindfuss et al., 2002). The technique we devised combined interview, focus
group, and GIS/remote sensing techniques. The details have been reported
elsewhere (Rindfuss et al., 2003), but the basic elements are as follows. For
all areas for which cadastral maps existed, they were obtained, digitized,
and overlaid on an aerial photograph for use in the field. If cadastral maps
were not available for a village, then just the aerial photography was
brought into the field. These aerial photos, with or without cadastral lines,
were used in focus groups containing village members with specialized
knowledge of local land use to mark the parcels used by village households.
In the household interviews, households were asked details about the agricultural parcels they used and they were asked to provide information on
those who used the neighboring agricultural parcels. Then the spatially
explicit focus group information and the relationally specific household
information were brought together, by hand, to determine the location of
the household plots, using skills similar to those used when working on a
jigsaw puzzle (Rindfuss et al., 2003).

Importance of Starting Point

Our project began as an evaluation of a community-based integrated
rural development intervention project. Its focus on a single district, a
significant proportion of the villages in that district, and all of the people
and households in those villages created opportunities for blending diverse
data and analytic techniques to address interesting questions about population change and landscape dynamics. However, the specifics of the starting

point also put limits on what is possible. For example, the original set of study villages excluded the southwest, the part of the district that has experienced the most dynamic land use change since 1984. Community-level data were collected on villages in the southwest starting in 1994, as well as some historical information included as part of that, but we lack the detail on households, household members, migrants, field plots, and land use available for the study villages. Village histories can be reconstructed (Entwisle et al., no date-a), and village-level analyses are possible, but the scale at which questions can be addressed is limited in this part of the district. As another example, the original design featured a census of households, but in the Nang Rong setting, this does not translate into a spatially continuous set of field plots, even locally, much less complete spatial coverage of the district. Many examples can be given of how our starting points—a social demographic survey and its design features—placed constraints on what was possible on the environmental side. Turning it around, if we had begun our project with the historical aerial photos, we might have proceeded very differently.

CONCLUSION

Our research on Nang Rong is based on a study of a single district in northeast Thailand, covering an area the size of a county in the eastern United States. Other investigators also focus on similarly constrained settings. Interconnections between human actions and the biophysical environment can be most easily observed at the local level, although, even at this level, there can be important spatial and temporal scale dependencies (Walsh et al., 1999, 2003). A focus on local as opposed to regional or global contexts and seasonal, annual, and decadal time periods directs attention to migration and household formation in addition to fertility and natural increase as master population processes with respect to land use and land cover change. A case study approach thus makes sense, given the goals. A case study is an intensive and focused examination of a phenomenon within and with attention to its context, often relying on multiple sources of evidence (Yin, 2003). It is representative only of itself, although it may be possible to draw larger inferences if the case study is embedded with other case studies in some kind of comparative design (Ragin, 1987). In the literature on population dynamics and land use change, case studies are often fairly local.

Our goal is a comprehensive account of social, economic, demographic, and environmental change in Nang Rong district. Our approach is cumulative, with research questions and data intimately connected. One element at a time, we have built a GIS database that is substantively broad, includes multiple levels of observation, and is unusual in its temporal depth. Each new element, whether a data source or an analytic result seems to create the need for other new or expanded elements. For example, village administrative histories were collected in 2000 that made possible a new look at village settlement and expansion over the past 50 years (Entwisle et al., no date-a). New settlement occurred relatively early in the period and was largely complete by 1970, just before our satellite time series begins. This in turn sparked renewed interest in the aerial photos (dating back to 1954) as a way to characterize land cover at the beginning of the period and led to the classification of portions of them. Land cover changes associated with village settlement and expansion now, which include the fragmentation and reconsolidation of the landscape as well as its composition, can be described on a decadal scale (Entwisle et al., no date-a). As the data set has grown in size and complexity, it has also increased in diversity, creating the need for new and more linkages between data of different types at different time and space scales. Our team has been particularly active in the development of linkages between survey-based social units and GIS-based land units (Rindfuss et al., 2002, 2003). Increasing knowledge of the case combined with the data we have assembled provides an opportunity for testing a broad range of new ideas and approaches. We have tended not to become engaged in policy issues or policy-relevant interpretations of our findings, but rather to emphasize fundamental research questions and analytical methods in the study of population-environment interactions.

For example, as part of our longitudinal social survey, we have tracked rural migrants to urban places. As a consequence, we are now engaged in a study of Bangkok using geocoded migrant locations and remote sensing to understand urban form and function, migrant destinations, and the scaling of remote sensing systems designed to study local neighborhoods and regional settings. We have expanded the team to include another geographer with urban remote sensing interests. Also growing out of our social surveys, we have linked people to the land that they use in our 2000 round of data collection. Using cadastral maps and expert discussion groups in study villages, we have been able to enhance our prior efforts in setting village territories by now spatially associating households to the land that they use. Borrowing from spatial analysis, we have developed approaches for characterizing the spatial organization of "functional" village territories by generating activity spaces, "radiance" diagrams that show the vector connections between the village centroids and the center of land parcel being used by village household, and triangulated irregular networks for characterizing village territories using facets whose nodes are land parcels in use by village households.

Building on our classifications of nearly 35 Landsat TM images, we are developing land cover trajectories or "pixel histories" so that we can examine space-time patterns of land cover change (Crews-Meyer, 2001, 2002).

This work has required customized programming in SAS (Statistical Analysis Software) to identify land cover sequences in a panel context for the generation of subsequent models of land cover dynamics that integrate multidimensional and scale-dependent drivers of change. Our models of land cover have also evolved from the statistical to the spatial. Using cellular automata and agent-based models, we are examining the patterns and processes of land cover dynamics by considering nonlinear relationships, emergent behaviors of agents, and complex adaptive systems. Beginning with "pseudo-agents," we are modeling the expansion of villages over space and time according to rules of behavior and an evolving landscape. Our agent-based models will soon begin to consider households and their decision-making processes that affect land use and cover change patterns and that integrate social, biophysical, and geographic factors and the interactions between agents and their environment. Cellular automata models are being used to simulate the environment (using the satellite time series for model calibration and validation) through patterns of land use and land cover change (set by initial conditions, transition or growth rules, and neighborhood relationships) that the agents use by generating surfaces of locational and biophysical change (Clarke, Hoppen, and Gaydos, 1996; Clarke, Gaydos, and Hoppen, 1997). Exogenous and endogenous factors will be represented in our models through rules and behaviors represented at the building block level (i.e., household). The potential value of integrating GIS, cellular automata, and agent-based technologies for modeling and simulating social and ecological phenomena has been discussed by Westervelt (2002) and Wright (2002) but not yet fully implemented in the study of population-environment interactions.

Findings from our research have contributed to the social, natural, and spatial sciences and have emerged as a consequence of our integrative and cross-cutting perspectives. For example, we have (a) chronicled patterns of land use and land cover change by developing a dynamic model of village settlement that depends on prior settlement patterns and on potential relevant contextual factors (Entwisle et al., no date-a), (b) determined that growth in the population of households is a stronger predictor of upland crop production than growth in the number of persons (Entwisle et al., no date-b), (c) related land use and land cover fragmentation patterns of forests located within village territories to the out-migration patterns of young adults to Bangkok and other urban destinations (Rindfuss et al., 1996), and (d) described the variation in landscape greenness as a function of demographic and biophysical variables that are space and time dependent (Walsh et al., 1999, 2001, 2003).

The challenges are many for interdisciplinary research in population-environment interactions, but the opportunities for insight are substantial. We continue to chart our research by posing questions rooted in theory and practices, but extending across traditional disciplinary borders. We are concerned with questions that link people, place, and environment in a spatially explicit context, in which endogenous and exogenous factors are considered, and in which the multiscale and multithematic determinants of land use and land cover change are examined. We use perspectives fundamental to the social, natural, and spatial sciences and also those that offer new theoretical insights and possible links to evolving analytical methods. Our questions are about human behavior, primarily migration and demographic characteristics at the household level, and the concommittal changes in the composition and spatial structure of the land. Space and time lags in population-environment interactions are examined to further consider the causes and consequences of land use and land cover dynamics. Geospatial data and spatial digital technologies are used to map and model the social, biophysical, and geographical landscapes. As spatial and spectral resolutions of remote sensing systems continue to increase, we will increasingly rely on such systems to add further insights about the land and the people that shape it. But images are only snapshots in time, they do not communicate intentions or memories, and they are only indirect measures of population and can only hint at questions of human behavior. Images are also spatially and temporally biased to certain human imprints on the land. People are mobile, discrete, and their links to the land may be through lands on which they reside or from some more distant location. Remote sensing and the land that it senses is generally static in place but may be dynamic through time, is continuous in pattern, but reflects patterns only at specified scales without providing insights about the motivations of people and how they might translate to actions that affect the land. In our research, it is the integrative power of our theories and perspectives, data and methods, and analyses and interpretations that informs our inquiries and offers insights to complex problems, some newly emerging, while others are cast in terms of traditional paradigms and perspectives, but served by new analytic approaches and syntheses that extend across the social, natural, and spatial sciences.

ACKNOWLEDGMENTS

The research reported here has been supported by a variety of mechanisms, including grants from the National Institute of Child Health and Human Development (RO1-HD33570 and RO1-HD25482). Additional support was provided by the Mellon Foundation (through a grant to the Carolina Population Center), the National Aeronautics and Space Administration (NAG5-6002), the National Science Foundation (SBR 93-10366), the Evaluation Project (USAID Contract #DPE-3060-C-00-1054), the MacArthur Foundation (95-31576A-POP), and a P30 center grant to the Carolina Population Center from the National Institute of Child Health and Human Development, HD05798. We are grateful for this support. We would also like to acknowledge, with gratitude, the help and cooperation of numerous individuals who assisted in the design of the research described here. Numerous staff members and graduate students at the Institute for Population and Social Research, Mahidol University, and the Carolina Population Center, University of North Carolina, participated, as well as colleagues at other universities. And finally, and perhaps most importantly, we would like to acknowledge the cooperation of the people of Nang Rong. Our requests for information have been many, and Nang Rong residents have cooperated completely, and for that we are in their debt.

REFERENCES

Ahl, V., and T.F.H. Allen
  1996   *Hierarchy Theory*. New York: Columbia University Press.
Allen, T.F.H., and T.B. Starr
  1982   *Hierarchy: Perspectives for Ecological Complexity*. Chicago, IL: University of Chicago Press.
Bak, P.
  1998   *How Nature Works*. New York: Copernicus/Springer-Verlag.
Biemer, P.P., and L.E. Lyberg
  2003   *Introduction to Survey Quality*. Hoboken, NJ: John Wiley and Sons.
Blaikie, P., and H. Brookfield
  1987   *Land Degradation and Society*. London, England: Methuen.
Carson, R.
  1962   *Silent Spring*. Boston, MA: Houghton Mifflin.
Clarke, K.C., S. Hoppen, and L. Gaydos
  1996   Methods and techniques for rigorous calibration of a cellular automaton model of urban growth. Paper presented ath the Third International Conference/Workshop on Integrating GIS and Environmental Modeling, Santa Barbara National Center for Geographic Information and Analysis, Santa Fe, NM.
Clarke, K.C., L. Gaydos, and S. Hoppen
  1997   A self-modifying cellular automaton model of historical urbanization in the San Francisco Bay area. *Environment and Planning B* 23:247-261.
Crews-Meyer, K.A.
  2001   Assessing landscape change and population-environment interactions via panel analysis. *Geocarto International* 16(4):69-79.
  2002   Characterizing landscape dynamism using paneled-pattern metrics. *Photogrammetric Engineering and Remote Sensing* 68(10):1031-1040.
Davis, K.
  1963   The theory of change and response in modern demographic history. *Population Index* 29:345-366.
Edmeades, J.
  2000   Rice farming in Nang Rong, Thailand. Unpublished paper. Department of Sociology and Carolina Population Center, University of North Carolina, Chapel Hill.

Elder, G.H.
  1974   *Children of the Great Depression: Social Change in Life Experience.* Chicago, IL: University of Chicago Press.
  1998   The life course and human development. Pp. 939-991 in *Handbook of Child Psychology, Volume I: Theoretical Models of Human Development,* R.M. Lerner, ed. New York: John Wiley and Sons.
Entwisle, B., R.R. Rindfuss, D.K. Guilkey, A. Chamratrithriong, S.R. Curran, and Y. Sawangdee
  1996   Community and contraceptive choice in rural Thailand: A case study of Nang Rong. *Demography* 33:1-11.
Entwisle, B., S.J. Walsh, R.R. Rindfuss, and A. Chamratrithirong
  1998   Land use/land-cover and population dynamics, Nang Rong, Thailand. Pp. 121-144 in National Research Council, *People and Pixels: Linking Remote Sensing and Social Science,* Committee on the Human Dimensions of Global Change, D. Liverman, E.F. Moran, R.R. Rindfuss, and P.C. Stern, eds. Washington, DC: National Academy Press.
Entwisle, B., J. Edmeades, G.P. Malanson, C. Podhisita, P. Prasartkul, R.R. Rindfuss, and S.J. Walsh
  no   Village Settlement, Deforestation, and the Expansion of Agriculture in a Frontier
  date-a Region: Nang Rong, Thailand. Carolina Population Center, University of North Carolina, Chapel Hill.
Entwisle, B., S.J. Walsh, R.R. Rindfuss, L.K. VanWey
  no   Population and Upland Crop Production in Nang Rong, Thailand. Carolina Popu-
  date-b lation Center, University of North Carolina, Chapel Hill.
Evans, T.P.
  1998   Integration of Community-Level Social and Environmental Data: Spatial Modeling of Community Boundaries in Northeast Thailand. Ph.D. dissertation, Department of Geography, University of North Carolina, Chapel Hill.
Forman, R.T.T., and M. Godron
  1986   *Landscape Ecology.* New York: John Wiley and Sons.
Freedman, D., A. Thorton, D. Camburn, D. Alwin, and L. Young-DeMarco
  1988   The life history calendar: A technique for collecting retrospective data. *Sociological Methodology* 18:37-68.
Fukui, H.
  1993   *Food and Population in a Northeast Thai Village.* (Translated by P. Hawkes.) Honolulu: University of Hawaii Press.
Gell-Mann, M.
  1994   *The Quark and the Jaguar.* New York: Freeman.
Hirschman, C., J. Tan, A. Chamratrithirong, and P. Guest
  1994   The path to below replacement-level fertility in Thailand. *International Family Planning Perspectives* 20:82-87, 107.
Houghton, R., J. Hackler, and K. Lawrence
  1999   The U.S. carbon budget: Contribution from land-use change. *Science* 285:574-578.
Hunter, L.M.
  2000   *The Environmental Implications of Population Dynamics.* Santa Monica, CA: RAND.
Jampaklay, A.
  2003   Migration, Marital Timing, and Mate Selection in the Context of Thailand. Ph.D. dissertation, Department of Sociology, University of North Carolina, Chapel Hill.
Johnston, R.J., P.J. Taylor, and M.J. Watts, eds.
  1995   *Geographies of Global Change: Remapping the World in the Late Twentieth Century.* Oxford, England: Blackwell.

Kanae S, T. Oki, and K. Musiake
  2001   Impact of deforestation on regional precipitation over the Indochina Peninsula. *Journal of Hydrometeorology* 2(1):51-70.
Kasperson, J.X., R.E. Kasperson, and B.L. Turner II, eds.
  1995   *Regions at Risk: Comparison of Threatened Environments.* Tokyo, Japan: United Nations University Press.
Konrad, C.E.
  2000   Summary Report: Nang Rong Precipitation Climatology. Unpublished manuscript. University of North Carolina, Chapel Hill.
Lambin, E.F., X. Baulies, N. Bockstael, G. Fischer, T. Krug, R. Leemans, E.F. Moran, R.R. Rindfuss, Y. Sato, D. Skole, B.L. Turner II, and C. Vogel
  1999   *Land-Use and Land-Cover Change Implementation Strategy.* Stockholm: IGBP Secretariat, Royal Swedish Academy of Sciences.
Limanonda, B.
  1992   Nuptiality patterns in Thailand: Their implications for further fertility decline. Pp. 101-120 in *Fertility Transitions, Family Structure, and Population Policy,* C. Goldscheider, ed. Boulder, CO: Westview Press.
Luhman, N.
  1985   *A Sociological Theory of Law.* London, England: Routledge and Kegan Paul.
Malanson, G.P.
  1999   Considering complexity. *Annals, Association of American* Geographers 89:746-753.
  2002   Extinction debt trajectories and spatial pattern of habitat destruction. *Annals of the Association of American Geographers* 92:177-188.
Messina, J.P., and S.J. Walsh
  2001   2.5D morphogenesis: Modeling landuse and landcover dynamics in the Ecuadorian Amazon. *Plant Ecology* 156:75-88.
Meyer, W.B., and B.L. Turner II
  1992   Human population growth and global land-use/cover change. *Annual Review of Ecological Systems* 23:39-61.
Moran, E.F., and E. Brondizio
  1998   Land use change after deforestation in Amazônia. Pp. 94-120 in National Research Council, *People and Pixels: Linking Remote Sensing and Social Science,* Committee on the Human Dimensions of Global Change, D. Liverman, E.F. Moran, R. Rindfuss, and P. Stern, eds. Washington DC: National Academy Press.
Moran, E.F., E. Brondizio, P. Mausel, and Y. Wu
  1994   Integrating Amazonian vegetation, land-use, and satellite data. *BioScience* 44(5): 329-338.
Phananinarai, M.
  1997   *Population Changes and Economic Development in Thailand: Their Implications for Women's Status.* (East-West Center Working Papers 88-11.) Honolulu, HI: East-West Center.
Ragin, C.C.
  1987   *The Comparative Method: Moving Beyond Qualitative and Quantitative Strategies.* Berkeley: University of California Press.
Rindfuss, R.R.
  1991   The young adult years: Diversity, structural change, and fertility. *Demography* 28:493-512.
Rindfuss, R.R., S.J. Walsh, and B. Entwisle
  1996   Land Use, Competition, and Migration. Paper presented at the Population Association of America Meeting, New Orleans, LA.

Rindfuss, R.R., B. Entwisle, S.J. Walsh, P. Prasartkul, Y. Sawangdee, T.W. Crawford, and J. Reade
    2002   Continuous and discrete: Where they have met in Nang Rong, Thailand. Pp. 7-37 in *Linking People, Place and Policy: A GIScience Approach*, S.J. Walsh and K.A. Crews-Meyer, eds. Boston, MA: Kluwer Academic Publishers.
Rindfuss, R.R., P. Prasartkul, S.J. Walsh, B. Entwisle, Y. Sawangdee, and J.B. Vogler
    2003   Household-parcel linkages in Nang Rong, Thailand: Challenges of large samples. Pp. 131-172 in *People and the Environment: Approaches for Linking Household and Community Surveys to Remote Sensing and GIS*, J. Fox, R.R. Rindfuss, S.J. Walsh, and V. Mishra, eds. Boston, MA: Kluwer Academic Publishers.
Rindfuss, R.R., A. Jampaklay, B. Entwisle, Y. Sawangdee, K. Faust, and P. Prasartkul
    2004   The collection and analysis of social network data in Nang Rong, Thailand. In *Network Epidemiology: A Handbook for Survey Design and Data Collection*, M. Morris, ed. Oxford, England: Oxford University Press.
Stark, O.
    1991   *The Migration of Labor.* Cambridge, MA: Basil Blackwell.
Urry, J.
    2001   The sociology of space and place. Pp. 5-13 in *The Blackwell Companion to Sociology*, J.R. Blau, ed. Malden, MA: Blackwell.
Walsh, S.J., T.P. Evans, W.F. Welsh, B. Entwisle, and R.R. Rindfuss
    1999   Scale-dependent relationships between population and environment in northeastern Thailand. *Photogrammetric Engineering and Remote Sensing* 65:97-105.
Walsh, S.J., T.W. Crawford, W.F. Welsh, and K.A. Crews-Meyer
    2001   A multiscale analysis of land use and land cover and NDVI variation in Nang Rong District, Northeast Thailand. *Agriculture Ecosystems and Environment* 85(1-3):47-64.
Walsh, S.J., R.R. Rindfuss, B. Entwisle, Y. Shao, D.J. Weiss, P.M. McDaniel, and R.E. Pullen
    2003   Characterizing land use/land cover change in northeast Thailand and analyzing the causes and consequences of landscape dynamics. (CD-ROM.) *Proceedings, 30th International Symposium on Remote Sensing of Environment*, Honolulu, HI.
Westervelt, J.D.
    2002   Geographic information systems and agent-based modeling. Pp. 83-104 in *Integrating Geographic Information Systems and Agent-Based Modeling Techniques for Simulating Social and Ecological Processes*, H.R. Gimblett, ed. New York: Oxford University Press.
Wright, H.T.
    2002   Agent-based modeling of small-scale societies: State of the art and future prospects. Pp. 373-385 in *Dynamics in Human and Primate Societies: Agent-Based Modeling of Social and Spatial Processes*, T.A. Kolher and G.J. Gumerman, eds. New York: Oxford University Press.
Yin, R.K.
    2003   *Case Study Research: Design and Methods* (3rd ed.). Thousand Oaks, CA: Sage Publications, Inc.

7

The Urban Ecology of Metropolitan Phoenix: A Laboratory for Interdisciplinary Study

Charles L. Redman

Because an ever-increasing proportion of the global population resides in cities, it is essential to improve understanding of the recursive relationship between population and the environment. Toward that end, seven years ago we undertook a comprehensive study of the long-term urban ecology of central Arizona's rapidly growing urban region. Called the Central Arizona–Phoenix Long-Term Ecological Research project (Grimm et al., 2000; Grimm and Redman, 2004), it is part of the Long Term Ecological Research Program, a program of 26 sites sponsored by the National Science Foundation (Hobbie et al., 2003). In addition to the challenges of investigating ecological patterns and processes over long temporal and broad spatial scales, an urban system involves the complexities of intense human participation. Associated with human participation in the system are economic and social drivers, radically altered land cover, flows of materials, and the impacts of a built environment. As in traditional long-term ecological research, interdisciplinary collaboration of ecologists, biogeochemists, earth scientists, and climatologists is fundamental, but added to the mix are sociologists, geographers, economists, political scientists, urban planners, anthropologists, civil and environmental engineers, mechanical and chemical engineers, and many community partners who share the zeal for understanding the urban ecosystem. Although we realize there is a significant difference among the perspectives needed to understand an urban system, in contrast to a system in which human participation is relatively modest, we think that lessons learned through wider collaboration will prove useful to all long-term ecological research programs and to others interested in integrating social and environmental perspectives (Redman, Grove, and Kuby, 2004).

The detailed examination of a human-dominated urban ecosystem has led us to question how and to what extent the patterns and processes in human-dominated systems require qualitative changes to traditional ecological theory (Collins et al., 2000). So far, most ecologists working in cities have relied on the view of humans as disturbing forces and equated urban environments with extreme conditions. Assigning the residual values from traditional analyses to the human component of the ecosystem appears to work, up to a point, just as the Ptolemaic explanation of the solar system could be elaborated to fit empirical observations. Rather than elaborate on what may be fundamentally insufficient, at some point it is more effective to reconceptualize the theory to better explain the patterns. This strategy calls for integrating new elements into ecological theory. Certainly not all ecological theory must be refined, nor will all changes be radical, but we think that the pervasive presence and impact of humans on all global environments, not just urban ecosystems, requires one to be open to change.

This chapter reviews the interdisciplinary approaches of the Central Arizona–Phoenix Long-Term Ecological Research project toward the interaction of land use change, population, and environment. It continues with a review of two related projects: Agrarian Landscapes in Transition, which examines the relationship between urban growth and regional transformation, and Networking Urban Ecological Models, which integrates data from several public agencies to solve problems of mutual interest to academic and nonacademic researchers. This review is a stepping-off point for a brief discussion of our efforts to work with local land managers and public officials and a new project that is explicitly aimed at improving the application of science to decision making. The chapter concludes with a discussion of how these projects have led to a refinement in the conceptual approach being used and suggests how our observations direct us to areas in which ecological theory should be reexamined.

CENTRAL ARIZONA–PHOENIX LONG-TERM ECOLOGICAL RESEARCH

The overarching goal of the broader Long-Term Ecological Research program is to understand patterns and processes that underlie long-term changes in ecosystem structure and function. For an urban ecosystem, success in achieving this goal also hinges on understanding the complexities of intense human participation in the system—with attendant economic and social drivers, radically altered land cover, accelerated cycling of materials, and heretofore unresearched ecological impacts of a built environment (Redman, 1999a). The particular challenge for our project is to conduct a comprehensive study of central Arizona, one of the most rapidly urbanizing regions in the country, which includes Phoenix and four of the state's five next-largest cities: Mesa, Glendale, Scottsdale, and Chandler. To address this challenge, our researchers have been committed to interdisciplinary collaboration from project inception, under the broad umbrella of earth, life, and social sciences; engineering; and planning and policy (Grimm and Redman, 2004).

The Phoenix metropolis, comprising over 20 municipalities, is situated in a broad, alluvial basin where two major desert tributaries of the Colorado, the Salt, and Gila rivers, converge (see Figure 7-1). The basin, dotted with eroded volcanic outcrops and rimmed by mountains, once supported a vast expanse of lowland Sonoran desert and riparian vegetation. The plant association of the upper Sonoran life zone (on outwash slopes and pediments) is the saguaro-paloverde, with creosote bush dominating in low-

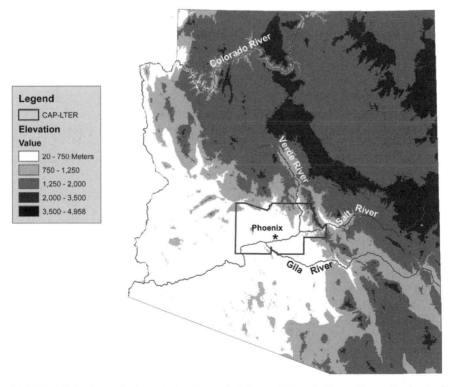

FIGURE 7-1 Boundaries of the Central Arizona–Phoenix Long-Term Ecological Research site (outlined) encompassing an area of 6,400 km².

land, flatter areas. The study site (6,400 square kilometers, km²) includes the rapidly expanding Phoenix area, along with its agricultural and desert surroundings. The region's population has increased by 47 percent since 1990 to over 3.2 million people (U.S. Census Bureau, 2000). Although the population growth rate was faster early in the twentieth century, numerically the growth of Phoenix has occurred mostly in the second half of the century (see Figure 7-2). Initially, that expansion consumed mostly farmland, but the newest housing has primarily replaced desert land, leading to spatial variation in the extant vegetation and the structure of residential landscapes. Reliance on irrigation to create and sustain agricultural production and urban landscapes hastened the sharp contrast between managed landscapes, with their exotic plants, and undeveloped desert, with its native vegetation (Hope et al., 2003). This process generated a frequently quoted newspaper series, which claimed that urban growth was consuming "an acre an hour" of desert lands. The costs of extending the water infrastructure and other social factors have resulted in a remarkable uniformity of residential lot size across the metropolitan region that defies national patterns (Knowles-Yánez et al., 1999; Gammage, 1999). Construction of local reservoirs and the Central Arizona Project canal (Kupel, 2003), the devel-

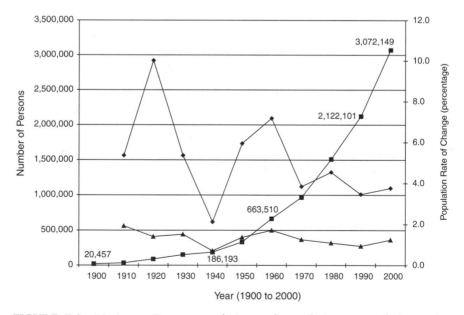

FIGURE 7-2 Maricopa County population and population rates of change by decade for Maricopa County and the United States, 1910-2000. Maricopa County population figures roughly correspond to the CAP LTER figures.

opment of air conditioning, and the widespread use of motor vehicles have been triggering factors, each accelerating the region's growth.

We began the project with an overarching research question that continues to guide us today:

> How do the patterns and processes of urbanization alter the ecological conditions of the city and its surrounding environment, and how do ecological consequences of these developments feed back to the social system to generate future changes?

This question focuses our thinking on the interaction within and between the ecological and human domains in the context of a changing, expanding urban metropolis. For us, the process of urbanization is at its heart one of land use change, reflecting the transformation of either the Sonoran Desert or irrigated farmland to municipal or industrial use. Increasing land surface coverage by buildings and roads as well as transformed landscapes, the redesigned hydrological system, the spread of impervious surfaces, and the transformation of habitats characterize this process. Although the study of change is a strong element of our approach, we are also concerned with relatively stable patterns and aspects of the system. Although dozens of researchers have investigated these issues, we are only a fraction of the way toward our goal. While identifying and monitoring the ecological consequences of urbanization, we have only begun to understand how these consequences influence the social system and generate future changes.

Our research question must also address a range of scales, with the focal scale being the whole ecosystem, but with interesting questions asked at lower and higher levels of a time-space scale hierarchy. In some cases, feedbacks may occur at scales different from the primary scale the research addresses. In describing our findings, we refer to the following scales:

1. Individual land use patch types: these can be land use or land cover patches or even smaller units (i.e., households, lots, parks). At this scale, our research has primarily characterized ecological and social patterns.

2. Mosaics of patches: here the focus is on the relationships among individual patches.

3. Whole ecosystem: several efforts have been made to describe ecological conditions without referring to the heterogeneity in the urban ecosystem, but by treating the system as a "black box."

4. The central Arizona–Phoenix ecosystem in a regional context: the ecosystem interacts with its surroundings in quantifiable ways. For example, the city can be seen as a source or sink for elements.

5. Urbanizing central Arizona in a global context: Can lessons learned in central Arizona–Phoenix be transferred to other dryland regions internationally?

The hierarchical, patch dynamics model developed for this project (Wu and David, 2002) provides a framework for integrating different kinds of models (e.g., population dynamics, ecosystem processes, land use, and land cover change) across these different spatial scales. Such a framework is necessary because both ecological and socioeconomic patterns and processes in any urban landscape occur on a variety of scales, and hierarchical linkages among scales often significantly affect the dynamics and stability of urban development. The patch dynamics approach focuses not only on the spatial pattern of heterogeneity at a given time, but also on the pattern's change over time and its impact on ecological and social processes. Because cities are both expanding and changing within their boundaries, the dynamic aspect of this approach is crucial to a complete understanding of urban ecological systems.

LAND USE AND LAND COVER CHANGE

An improved understanding of past, current, and future land cover and land use transformations is essential to investigating the urban ecosystem and, in particular, its relationship to population and environment. Crucial to the patterns we witness is the region's population growth. Having acknowledged the central role that the growing presence of humans plays in these changes, we turn our attention to what governs the perception of the current patterns and of the implications of each alternate perception. Land use change ensues from human decision making that occurs in the context of social institutions and is influenced by drivers that range from economics and cultural traditions to expected economic or ecological benefits. It is vital to recognize that broad-scale social and environmental conditions, as well as local ecological and human legacies, constrain and sometimes guide the range of possible trajectories for land cover and land use. At an earlier workshop on integrating social science into the Long-Term Ecological Research network (Redman et al., 2004), we developed a conceptual model to articulate these diverse approaches. At the center of the model and at the core of integrated inquiries is a set of interactions, the foremost being land use change (see Figure 7-3). We suggested that to implement this model requires three iterative stages of research: (1) collecting background information on "external" biogeophysical, political, economic, and demographic conditions; (2) describing and monitoring changes in both ecological and social patterns and processes that drive the system we define; and (3) investigating the nature of, and monitoring changes in, interactions resulting from the patterns and processes. Land use change is probably the most direct indicator of system change of those indicated.

Land use change alters the hydrological system, air movement, settlement spread, trophic communities, primary productivity, land surface char-

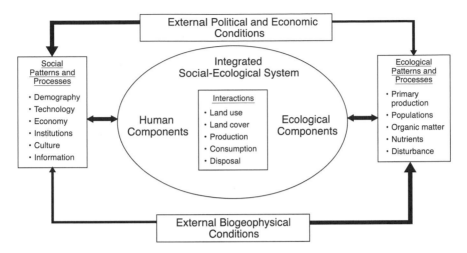

FIGURE 7-3 Conceptual framework for long-term investigations of social–ecological systems from Redman, Grove, and Kuby (2004).

acteristics, and the overall ecological footprint of the city. Open-ended questions, such as determining the level at which excessive urban growth impacts water supply, air quality, or agricultural viability, are of paramount importance to the citizens of central Arizona. At what point in the urbanization process do cities contribute to, or become susceptible to, catastrophic vulnerability such as infrastructure inadequacy, transportation gridlock, air pollution extremes, geologic hazards, and health risks?

Drawing on extant resources for the analysis of land use change has allowed us to proceed quickly and provide summary analyses that are of immediate interest to our local collaborators. Nowhere is that scenario more apparent than with our Historic Land-Use Project. We drew on available aerial photography, satellite imagery, and municipal and county records from 1912, 1934, 1955, 1975, 1995, and 2000, and, with modest additional analysis, developed maps of broad land use categories (agricultural, desert, recreational, and urban) that provided a context for many of our subsequent studies (see Figure 7-4). Local media and government agencies have also used these maps, giving our project early recognition. This historical analysis of land use has revealed that one aspect of spreading urbanization and the dominant land use transition has changed over the past century. Phoenix and neighboring municipalities began a decade after the Civil War as a series of scattered communities in a broad expanse of farmland. The amount of land in agrarian use continued to increase rapidly from 1912 to 1934, increased more slowly from 1934 to 1975 (expanding at the periphery as land was converted to urban at the core), and declined

1912

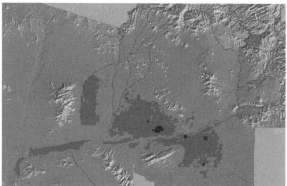

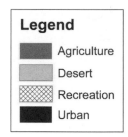

1934

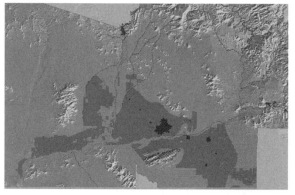

1955

FIGURE 7-4   Land use maps of central Arizona–Phoenix.

1975

1995

2000

from 1975 to 2000. Until 1975, the urban fabric expanded to adjacent
land, soon transforming the discrete communities into a continuous metropolitan zone. Although this spread into adjacent farmland continues today,
most new developments since 1975 have occurred on former desert lands,
often some distance out from the nearest residential area. This shift—from
urban residential development on former farmland, in which water once
used on the farm was diverted for municipal uses, to development in pris-
tine desert areas farther from canal and surface water distribution systems—has profoundly impacted water policy and real estate opportunities
(Knowles-Yánez et al., 1999; Gammage, 1999). Interestingly, the need to
build expensive infrastructure to service these new residential developments
has led to the construction of housing on small lots in a relatively compact
fashion. In a Brookings Institution study of 13 large U.S. cities, Phoenix,
surprisingly, was found to be one of two cities that became more compact
between 1970 and 2000 (Fulton et al., 2001). New, and often very expensive, homes are being built on lots that are the same size or even smaller
than the lots of modest homes near the center of the city. This pattern has
resulted in a relatively uniform density across virtually all of the metropolitan area.

200-POINT SURVEY

Given the broad expanse of the central Arizona–Phoenix ecosystem—
6,400 km^2 defines the study area, and the watershed is several times that
size—and its spatial heterogeneity (Luck and Wu, 2002), characterization
of the landscape at a finer scale than the Historic Land-Use Project would
require a major field survey and a sampling strategy. To ensure widespread
spatial distribution and allow more intense sampling of the urban core, we
used a dual-density, tessellation-stratified random sampling design (see Figure 7-5). This design, which established 204 sampling points randomly
selected in a grid cell of 5 by 5 km (with outlying points established in every
third grid cell, hence the dual density), allows us to measure numerous
environmental variables in a 900 m^2 plot. Among the collected data at each
plot is information on meteorology, soil chemistry, surface characteristics,
pollen, arthropods, bird abundance and diversity, woody plant genera, and
above-ground biomass. In addition, because the entire data set is
georeferenced in a series of ArcInfo files, we can superimpose social data
(from the census, the Historical Land-Use Project, and other available information) on this extensive snapshot of the central Arizona–Phoenix ecosystem, which we intend to repeat every five years.

Although data analysis from our first (spring 2000) application of the
200-point survey design is ongoing, already we have discerned a difference
in potential driving and controlling variables between urban plots and

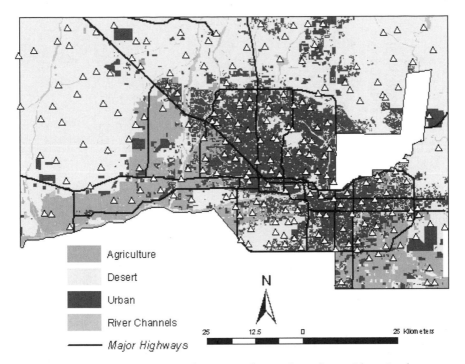

FIGURE 7-5   Central Arizona–Phoenix study area boundary with major freeways
and 200-point survey locations (white triangles).

desert plots, as well as within socioeconomic divisions of the urban plots. A
basic finding from our survey of how human activities inadvertently alter
the environment is that while soil nitrate concentration is spatially auto-
correlated in the desert plots, as one would expect from traditional ecological experiments, no such spatial relationship exists for the urban plots
(Hope et al. no date). We think this difference reflects the extent to which
human management has introduced heterogeneity into the soil's chemical
properties at a scale much smaller than that found in deserts where non-
anthropogenic processes dominate. One example of how explicit human
choice can lead to an association between social and ecological variables is
the positive correlation of the richness of woody vegetation (recorded to
genus), a measure of plant diversity, with median family income (derived
from the 2000 census) for the urban plots (see Figure 7-6; Hope et al.,
2003). Although this intriguing pattern is a correlation and does not necessarily imply causation, the finding leads us to new research questions about
the mechanisms by which humans control their environment. The data
indicate that plant diversity (resulting from landowner choice) increases
with family income, yet this relationship appears to level off when income

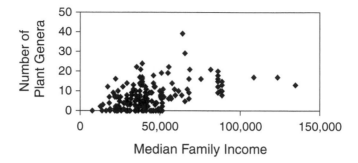

FIGURE 7-6   Illustration of the direct relationship between plant diversity and economic wealth for the CAP LTER study area. The data are taken from the 200-point survey (Hope et al., 2003).

exceeds a certain level (above $70,000). This leveling implies that aesthetic or other drivers of choice are satisfied even though there is available wealth to expand the diversity.

The 200-point survey monitors slowly changing variables over a broad expanse in space at a low sampling frequency (once every 5 years). The picture that we get of the ecosystem is thus coarse-grained and cannot resolve dynamics that occur in shorter time frames. Moreover, although it is possible to distinguish land cover and land use types (patches; for example, our comparison of desert and urban plots), this approach is perhaps best suited to gaining an understanding of the whole from viewing the mosaic of patches. We can question, for example, whether desert plots embedded in urbanized surroundings differ from those on the periphery of the study area. Thus, we are working at the scale of the mosaic of patches within the ecosystem. A more intensive examination of permanent plots is likely to identify the mechanisms that explain the patterns found at this broad extent and coarse grain. Our permanent plots, established to date in a few residential urban as well as desert sites, are used to investigate the variables that change more rapidly (e.g., seasonally) and potentially show the direct and indirect effects of human action.

The 200-point survey provided detailed land use and land cover information from 900 m² units—relatively small and widely dispersed sampling units. To put these sampled areas in a somewhat broader context, the second phase of the Historic Land-Use Project investigated the square mile around the sample point (defined by arterial streets that follow the original Government Land Office survey). Aerial photos were the main source of information until 1990, when these sources were supplemented with land use maps produced by the Maricopa Association of Governments. It was decided to attempt matching with decadal census years, something possible only from 1970 to 2000. The individual parcels in the section around each of the 200 points were categorized according to 26 land use types adapted from Anderson et al. (1976) for 1970, 1980, 1990, and 2000, and as many points as possible were also classified for 1961, 1949, and 1934 (Plate 5). The history of a given parcel of land and its immediate surroundings has important consequences for ecological variables. For example, whether a site was farmed in the past century determines present-day soil nitrate concentration (Hope et al., no date). Nitrate is the predominant form of nitrogen in soils of the region, and nitrogen is an important plant nutrient that, given sufficient water, may enhance or limit primary productivity. This backbone of data from the survey as well as extant data sources have allowed us to develop expectations of the ecological and social conditions in similar modern land use patches with different histories. A number of analyses are being conducted with this information. The central focus is on sequences of land use transitions as they occurred across the region. We can trace the composition of each section across the region regarding its proportion of desert land developed for residential, commercial, or industrial use—hence, tracing the timing of the development of that neighborhood. By reconstructing the trajectory of development for each area and categorizing them according to trends that occurred at different times, we can gain insights into the alternate developmental patterns followed in the region (Zoldak, 2003).

URBAN MODELS AND SOCIAL PROCESSES

Data describing historical patterns of urban growth in central Arizona are being used as input for a series of models that characterize these patterns and to spark projects related to future growth. Wu has led an effort to examine the growth patterns under different conditions and assembled them into a series of related models called the Phoenix Urban Growth Model. The cellular automaton assumption of next unit of growth occurring adjacent to current habitation (Berling-Wolff and Wu, 2004; see Figure 7-7) drives the model. We have added several rules to the basic model, such as new housing follows transportation routes and avoids public lands. Of special interest to our community partners are projections of how long it will take before all available land is urbanized under different conditions (rates of growth, changes in land availability, etc.). Urban planners on our team are leading complementary efforts to use historical patterns to project growth scenarios by incorporating the UrbanSim model developed for other Western cities (Guhathakurta, 2002; Waddell, 2000).

Although these approaches are yielding important information, we still need to develop a system for monitoring land use change at a relatively detailed spatial scale, more frequently than once a decade, and with con-

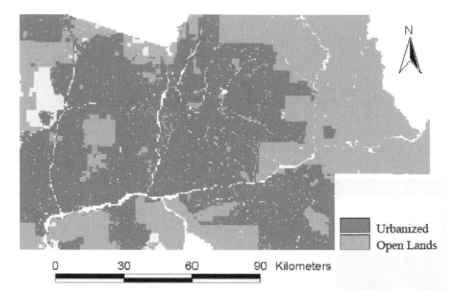

FIGURE 7-7 Land use projections for 2029 when all private land in central Arizo-na–Phoenix is projected to be urbanized, with an estimated population of 8.2 million (Berling-Wolff and Wu, 2004).

tinuous spatial coverage of this very large region. Remote sensing appears to be the most promising strategy to achieve these goals in a reasonable cost structure. Using Landsat coverage and an expert classification system of multispectral information, we have been able to create continuous spatial coverage (30 m pixels) classified into 12 land use categories (Stefanov, Ramsey, and Christensen, 2001). Researchers have devoted significant energy to verifying this classification system so that eventually we can adopt it as our basic monitoring procedure for land use and land cover change. As we use the imagery to classify the land cover, we are also applying a variety of metrics to the spatial patterns observed by satellite, including texture, patchiness, density of edges, etc. (Netzband and Stefanov, 2003). Through the analysis of these geographic metrics as they relate to sociodemographic data from the U.S. census, county records, and our own 200-point survey, we hope to improve the effectiveness of remote-sensing techniques in examining urban structure and change.

As a city like Phoenix grows under the pressure of continual immigration, patterns of land use impact the environment in ways that place certain segments of the population at greater risk. Unsurprisingly, the distribution of environmental risk often correlates with groups with less wealth, status, or power. This inequity may take the form of living in neighborhoods with greater likelihood of exposure to hazardous materials, breathing polluted air, or exposure to physical hazards such as floods. One part of a multivariate study of environmental risk and sociodemographics found that high values for air emissions from the U.S. Environmental Protection Agency's Toxic Release Inventory correlated strongly with neighborhoods with high proportions of minority residents (see Figure 7-8; Bolin et al., 2002). However, we did find that some less obvious environmental risks, such as high ozone levels, often cross-cut socioeconomic class. A key objective of our studies is to distinguish between conditions in which facilities producing environmental risks choose to locate in poorer neighborhoods and conditions in which people with less wealth have little choice but to locate in affordable neighborhoods that are adjacent to these facilities.

One case of confronting the human factors in land use and land cover change focuses on changes occurring at the geographic fringe of urban development. The researchers on our project used county records of individual housing starts to trace the appearance of residential neighborhoods on former desert or agricultural lands. This work resulted in a preliminary understanding of a key process of urbanization in the region: the establish-

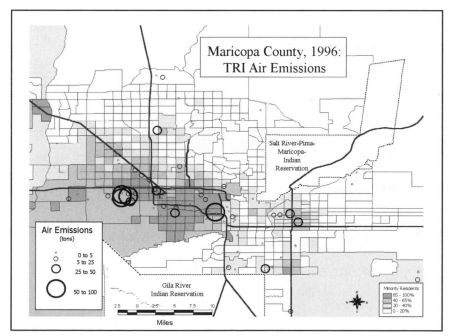

FIGURE 7-8   Toxic air emissions from the U.S. Environmental Protection Agency's Toxic Release Inventory, correlated with neighborhood sociodemographic characteristics, minority residents (Bolin et al., 2002).

ment, and outward migration, of an urban fringe. Migration is defined as the geographic movement of a zone, or a series of linked zones, outward from urban centers into unoccupied or lightly occupied landscapes. The composition of new residents in this zone is a mix of new migrants from other states and people from the Salt River Valley moving to larger houses or less congested areas. Gober and Burns (2002) described the urban fringe as a "wave of advance" that migrates into the outlying desert and agricultural lands, is preceded by predictable changes in types of businesses and microclimate, and progresses through stages of development (i.e., pioneer settlement, peak, zone of infill; see Figure 7-9). During the past 20 years, this fringe has advanced in a checkerboard fashion as development often hops over the established urban edge in a leapfrog pattern. At a more local scale, urban fringe morphology can be modeled as a colonization process (Fagan et al., 2001). Such basic models can be used as starting points for further investigation into the pattern of development and incorporate the effects of individual or group decisions by inhabitants, the composition of the population along the fringe, and the effects of external triggering events.

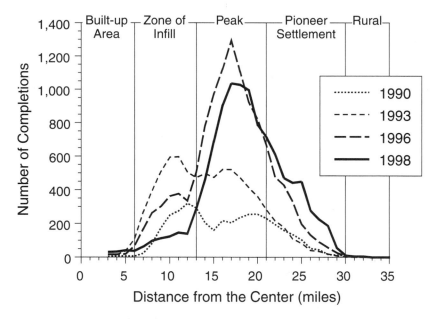

FIGURE 7-9   Zones of residential completions, 1990-1998, for the southeast zone of the Phoenix metropolitan area. Note that fringe development covers a wide geographic area and that there are well-defined zones of development (Gober and Burns, 2002).

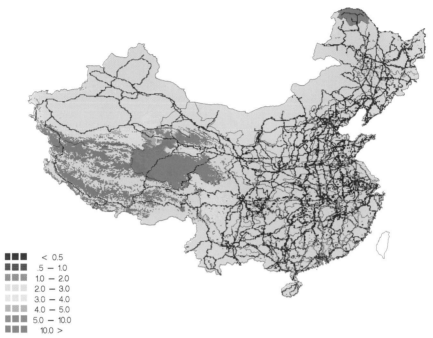

PLATE 1 Average transport cost (Yuan per ton-kilometer).

Legend:
- < 0.5
- .5 — 1.0
- 1.0 — 2.0
- 2.0 — 3.0
- 3.0 — 4.0
- 4.0 — 5.0
- 5.0 — 10.0
- 10.0 >

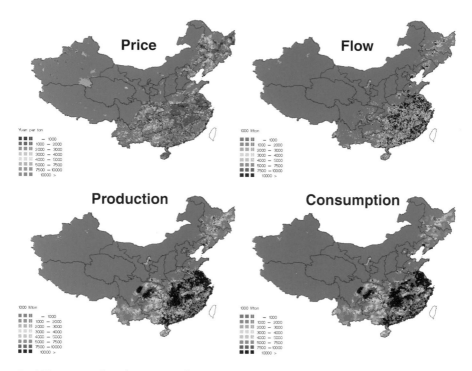

PLATE 2 Results of transport flow model for rice.

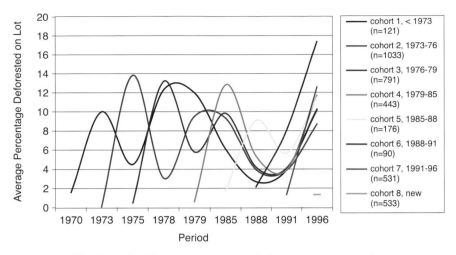

PLATE 3 The Colonist Footprint: Average deforestation trajectories across cohorts. The cohorts refer to dates when groups of settlers first arrived at this
location and the deforestation trajectory is the average area deforested by each
group or cohort. Adapted from Brondizio et al. (2002).

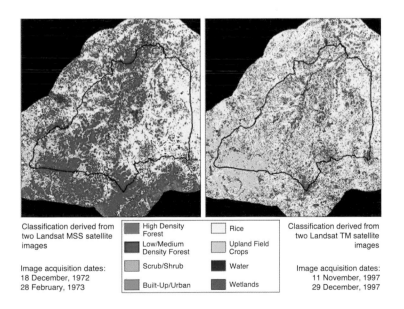

PLATE 4 Image comparison of land use and land cover in Nang Rong district
(bounded by dark irregular line) and a surrounding 10 km buffer area, 1972-1973
and 1997.

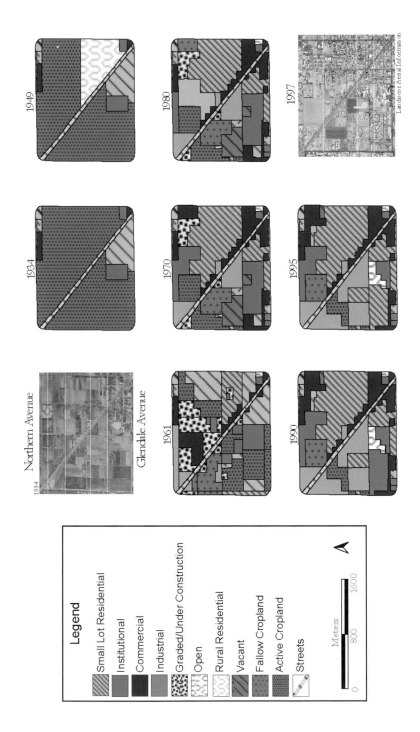

PLATE 5 Finer scale analysis of historic land use change, historic land use, Phase II, for one square mile section around a 200-point survey point

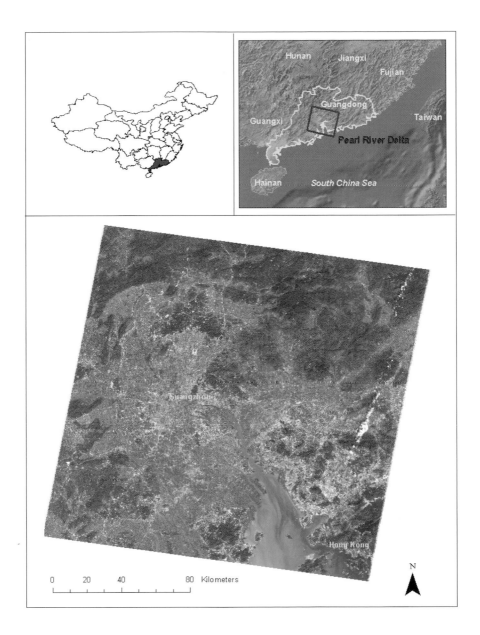

PLATE 6 Pearl River Delta study area. The upper left inset shows the Guangdong Province within China; the upper right inset pinpoints the study area in relation to the province; the bottom inset is a satellite composite image of sample data from the Landsat Thematic Mapper circa 1992.

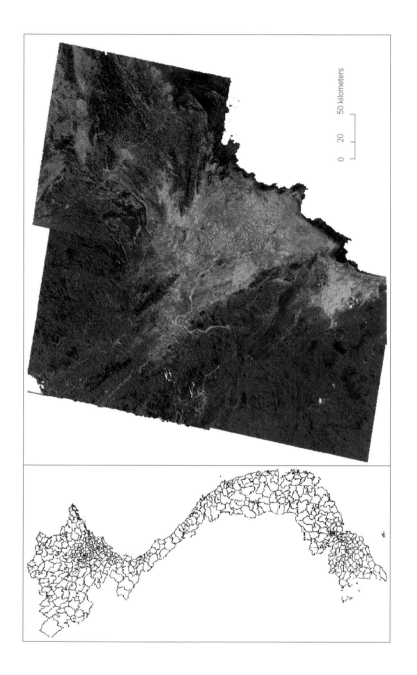

PLATE 7 Red River Delta study area. The left inset shows the study area in relation to the country (Vietnam). The right inset is a satellite composite image from the Landsat Thematic Mapper circa 1992.

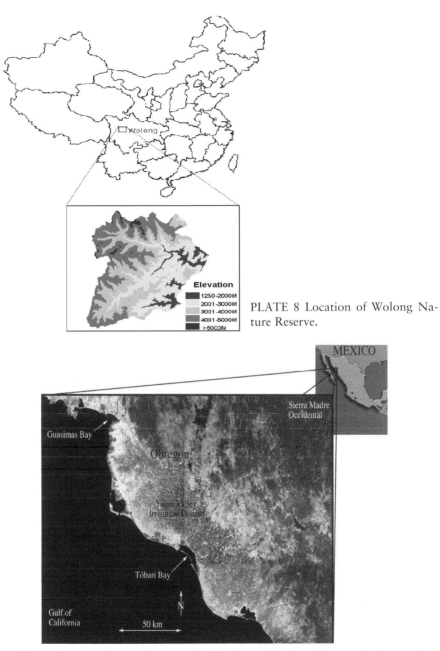

PLATE 8 Location of Wolong Nature Reserve.

Elevation
- 1250-2000M
- 2001-3000M
- 3001-4000M
- 4001-5000M
- >5000M

MEXICO

Sierra Madre Occidental

Guasimas Bay

Obregon

Yaqui Valley Irrigation District

Tóbari Bay

Gulf of California

N

50 km

PLATE 9 Yaqui Valley study region in Northwest Mexico. The satellite image is a three-band color composite from Landsat data. Agriculture and other regions of green vegetation show up as red. Water shows as black or blue and urban or barren land show as grey or white.

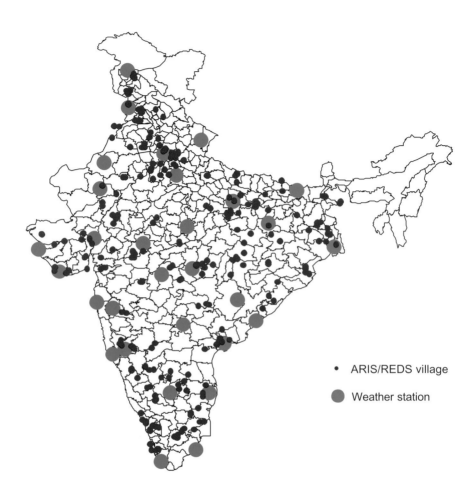

PLATE 10 Survey villages and weather stations used to impute rainfall.

REGIONAL DEMOGRAPHY

Another interesting study by Gober looks at the age profiles of a number of cities situated differently with respect to the advancing urban fringe (see Figure 7-10; Gober, in press). The cities of Tempe and Guadalupe are located in parts of the metropolitan area that have been built up for some time. Tempe's profile is skewed by the presence of college-age students but otherwise fits a normal urban structure. Guadalupe is a small Hispanic enclave that reflects a population with unusually high proportions of the very young and young adult males. Scottsdale has both old and fringe neighborhoods that attract a higher than normal proportion of mature inhabitants, given its high socioeconomic level. Gilbert and Sun City are located on the advancing urban fringe, but they attract very different populations. Young families looking for bigger houses at modest prices characterize Gilbert, whereas Sun City is known as a large development restricted to senior citizens. Further analysis is needed to examine characteristics of the various zones of the expanding city, especially studies of ethnicity and movement within the city. Although these settlement patterns reflect economic realities, we need to examine residential choice as it reflects the mental models people hold about the city and region they inhabit (see below for how we are working with changing mental models).

AGRARIAN LANDSCAPES IN TRANSITION

Given that central Arizona is among the most arid environments in North America and that highly successful farming communities initiated Phoenix's historic (and prehistoric) growth, the control of water is at the core of development and the continued operation of the urban ecosystem. Factors that govern water availability and patterns of use intersect the domains of climate, geography, population dynamics, economy, energy, aesthetics, and political power. Each factor has its own drivers and operates at various scales of space and time. Over the past 150 years, residents of central Arizona have chosen to reengineer 100 percent of the surface water flow through the Salt and Gila river valleys, extract groundwater, and import water from the Colorado River watershed via a 350-mile canal. Water allocation for farming, municipal and industrial consumption, riparian vegetation, residential landscaping, and groundwater replenishment grows increasingly contentious and is fundamental to the structure and population of the urban ecosystem.

Researchers from six Long-Term Ecological Research projects have collaborated to study the intersection of humans, climate, and water in the context of agrarian transformations, both current and historical, because of their ubiquity and the tight coupling of human and environmental dynamics

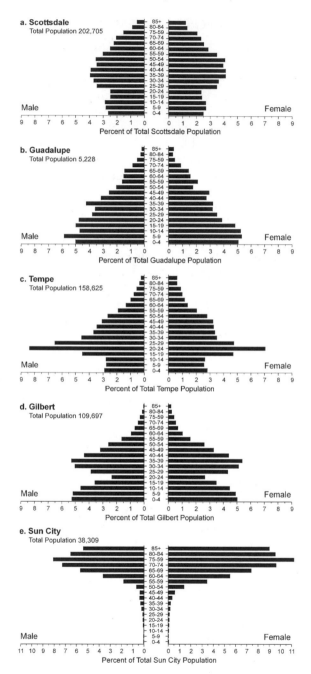

FIGURE 7-10   Age profiles of different cities in Maricopa County, Arizona (Gober, in press).

inherent in agrarian landscapes (Redman et al., 2002). Our central objective is to understand what happens when humans impose their spatial and temporal signatures on ecological regimes and then respond to the systems they helped create, further altering the dynamics of the coupled system and the potential for ecological and social resilience. The transitions of agrarian landscapes and life ways continue to take many forms, ranging from abandonment, to urban development, to more intensified agriculture. In the United States alone, 105 acres of agricultural land go out of production every hour; urban or suburban growth consumes about half that amount, and the remainder is used less intensely or actively conserved for its habitat values (U.S. Department of Agriculture Policy Advisory Committee, 2001). We conceptualize an integrated cycle of land use change affecting landscapes, altered landscapes affecting ecological processes, both influencing the ways in which humans monitor and respond to their surroundings, and those responses engendering further cycles of change.

Agrarian Landscapes in Transition or "Ag Trans," as it is called, uses quantitative and qualitative approaches to link human and environmental dynamics. Quantitative patterns of climate, land use, and population are being encoded as a series of levels in a geographic information system (GIS) analysis for each area by county or smaller unit based on U.S. and agricultural census information. Spatial patterns of change are being monitored from historical records and for the last 30 years from remotely sensed imagery. Although these quantitative approaches allow us to create graphs of changing demography and land use, they do not take advantage of rich historical information on the changing context of social, political, and economic changes that might be driving the observed patterns. As a result, Ag Trans is experimenting with a qualitative approach that focuses on the impact of specific events and their perception on social, demographic, and landscape transformations. To apply this approach to the socioecological history of the central Arizona–Phoenix region, we have delineated three historical periods representing major transformations in the relationship between the citizens of this region and their environment: emergent years, boom years, and Southwest metropolis years. Multiple factors drive agrarian landscape transformations, such as climate, population dynamics, economics, politics, technology, and perception. Rather than separating these factors, we seek to recognize and interpret the perception, impact, and response to the extant mental models held by elements of the population and the key triggering events (both crises and opportunities) during each period that may reinforce or change these models and the accompanying decision making.

These events derived from local, regional, and national scales and occurred at differing tempos, ranging from rapid, which may shock the system, to enduring, often pervasive influences. Depending on the mental models, regulatory institutions, and economic dynamics at the time, people responded to these events by transforming one or more domains of the local coupled system. Box 7-1 presents a series of triggering events as they drove changes during the three periods. We apply the term "events" broadly, encompassing both challenges to the system and opportunities for advance, as well as those that emanated from within or derived from outside the region. At this point in our analysis, we have focused on events and opportunities that are easily recognizable to us and probably also to many of the residents living during those times. We expect that there also were more

---

BOX 7-1   Triggering Events in the Interaction of Population, Agriculture, and Environment in Central Arizona

The Emergent Years (1867-1940)

• Recognition of a vacant productive environmental niche (irrigable lower Salt River Valley) for producing crops to supply local soldiers and miners led to reexcavation of prehistoric canals and establishment of successful agriculture.
• Catastrophic floods followed by severe drought (1890-1903) led to cooperative action and use of federal funds to build the first major reservoir.
• World War I sparked greater demand for copper and cotton, leading to a boom in population, agriculture (see Figure 7-11), and commercial activity.

The Boom Years (1941-1970)

• World War II generated military industry, air bases, and attendant infrastructure, familiarizing people with the region.
• In 1948, Motorola established an electronics facility in the valley, the first step in what was to reshape Phoenix's economic base, attracting an influx of people looking for good jobs, and transforming the region's rural character.
• Successful builders of large housing developments (e.g., John F. Long, Del E. Webb) provided abundant, low-cost housing that created the region's characteristic suburban sprawl.

Southwest Metropolis (1971-2003)

• National migration to the Sunbelt; people, industry, and commercial activity relocated to Phoenix.
• Groundwater Management Code, enacted in response to the threat of funding cut from the federal government, limited the expansion of farming, resulting in decreased agricultural acreage and the redirection of water from the agricultural to urban sector (Figure 7-11).
• Increased migration from Mexico and Central America altered the city's demographic character.
• The drought from 1999 to the present combined with concern over quality-of-life issues may be leading to a shift in attitude concerning population growth as the necessary engine for the region's economic viability.

subtle triggering events that reflected the slow buildup of ecological factors, such as soil salinization and groundwater depletion, or that reflected socio-demographic forces, such as shift in ethnic composition or the source of migrants to the region.

Figure 7-11 summarizes the above conceptual approach in a simplified model. The model clearly represents an iterative process, one that begins with the current state of knowledge and the impact of one or more triggering events that may emanate locally or be the result of external forces. Given the condition of the socioecosystem and current mental models, the perception and impact of the triggering event may change the mental models about appropriate decision making, leading to a change in management strategies, which may lead to a change in some aspect of the coupled human-natural system, which, in turn, may create new vulnerabilities to the system's sustainability. This transformation may, in turn, lead to a change in the initial condition of knowledge and mental models. This cycle plays out at multiple scales from the individual to international, and the system is often driven by impacts of events across scales (e.g., national policy impacting local decisions or local lobbying leading to national policy change). The import of formulating this type of model is to determine the processes

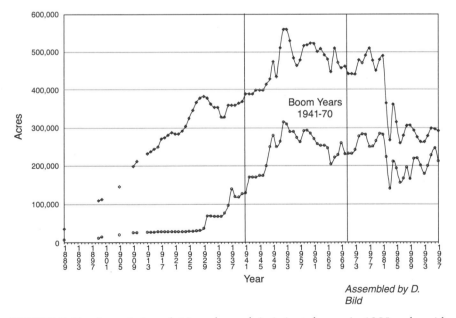

Assembled by D. Bild

FIGURE 7-11   Acres irrigated. Note the peak in irrigated acres in 1955 and rapid drop after passage of the Groundwater Management Act in 1980, which prohibited new irrigation pumping.

underlying past cycles and thus improve our ability to propose future scenarios and understand their implications.

NETWORKING URBAN ECOLOGICAL MODELS AND ENGAGING PUBLIC AGENCIES

Although we academics have conducted our own data collection and model building, working in an urban environmental context makes it clear that scientists working for federal, state, and local agencies have developed sophisticated models of subsystems of the urban phenomenon and collected data at a scale unobtainable with academic resources alone. We embarked on an ambitious project to bring together these two different domains of activity without sacrificing the autonomy of any party. Our early belief that the research of the Central Arizona–Phoenix Long-Term Ecological Research project scientists could and should be relevant to local public officials infuses this integrative effort. Although there have been instances of clear utility, there was an obvious gulf between our academically defined research agendas and the perceived needs of local public managers. Although recognizing this mismatch, we realized early on that we could not expect public officials to ignore legal restraints or public opinion, just as we hesitated to apply our academic research to immediate local needs. Instead, we embarked on a multiyear journey, initially called Greater Phoenix 2100, in which many of us have collaborated with public officials to find common approaches. In addition to learning more about the perspectives and needs of each party, we had to construct a bridging mechanism that was outside either entity and would function to inform and transform the mission-oriented work each of us did to something more useful to the other. The first tangible product of this collaboration was the Greater Phoenix 2100 Atlas, which defined 10 major challenges facing the metropolitan area.[1] We then sought extant data that could be expressed in maps and tables, which would illuminate these issues and their possible trajectories 50 years into the future. We found that most of the maps did not derive from our own academic research but were drawn from the work of eight public agencies. Yet we at the university were uniquely well suited to bring together this disparate information. Moreover, our role in assembling this resource allowed us to convey what we think are the three operating assumptions that would make data like these valuable. To effectively address the socio-environmental challenges that confront modern society, information gath-

---

[1]The 10 challenges are regional transportation; water: supply, use, and quality; air quality; pollen and allergies; changing demographics; Hispanic education; housing affordability; the high-tech new economy; open-space preservation; and the urban heat island.

ering, analysis, and decision making must take into account these principles. (1) Regions are often greater than their current political boundaries. (2) Time depth (both into the past and future) is longer than officials normally consider. (3) Virtually any issue of real concern is so complex that it requires information from a wide variety of sources. An on-line demonstration of this atlas connects users to a host of dynamic data resources at http://www.gp2100.org/eatlas.

Assembling information for the atlas, providing electronic links to agency and university data sources, and focusing academics and the community on shared issues and data needs are important first steps, but we also wanted to develop tools for more effective collaborations. With funding from the National Science Foundation, we are building and deploying a distributed-information infrastructure so that the diverse demographic and ecological researchers as well as the management and policy communities in central Arizona can benefit from integrated urban models. This innovative approach can be used to overcome the barriers to access and use of regional models, while retaining their complexity. The project draws from recent developments in the Internet industry that seek to integrate distributed services through peer-to-peer networks based on standard communication protocols. A modeling exercise that couples climate, water, and land use change models from the Arizona State University's Office of Climatology, the National Oceanic and Atmospheric Administration, the Arizona Department of Water Resources, and the Maricopa Association of Governments is evaluating the system's effectiveness (see Figure 7-12). Each agency maintains responsibility for operating and updating their model and databases, while an external platform draws on the current version and data of each model and feed results from one as input to the next. The net result is an integrated analysis that was not possible heretofore. Researchers, informatics specialists, and community members are enthusiastic about expanding this line of research and collaboration.

Close connections with agency personnel on this project as well as the Long-Term Ecological Research project laid the foundation for a new project that aims to develop decision-making tools. The Decision Center for a Desert City, begun September 2004, will focus on how to integrate science into policy and management decisions that have to confront the uncertainty created by climate variability as it relates to water supply in the central Arizona region. Officials from the top water providers, regulatory agencies, and municipalities have been engaged from the very beginning of this project, helping to craft the original proposal. Although related to all the other projects described in this chapter, this is the first instance in which the primary measure of success will be whether we have improved the way public policy decisions are being made.

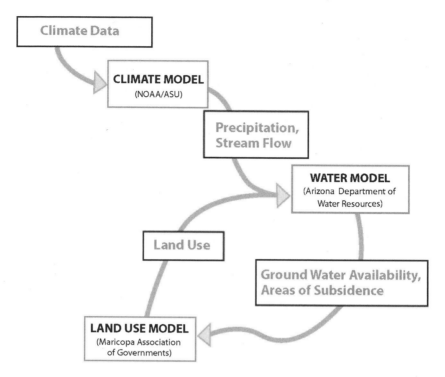

FIGURE 7-12   Chart illustrating networking to share models and data among three public agencies.

GOING FORWARD WITH ACADEMIC AND APPLIED OBJECTIVES

With insights gained from six years of urban ecological research and the foundation built with several interrelated projects, we are now ready to embark on a new phase of the endeavor. Until now we have (1) focused our investigations on an arid, urban ecosystem; (2) experimented with strategies that will be effective in this new study domain; and (3) found ways to work together across disciplines, especially in bridging the life and social sciences. In the initial years, we have had to emphasize background studies, baseline monitoring of a suite of variables, and experimentation that have led us to better define the processes that engage us. With these definitions in hand, we now can refine the substantive models and the patterns we observe and contribute to a more general understanding of urban ecosystems. At the same time, we hope to improve paradigms for the collaboration of ecology and social sciences.

We have proposed three conceptual themes that we think will cast our empirical research into an integrative context. It is our goal that these interpretive themes will link field projects to the overarching research question on the feedbacks among patterns of urbanization, population dynamics, ecological consequences, and human responses.

1. **Scales and periodicities of ecological and human phenomena.** Biological and physical processes occur at multiple scales intrinsic to the organism or to the geophysical context. Humans operate at varying scales as well, due to their physiology, social organization, economy, politics, and culture. The scales and periodicities of ecological and human phenomena sometimes match well and integrate easily, and sometimes they do not. These mismatches may introduce the risk of breakdown into the system or may, in fact, offer opportunities for growth or change.

2. **Human actions that control variability at various scales and periodicities at which ecological systems operate.** Humans act either to keep this variability within acceptable limits or to gain economic or political advantage from managing the variability. In what ways and to what extent does human control transform the socioecological system? For example, replacing dead plants, adding fertilizer, and irrigating all serve to buffer the plant community against climatic pressure, creating a socioecological system that would not survive without human intervention.

3. **Resilience of socioecological systems.** Cities (i.e., urban ecosystems) are complex, nonequilibrium, and adaptive systems. To what extent are human-dominated systems resilient? What are the threats to these systems, and what are their vulnerabilities? What qualities should we maintain, what aspects are we willing or anxious to eliminate? Can we build institutions that will protect urban socioecological systems from dramatic, undesirable changes and also promote qualities and functions deemed positive?

Even with the addition of the new conceptual themes, the Central Arizona–Phoenix Long-Term Ecological Research and other projects described here continue to use traditional ecological and spatial theories to interpret the data patterns we observe. It is possible to explain data patterns by traditional ecological theory, but some patterns do not fit well and require special consideration. Researchers have often accounted for these deviations from normal pattern expectations by attributing them to human influence. However, these situations—and those in which the deviations are greater—may be domains in which devising a new integrated human ecological theory would be fruitful.

Reviewing the results of our early environmental monitoring, three domains stand out as candidates for theoretical refinements:

1.   Uniquely human elements of perception, valuation, and goal orientation are major elements of decision making that influence virtually all

aspects of ecosystem stability and change. We are specifically exploring this subject in our Ag Trans investigations (see Figure 7-13).

2. Flows of nutrients, materials, and energy are often an order of magnitude greater in urban environments when compared with nonurban locales. In addition, there are new materials and new mechanisms for conveying flows in urban environments, both of which may act differently from their natural counterparts.

3. Fragmentation of the environment into patches seems to follow some ecological guidelines but also seems to run contrary to basic ecological principles, with unexpectedly high levels of fragmentation often marking human-dominated environments.

In our own fieldwork, we have found that the city of Phoenix, and we expect most others, have many more and smaller patches than the surrounding environment (Luck and Wu, 2002: Figure 3c). In the analysis of 200 plots across our study area, spatial autocorrelation explained plant genera diversity outside the city, but not within the built-up areas (Hope et. al., 2003). Applying linear gradient analysis to explain these differences, as is often done in ecological studies based on elevation differences or distance from the point of origin of a species, has limited utility in human-dominated cases. Rural-to-urban gradient analysis developed by urban ecologist Steward Pickett (Pickett et al., 1997) came closer to explaining the extant variability, but I would argue that a more complex, multicentered network model would be even more useful. An interesting additional observation is that, in the urbanized area we have studied, the expected species-

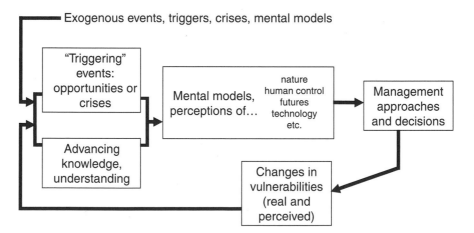

FIGURE 7-13 Conceptual model of Agrarian Landscapes in Transition project, whose ultimate goal is to understand past cycles of land use and human response in order to propose future scenarios.

area relationship of larger patches of the same type containing greater species diversity often did not hold. In many cases, small residential lots had high plant diversity and, although larger lots often had more diverse assemblages, sometimes they did not, and in many cases there seemed to be an artificial point at which diversity did not increase with size or wealth (see Figure 7-6).

Thinking about this subject more generally, human-dominated systems, land use changes and, in particular, habitat fragmentation, are conditioned by all of the traditionally cited biogeophysical forces that are thoroughly discussed in the ecological literature—*plus* a complex, and sometimes intense, set of human factors. Throughout their history, humans have modified their environment to suit their perceived needs (Redman, 1999b). It is often suggested that humans have acted to homogenize habitats, reducing the diversity of landscapes and even entire regions. This consequence is particularly true of contemporary agrarian landscapes in which extensive monocropped fields have replaced naturally occurring plant diversity. However, I would argue that, at least as often, humans have acted to create additional boundaries in their environments, resulting in smaller patches than would exist without their presence. Having partitioned their world, humans then create mechanisms to bridge or permeate these boundaries. I think the tendency to further fragment the natural landscape relates to a combination of four powerful drivers. Through habitat fragmentation, humans act to better understand their surroundings, reaffirm their identity, create economic value, and construct asymmetric power relations. How these human drivers lead to boundary formation is discussed in anthropological and other social scientific literature, but not usually in reference to habitat fragmentation. One benefit of interdisciplinary research teams is that they bring together researchers who look at the same phenomena from different perspectives. Moreover, urban ecosystems, because of the clearly dominant influence of people, institutions, and the built environment, offer an exciting laboratory for examining alternative perspectives and formulating possible refinements for both social and ecology theory.

ACKNOWLEDGMENTS

This paper results from the work and cooperation of many researchers who have defined and carried out the projects I have described. Realizing that the number is large, I will point out the leadership of each project, and one can see from the reference list the names of others to whom I am indebted. The Central Arizona–Phoenix Long-Term Ecological Research project (NSF/DEB-9714833) is codirected by Nancy Grimm, who has left her talented imprint on much of what we do and what I think. I codirect the Arizona State University component of the Biocomplexity in the Environment project, Agrarian Landscapes in Transition (NSF/DEB-0216560), with Ann Kinzig; communication with other partners, as well as help with this and other manuscripts, is overseen by Lauren Kuby, each of whom are key to making this complex program advance. The Networking Urban Ecological Models Through Distributed Services (NSF/EIA-0219310) is directed by Peter McCartney, who is able to perceptively understand barriers to collaboration and devise informatics approaches to bridge these barriers. The Decision Center for a Desert City (NSF/SES-0345945) is codirected by Patricia Gober, who has also been a key researcher in the Central Arizona–Phoenix Long-Term Ecological Research project, as seen in two of her creative projects described here.

REFERENCES

Anderson, J.R., E.E. Hardy, J.T. Roach, and R.E. Witmer
  1976   *A Land Use and Land Cover Classification System with Remote Sensor Data.* (USGS Professional Paper 964.) Washington, DC: U.S. Geological Survey.
Berling-Wolff, S., and J. Wu
  2004   Modeling urban landscape dynamics: A case study in Phoenix, USA. [Special Issue.] *Urban Ecosystems* 7:215-240.
Bolin, R., S. Smith, E. Hackett, A. Nelson, T. Collins, and K.D. Pijawka
  2002   Toxic Tracts: The Development of Environmental Inequality in Phoenix Arizona. Presentation at the 2002 meeting of the American Geographical Association in Los Angeles, CA.
Collins, J.P., A.P. Kinzig, N.B. Grimm, W.F. Fagan, D. Hope, J. Wu, and E.T. Borer
  2000   A new urban ecology. *American Scientist* 88:416-425.
Fagan, W.F., E. Meir, S.S. Carroll, and J. Wu
  2001   The ecology of urban landscapes: Modeling housing starts as a density-dependent colonization process. *Landscape Ecology* 16:33-39.
Fulton, W.R. Pendall, M. Nguyen, and A. Harrison
  2001   Who Sprawls Most? How Growth Patterns Differ Across the U.S. A Report to the Brookings Institution. Available: http://www.brook.edu/es/urban/fultonpendall.htm [accessed February 10, 2005].
Gammage, G., Jr.
  1999   *Phoenix in Perspective: Reflections on Developing the Desert.* (Herberger Center for Design Excellence.) Tempe: College of Agriculture and Environmental Design, Arizona State University.
Gober, P.
  in   *Greater Phoenix: Dynamics of Change in a Postmodern Metropolis.* Philadelphia,
  press PA: University of Pennsylvania Press.
Gober, P., and E.K. Burns
  2002   The size and shape of Phoenix's urban fringe. *Journal of Planning Education and Research* 21:379-390.
Grimm, N.B., and C.L. Redman
  2004   Approaches to the study of urban ecosystems: The case of central Arizona–Phoenix. *Urban Ecosystems* 7:199-213.
Grimm, N.B., J.M. Grove, S.T.A. Pickett, and C.L. Redman
  2000   Integrated approaches to long-term studies of urban ecological systems. *BioScience* 50:571-584.

Guhathakurta, S.
  2002   Urban modeling as storytelling: Using simulation models as a narrative. *Environment and Planning B* 29(6):895-911.
Hobbie, J.E., S.R. Carpenter, N.B. Grimm, J.R. Gosz, and T.R. Seastedt
  2003   The U.S. Long-Term Ecological Research Program. *BioScience* 53:21-32.
Hope, D., C. Gries, W. Zhu, W.F. Fagan, C.L. Redman, N.B. Grimm, A. Nelson, C. Martin, and A. Kinzig
  2003   Socio-economics drive urban plant diversity. *Proceedings of the National Academy of Sciences* 100:8788-8792.
Hope, D., W. Zhu, C. Gries, J. Oleson, J. Kaye, N.B. Grimm, and B. Baker
  no   Spatial variation in plant diversity and soil nitrate concentrations across an urban
  date   ecosystem. Unpublished paper, Arizona State University, Tempe.
Knowles-Yánez, K., C. Moritz, J. Fry, C.L. Redman, M. Bucchin, and P.H. McCartney
  1999   *Central Arizona–Phoenix Long-Term Ecological Research Contribution No. 1. Historic Land Use: Phase I Report on Generalized Land Use.* Tempe: Center for Environmental Studies, Arizona State University.
Kupel, D.E.
  2003   *Fuel for Growth: Water and Arizona's Urban Environment.* Tucson: University of Arizona Press.
Luck, M., and J.G. Wu
  2002   A gradient analysis of urban landscape pattern: A case study from the Phoenix metropolitan region, Arizona, USA. *Landscape Ecology* 17:327-339.
Netzband, M., and W.L. Stefanov
  2003   Assessment of urban spatial variation using ASTER data. *International Archives of the Photogrammetry, Remote Sensing, and Spatial Information Sciences* 34(7/W9):138-143.
Pickett, S.T.A., W.R. Burch, Jr., S.E. Dalton, T.W. Foresman, J.M. Grove, and R. Rowntree
  1997   A conceptual framework for the study of human ecosystems in urban areas. [Special Issue, Baltimore-Washington Integrated Regional Framework.] *Urban Ecosystems* 1(4):185-200.
Redman, C.L.
  1999a   Human dimensions of ecosystem studies. *Ecosystems* 2:269-298.
  1999b   *Human Impact on Ancient Environments.* Tucson: University of Arizona Press.
Redman, C.L., A. Kinzig, D. Foster, M. Gutmann, and P. Kareiva
  2002   Agrarian Landscapes in Transition: A Cross-Scale Approach. Biocomplexity: Coupled Human-Natural Systems Award, National Science Foundation, BCE-0216560. Available: http://www.ces.asu.edu/agtrans [accessed February 10, 2005].
Redman, C.L., J.M. Grove, and L.H. Kuby
  2004   Integrating social science into the long-term ecological research network: Social dimensions of ecological change and ecological dimensions of social change. *Ecosystems* 7:161-171.
Stefanov, W.L., M.S. Ramsey, and P.R. Christensen
  2001   Monitoring urban land cover change: An expert system approach to land cover classification of semiarid to arid urban centers. *Remote Sensing of Environment* 77:173-185.
U.S. Census Bureau
  2000   Census 2000 PHC-T-5. Ranking tables for incorporated cities. Available: www.census.gov/population [accessed April 22, 2005].
U.S. Department of Agriculture Policy Advisory Committee on Farm and Forest Land Protection and Land Use
  2001   *Maintaining Farm and Forest Lands in Rapidly Growing Areas.* Report to the Secretary of Agriculture. Washington, DC: U.S. Department of Agriculture.

Waddell, P.
  2000   A behavioral simulation model for metropolitan policy analysis and planning: Residential location and housing components of UrbanSim. *Environment and Planning B: Planning and Design* 27(2):247-263.

Wu, J., and J.L. David
  2002   A spatially explicit hierarchical approach to modeling complex ecological systems: Theory and applications. *Ecological Modeling* 153:7-26.

Zoldak, M.
  2003   Interpreting Complex Land Use Patterns Through Generalization: Applying Unsupervised Classification to Categorical Data. Unpublished paper. International Institute for Sustainability, Arizona State University, Tempe.

8

Economies, Societies, and Landscapes in Transition: Examples from the Pearl River Delta, China, and the Red River Delta, Vietnam

Karen C. Seto

This chapter describes work that links multiple data sources and research perspectives to advance understanding of the dynamics and human causes of land use change, particularly urban growth, in the Pearl River Delta of southern China and the Red River Delta of northern Vietnam. Thus far, the research effort has concentrated on three interrelated questions:

- How has land cover and land use changed over the last 20 to 30 years in both of these regions? What are the spatial dynamics of these changes and over what time scales do they occur?
- What are the major human causes of the observed land cover changes? How does the transition from a centrally planned to a market-oriented economy affect land use? What are the broader social, political, and economic factors at the macro level that influence local land use decisions?
- What are the environmental consequences of changes in the land system? How will land use change affect biophysical properties and biogeochemical cycles?

The chapter includes discussions of completed and ongoing research in the context of theoretical frameworks, methods used, and lessons learned, including a description of the two study regions; the history of the projects; the assembly and processing of remote sensing, spatial, field, and survey data; and conceptual and methodological challenges in implementing the research.

A TALE OF TWO DELTAS

In 1979, China embarked on an ambitious plan to reform its economy. These liberalization policies spurred remarkable rates of economic development and transformed the social, economic, and environmental landscape of the country. Less than one decade later, Vietnam followed suit and implemented nearly identical policies in 1986. The legacy of central planning in China and Vietnam has generated land use patterns that differ significantly from those in market economies (Scarpaci, 2000; Lin, 2002; Tammaru, 2002). Our projects focus on land dynamics in two coastal deltas that share similar geography, climate, ecology, political history, and policy changes.

Pearl River Delta, China

Over the last two decades, China has been experiencing an urban revolution that is likely to continue through the first half of the twenty-first century. Currently, one-quarter of the 500 largest urban areas in the world are in China, and the country's urban population is predicted to increase to nearly 900 million by 2030 (United Nations, 2002). In China, the Pearl River (*Zhujiang*) Delta in the southern province of Guangdong is one of the most economically vibrant regions; it is also where urban growth and land conversion are the most dramatic (Plate 6). The Pearl River Delta is an area of approximately 26,000 square kilometers (km^2). Crossed by the Tropic of Cancer, it has a long agricultural history with fertile alluvial soils that can support two to three crops per year.

From 1980 to 2000, the average real rate of increase in gross domestic product for the delta was greater than 16 percent, and the economy expanded more than eleven-fold (Statistical Bureau of Guangdong, 2002 [various years]). High rates of economic and urban growth in the region have their origins in 1979, when the central government promulgated decentralization policies and market reforms. The most significant of these reforms included (1) abolition of collective farming in favor of the "household responsibility system," which introduced subcontracting and allowed communes to divide their land among farmers; (2) agricultural price reforms that eliminated output quotas and permitted farmers to sell their product at market prices; (3) relaxation of *hukou*, China's stringent household registration system, which limited people's residential mobility; (4) diminished importance of *danwei*, the work unit that provides basic goods and social services, such as housing, health care, food ration tickets, and education; (5) establishment of special economic zones and policies to attract foreign direct investments; (6) decentralization of fiscal policy, which allowed the provincial and regional governments more autonomy to create their development priorities and issue loans; (7) transfer of state-owned enterprises from the central to the provincial government; (8) land tenure reform that allows transfers of land use rights; and (9) establishment of land markets that permits purchase of land through bid or auction (Table 8-1).

Before the reforms, migration from rural to urban areas was tightly controlled by the state. Together, the *hukou* and *danwei* limited geographic mobility and curbed urbanization. Social reforms and gains in agricultural efficiency have led to an increase in the number of "floating" or temporary workers. Since the reforms, migration has been a growing component of population growth in the delta and the province as a whole. In 1995, nearly 13 percent of all temporary migrants in China were located in Guangdong Province (Liang, 2001). In 1998, the official population estimate for the Pearl River Delta was 29 million (Statistical Bureau of Guangdong, 2002), up from 8 million in 1970 (Indian National Science Academy, Chinese Academy of Sciences, and U.S. National Academy of Sciences, 2001). Unofficial estimates of the floating population in the delta range from 10 million in 1997 (Shen, 2002) to 20 million in 2003.

Red River Delta, Vietnam

Similar economic, social, and political transitions are under way in Vietnam. In 1986, the Vietnamese government promulgated the *doi moi* (renovation) reforms to increase national productivity, stimulate foreign direct investment, and modernize the country's infrastructure. The most salient components the reforms were (1) abolition of collective farming; (2) agricultural price reforms; (3) establishment of industrial zones, export processing zones, and high-tech zones; (4) policies to attract foreign direct investment and official development assistance; (5) decentralization of fiscal policy; (6) promotion of small and medium enterprises; (7) land tenure reform; and (8) establishment of land markets (Table 8-1).

One of the major successes of the *doi moi* is that Vietnam shifted from being a rice importer in the 1980s to the world's third largest exporter of rice in the late 1990s, and since 1986, the gross domestic product has grown on average 7 percent per year (General Statistical Office, 2001, 2003 [various years]). The reforms have also led to an increase in rural-urban migration, agricultural expansion and intensification, a focus on export cash crops, urban expansion, and coastal land conversion. Although the size of the urban population is still relatively small at 19 million in 2000 (24 percent of total population), it is expected that the country will urbanize rapidly over the next three decades, with estimates of the urban population reaching 45 million, or 41 percent of total population, by 2030 (United Nations, 2002).

Our study area in Vietnam is the Red River (*Song Hong*) Delta, located

TABLE 8-1   Policy Reforms in China and Vietnam

China		Vietnam	
Sector	Policy	Sector	Policy
Agriculture	Eliminated collective farming, agricultural price reforms	Agriculture	Eliminated collective farming, agricultural price reforms
Land use	Established private land use rights and land markets	Land use	Established private land use rights and land markets
Decentralization	Gave lower level governments more autonomy from central government	Decentralization	Gave lower level governments more autonomy from central government
Foreign investments	Provided incentives to foreign entities	Official development assistance	Provided incentives to foreign entities
Special economic zones	Encouraged foreign investments and export economies	Export, industrial, and high-tech zones	Encouraged foreign investments and export economies
Town and village enterprises	Evolved agriculture collectives into industrial units	Small and medium enterprises	Promoted small-scale industries
Population mobility	Relaxed the household registration system and reduced importance of the work unit		

in the northeast (Plate 7) with a population of 17 million in 2000, 80 percent of whom live in farming communities (General Statistical Office, 2001). Shaped like an inverted triangle covering 16,000 km², the Red River Delta is often called the "cradle of the Vietnamese civilization." It is one of the country's two major agricultural regions, and produces nearly 40 percent of the country's total output of rice (General Statistical Office, 2003). Yet despite its agrarian landscape, the Red River Delta is a region responding to multiple stressors and undergoing numerous socioeconomic and environmental transitions. With the end of the U.S. trade embargo in 1994, normalization of relations with the United States in 1995, and an increase in foreign trade, the central government has focused on a multifaceted export economy: one track gears Vietnam to be the largest rice exporter in the world, another track directs the country toward high-value, export-oriented commodities, such as farmed shrimp. In less than a decade, large coastal sections of the Red River Delta have been converted to shrimp aquaculture ponds, transforming wetlands and societies.

Given the agricultural and economic importance of the Red River and Pearl River deltas, the social and political dynamics of transition economies, and the potential for each region to be held up as success cases and duplicated throughout their respective countries, the two deltas were chosen as our study sites to evaluate human–environment interactions. Both deltas are particularly rich areas in which to monitor and measure land use dynamics, understand the factors that drive land use change, and evaluate the social and ecological impacts of these changes. The strength of this comparative framework lies in similar prereform conditions and policy reforms in both countries, as well as the ability to identify common interrelationships among population, land use, and environment across geographic settings. Clearly, there are differences between the two regions, but the shared similarities allow for isolation of distinguishing features and policies related to land use, as well as to identify higher level generalities beyond an individual case study. Although there exist numerous studies of land use dynamics, to date there are few comparative studies across regions and countries. The comparative studies that do exist tend to be either intracountry (Schweik, Adhikari, and Pandit, 1997; Liu et al., 2003) or conducted with different teams of researchers in disparate political, cultural, and geographic settings (Indian National Science Academy, Chinese Academy of Sciences, and U.S. National Academy of Sciences, 2001).

CONCEPTS, DATA, AND METHODS

Our project has two overarching questions: What are the land use impacts of rapid economic growth that occurs after the restructuring of an economy? How generalizable are these dynamics across similar—yet different—contexts?

Conceptualizing Population, Land Use, and Environment

Our conceptualization of the relationship among population, land use, and environment builds on the perspective that social, cultural, and institutional factors play mediating roles (Turner and Meyer, 1991; National Research Council, 1992). Population growth and changes in lifestyle, consumption, institutions, and industrialization all contribute to land use change in China and Vietnam, although each factor's relative impact is unclear (Heilig, 1997). It has been argued that institutions, such as the state play a larger role in land use change than other factors in China (Song and Timberlake, 1996). While the government can direct the spatial structuring of foreign and domestic capital investments, thereby affecting the pattern of land use (Sit and Yang, 1997), we hypothesize that land use change is primarily driven by foreign interests in the form of investments and development assistance aid. In both countries, the combination of regional differences in economic opportunities between coastal and interior provinces and reforms have contributed to large intracountry migration and a significant floating labor population (Liang, 2001). Population migration is not the underlying cause of land use change, but rather is the effect of economic opportunities made available by investments by foreign firms and governments. As such, the interrelationship among population, land use, and environment is conceptualized as a "two-by-two" framework that operates in two scales and in two phases.

In the first phase, land use change is driven by investments by foreign interests (e.g., foreign direct investment, official development assistance). These investments usually concentrate on construction, transportation, and export industries. Investments for roads and construction are financially substantial, and they also drive large-scale and wholesale land use change, which occurs in short time periods. For example, a new residential development zone can be constructed in one year and pave over all farmland in a village. In the second phase, land use change is driven by domestic forces: population migration, regional differences in economic opportunities, property rights, and political factors. These land use changes occur over longer time intervals and are smaller in scale. For example, coastal mangrove conversion in Vietnam has occurred over a 10-year period and is undertaken largely by households. Hence, we hypothesize that land use change largely depends on political institutions and their effectiveness in attracting local versus foreign investments, as well as the manner in which these industries drive population movements.

Prior research suggests that locally based firms result in different scales and patterns of urban land use change than foreign investment (Sit and Yang, 1997). Concentrated manufacturing feeding on large local labor forces, for example, may lead to a more *desakota*-style expansion, one that involves an intense mixture of agriculture, cottage industry, residential development, and industrial zones (McGee, 1991). Regardless of ownership, the scale and kind of industries (capital-intensive versus labor-intensive) will lead to different types of land conversion. Similarly, investments based on local labor supplies will produce very different patterns of urban land use change than development that draws much of its labor through in-migration. Furthermore, urban development can spur additional in-migration and attract higher levels of investment.

Scale of Analysis

One motivation for our research is to develop an understanding of how policy levers can be used to affect land use outcomes. As with most countries, decision making regarding land use in the Pearl River Delta and the Red River Delta occurs at multiple scales. Before the reforms, land use decision making in China was done at the central state level, with local governments facilitating individual transactions. Central control over land management and urban planning ended with the Land Administrative Law in 1986, which gave ownership of rural land to the collective organization of farmers and the amendment of the constitution in 1988, which allowed transfers of land use rights. The Land Administration Law permitted a hierarchical approval system of land use transformation, in which lower administrative levels, such as rural townships and counties, were allowed to transfer smaller parcels of land than higher levels of administration such as the central state or provinces. With multiple levels of government, all part of "the State," the Land Administrative Law encouraged a mélange of individual municipal-level development plans, uncoordinated land transfers, and rapid land use change. This allowed cities and counties to develop their own policies and incentives to encourage investment and development.[1] Political and economic independence to sanction urban development at lower administrative levels ceased when the Land Administrative Law was amended in 1999 and local governments were no longer allowed to make decisions on land use change (Cartier, 2001). Recognizing that land use planning occurs at various administrative levels, our choice in selecting the county as the unit of analysis is predicated in part by the availability of rich and consistent socioeconomic data at this level.

In the Red River Delta, our analysis is conducted at two scales, the province and the household. There are several reasons for multiscale analysis. One reason is that we evaluate two types of land dynamics: the conversion of agricultural land to urban uses and the conversion of mangroves and rice paddy farms to aquaculture. The decision-making process behind urban land conversion is similar to that in the Pearl River Delta, where multiple administrative levels, but not farmers, are involved with regional and urban planning. Therefore, in order to facilitate cross-study comparisons, in the Red River Delta we chose the province, a spatial and decision-

---

[1]Cities in China are stratified into a hierarchy of five tiers: (1) central level, directly administered by the central government (e.g., Beijing); (2) provincial level, large cities whose administrative status is lower than a provincial government but are not administered by the province (e.g., most provincial capitals such as Guanghzou); (3) prefecture level, an administrative division between the province and the county; (4) county level, cities with a relatively large agricultural sector; and (5) townships, urban centers in rural areas.

making unit that is comparable to the county in the Pearl River Delta. In terms of coastal land use change and aquaculture development, decision making also occurs at multiple administrative units. For example, farmers who want to convert rice fields to other uses must first receive approvals from commune officials, who submit an application to the provincial government to seek permission to take farmland out of agricultural production for aquaculture. However, once this application is approved, the decision to switch to aquaculture is a household choice and the decision maker is the farmer. Consequently for questions relating to urban expansion, we analyze the data at the provincial level. For questions relating to aquaculture development, our unit of analysis is the household.

Landscapes in Transition

Urban growth in the Pearl River Delta has been and continues to be a highly dynamic process. Although Rome was not built in a day, cities in the Pearl River Delta are—or nearly. New cities, industrial zones, and high-tech centers spring up across the countryside in a matter of months. Entire farming villages and vast tracts of agricultural land become the drawing board for master-planned communities and shopping malls. Due to the high degree of land conversion in the region, it was important to obtain a high-frequency time series of satellite data to capture land system dynamics. Most land use change studies evaluate satellite data at three or four points in time, but this would not capture the rapidly changing land processes in the Pearl River Delta. With this in mind, we developed a Landsat Thematic Mapper (TM) data set of 19 images of the Pearl River Delta, representing the period 1973-2001. We subdivided the data set into two periods, pre- and postreform, and analyzed each set separately. During the first phase of the project, we analyzed 9 TM images acquired annually over the period 1988-1996. Collecting these data took much longer than expected due to unforeseen obstacles in obtaining an accurate inventory of cloud-free images.

After acquisition of the imagery, our next challenge was to develop methods to radiometrically calibrate the data and evaluate land use change. What began as a simple question about the most appropriate method of calibration given our long time series evolved into a lengthy, but invaluable, comparison of techniques that provide guidance on appropriate atmospheric correction for change detection studies (Song et al., 2001).

With some exceptions, most existing change detection methodologies have been developed for two images. The aim of many of these methods is to accurately identify land cover change, not necessarily to develop a land change data set with desirable statistical characteristics (e.g., unbiased). Yet in order to couple remote sensing data with population and economic data for statistical modeling, the remote sensing estimates must be both accurate and unbiased. Using econometric techniques, we developed a methodology that generates such a data set (Kaufmann and Seto, 2001). The value of new methodologies based on time-series techniques will increase as the Landsat database continues to expand and as opportunities arise to compare more images through time. We also explored the utility of classification and change detection methods based on logit models and artificial neural networks to identify urbanization (Kaufmann and Seto, 2001; Seto and Liu, 2003; Seto and Kaufmann, 2005).

Several of the approaches undertaken by other studies in this volume have similar goals of identifying the life cycle or land use path of a pixel or an area beyond two or three points in time. The method employed by Central Arizona–Phoenix Long-Term Ecological Research study, to develop trajectories for neighborhoods using satellite and historical data (Chapter 7), and the approach taken by the Nang Rong study, to follow a classified pixel through a series of images (Chapter 6), are both attempts to resolve the issue of capturing the land dynamics of a region and could be applied to our case studies. Other new and promising image-processing methods for evaluating land use change include subpixel classification approaches (Haertel, Shimabukuro, and Almeida, 2004; Yang et al., 2003), the incorporation of very high resolution data from sensors such as IKONOS and Quickbird (Goward et al., 2003; Hurtt et al., 2003), spatiotemporal modeling using geostatistics (Boucher, Seto, and Journel, no date; Melgani and Serpico, 2003), and data fusion techniques (Le Hegarat-Mascle and Seltz, 2004).

Our remote sensing analyses in the Pearl River Delta showed that urban expansion in the postreform period occurred largely at the expense of productive farmland (Seto et al., 2002), and that the rate of this land conversion is much higher than officially reported (Seto, Kaufmann, and Woodcock, 2000) (Figure 8-1). Urban areas increased by more than 300 percent during the 1988-1996 period, from 720 to 2,625 km^2. Although this is not completely surprising given the rate of economic development, the rates of land transformation are nonetheless impressive. The widespread conversion of agricultural land to urban areas in China is not limited to the Pearl River Delta. Similar patterns of land use change have been documented throughout the country, including the Yangtze Delta (Liu et al., 2003), Beijing (Qi et al., 2004), and greater Chengdu (Schneider, Seto, and Webster, in press). In recent years, many Chinese institutions have used multitemporal Landsat data to complete country-scale studies on the status of agricultural land and urban growth (Liu et al., 2003; Young and Wang, 2001). Our work contributes directly to this body of knowledge by comparing the official rates of agricultural land loss to satellite estimates and linking policy with land use change.

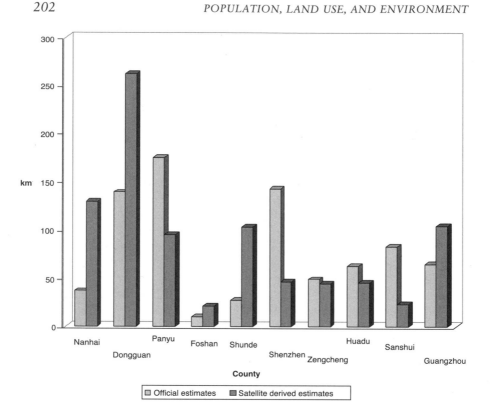

FIGURE 8-1   Agricultural land loss for selected Pearl River Delta counties, 1990-1996.
SOURCE: Seto, Kaufmann, and Woodcock (2000).

One notable unexpected finding is the extent to which waters in the delta are being reclaimed for agriculture to offset the loss of farmland elsewhere in the region. The reclamation of coastal waters and wetlands for agriculture has been a common practice in China for decades. However, the scale of the current reclamation projects was unexpected. We are currently working on evaluating the effects of urban growth patterns on local climate and conducting comparable studies in western China (Schneider et al., 2003, in press).

For our study in the Red River Delta, the remote sensing data and processing methods have proven to be more complex than for the Pearl River Delta. The Pearl River Delta as defined by our study lies completely within one Landsat scene (WRS 122-44). However, the Red River Delta spans a mosaic of 4 scenes (WRS 126-45, 126-46, 127-45, 127-46). Despite our best efforts to develop a cross-path calibration technique that allows the four scenes to be processed simultaneously, we were unable to achieve satisfactory results. We have had to analyze each scene individually—an inefficient method and not practical for regional-scale studies. Because the land transitions in the Red River Delta are not dominated by urbanization and involve other changes (e.g., coastal aquaculture development), we have looked at different remote sensing techniques for different landscapes. For example, the dramatic changes on the coast (Seto et al., no date) are best identified with algorithms different from those used to map urbanization around Hanoi (Seto and Nguyen, 2002; Duong et al., 2003).

We found that aquaculture is expanding rapidly throughout the delta, with an increase of more than 30 km^2 over 15 years. Shrimp aquaculture was introduced to the Red River Delta in the early 1980s. After the introduction of *doi moi*, nearly all the mature mangroves—approximately 20 km^2—were cleared for shrimp production (personal communication, Xuan Thuy Ramsar Office; Seto et al., no date). The Red River Delta is home to the last significant remnant of mangrove and mudflat habitat on the Vietnam coast and the only wetland in the country on the Ramsar List of Wetlands of International Importance.

Other land system changes under way in the Red River Delta are more difficult to assess with remote sensing. Concurrent with urban and aquaculture expansion is the intensification of farming methods. To meet the goal of making Vietnam the world's number one rice exporter, the central government is making widely available agricultural price supports, microfinancing and farm credit, and input subsidies. The net result is an increase in yields (Figure 8-2) but also increasing fertilizer and pesticide applications. Other farming practices also have changed. Crop types are more for market and export than for family and local consumption, crop rotation cycles have shortened, and water management—especially midseason drainage—is a common practice to increase yields. The spread of fish, shrimp, and crab aquaculture has replaced the wet-season rice–dry-season fish system. One effect of dry-season irrigation pumping for aquaculture ponds is that saltwater intrusion is increasingly a problem.

Economies and Societies in Transition, Drivers of Land Use Change

We combined the remote sensing estimates of land use change with county-level demographic and economic data obtained from the Guangdong Statistical Yearbooks to develop land use models of the region. Examples of socioeconomic variables include agricultural population; urban population; the number of town or village enterprises; output of grain; gross output value of agriculture; gross output value of industry; output in primary sector, which comprises mainly agriculture (farming, forestry, animal husbandry, and aquaculture); output in the secondary sector, which is mainly industry; and output in tertiary sector, which includes all industries not

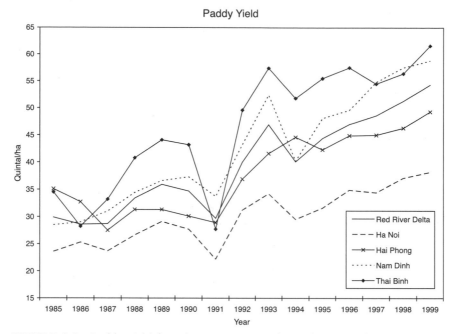

FIGURE 8-2   Paddy yield for select provinces in the Red River Delta, Vietnam.

included in the agriculture or industrial sectors. Field interviews with farmers and target meetings with city planners and key decision makers provided a historical narrative and filled information gaps about the urban
land conversion process.

The temporal sample used for the model spanned nine years, and land
use change estimates spanned eight years. Both sample sizes are too small
to allow models to be developed for individual counties in a statistically
meaningful manner. Instead, the land use change and socioeconomic data
were pooled to form a set of panel data that includes 8 years of observations for 12 counties. One reason for pooling the data in this manner is that
panel econometric techniques allow account and control for heterogeneity
across samples and the ability to develop more complex models; the increase in data points results in more degrees of freedom and hence reduces
multicollinearity, provides gains in statistical efficiency, and reduces problems with omitted variable bias.

We used fixed and random coefficient models to estimate the rates of
land use change from natural ecosystems to urban and from farmland to
urban in the Pearl River Delta. The results indicate that the annual rate at
which agricultural land is converted to urban uses is correlated with invest-

ment in capital construction, the productivity of land productivity in agriculture versus urban uses, agricultural labor productivity, and off-farm wage rates (Table 8-2). As expected, the sign on the coefficient associated with investment in capital construction is positive. This is consistent with observations that much of the capital construction in the Pearl River Delta is directed at residential and industrial complexes and new roads. The sign on the coefficient associated with returns to agricultural land relative to industrial uses is also positive. The conversion of agricultural land is negatively related to agricultural labor productivity. This variable is an indicator of agricultural wages. As on-farm income increases, the opportunity cost of converting farmland increases, and farmers are less inclined to convert agricultural land to nonfarm uses. Finally, average off-farm wages have a positive effect on agricultural land conversion.

The annual rate at which forests, shrubs, and water bodies are converted to urban uses is correlated with investment in capital construction, the return to agricultural land relative to industrial uses, and labor productivity in agriculture relative to industry (Table 8-2). Again, investment in capital construction tends to accelerate the rate at which natural ecosystems are converted to urban uses. Despite the similar signs, the interpretation of the relative land productivity variable is different from the *agriculture→ urban* model. For this model, we interpret relative land productivity as a proxy for the opportunity cost of land conversions. For counties in which

TABLE 8-2   Results from Analysis of Land Use Change in the Pearl River Delta

Variable	Agriculture→ Urban	Natural→ Urban
Constant	−0.109 (−4.95)	0.028 (3.13)
Value of gross agricultural output/Agricultural land / Value of gross industrial output/Urban land	1.496 (1.97)	6.53 (3.55)
Value of gross agricultural output/Agricultural population / Value of gross industrial output/Nonagricultural land		−1.39 (−3.37)
Value of gross agricultural output / Agricultural population	−3.965 (−4.58)	
Completed investments in capital construction / Population	1.24 (2.74)	2.85 (3.27)
Low (Average total wage)	0.032 (5.98)	

the productivity of agricultural land is high relative to urban uses, the opportunity cost associated with converting agricultural land is high relative to converting forest and water. This higher opportunity cost tends to favor the conversion of natural ecosystems and, hence, a positive relationship with natural land conversion. Relative labor productivity is defined as the ratio of agricultural labor productivity to industrial labor productivity. If agricultural labor productivity is high relative to industrial labor productivity, there is little incentive to convert natural ecosystems to industrial uses. Rather, higher relative agricultural labor productivity suggests that agricultural land produces greater returns than industrial land. Therefore, there is less incentive to urbanize natural areas. On the contrary, there may be more pressure to convert natural areas to agricultural land to take advantage of the relative high labor productivity.

Our models showed that international investments are one of the primary drivers of urbanization in the Pearl River Delta (Seto and Kaufmann, 2003). Investments from abroad generally fuel large-scale projects, whereas domestic investment sources generally fund small or medium-scale projects. Large projects employ numerous local workers, whose incomes rise as a result. As disposable incomes rise, workers may improve their housing conditions by constructing new homes or refurbishing their existing homes. In many towns, higher incomes increase local demand for shopping arcades, cars, and luxury restaurants. This rise may further provide incentives to build residential and commercial complexes, which are funded by overseas investors. The results suggest that the causes of land use change have multiple feedbacks that include income growth, consumer demand, and population migration. Higher incomes have fuelled a shift from agricultural to nonagricultural livelihoods. Similarly, township and village governments have been agents of urbanization in their levels of jurisdiction by facilitating development of town village enterprises in the region and by endorsing local efforts to cluster privately owned firms through the development of industrial estates and technology corridors. Our results also indicate that local land users do not have much influence over large-scale projects.

Another reason for the conversion of agricultural land to nonagricultural uses is the difference in farm wages versus fees from leases. When farmers can make more money from renting out or leasing their land, there is very little incentive to keep land under cultivation. Poor economic returns to agricultural land could be in part due to the household responsibility system which divided land into plots based on family size and land quality. A single family could have multiple disconnected plots due to differences in land quality and the number of households in a commune. In other words, many households held small parcels of land rather than contiguous property. This fragmentation discourages economies of scale and prevents some farmers from cultivating cash crops, a practice that requires a larger continuous tract of cropland.

Farmers also have little incentive to make long-term investments or improvements on their land. One of the problems with the household responsibility system is that it does not give farmers land tenure. Farm households have usufruct rights for 30 years and can lease and rent their land, but ownership of the land ultimately belongs to the state. Village leaders and local authorities may occasionally make readjustments to the location and number of parcels each family farms. This has the effect of further reducing incentives for farmers to invest in their land and increasing incentives to seek off-farm work. Officially, land can be acquisitioned by government officials for infrastructure development, such as highways, and farmers should receive compensation for lost farmland. Unofficially, however, local leaders have acquisitioned land from farmers and resold them at higher prices, usually to developers, and farmers have not received compensation.

Our preliminary analysis in Vietnam suggests that urban growth is driven primarily by rural to urban migration and the expansion of existing urban centers rather than by new town development (as was the case in the Pearl River Delta). Large-scale development projects are funded mainly by official development assistance and are limited to the periphery of Hanoi and Haiphong. There is little large-scale conversion of agricultural land outside these two cities. However, periurbanization is accelerating, driven in part by village cottage industries in handicrafts. With official development assistance, the central government is currently developing a modern transportation network that links the three major nodes of the delta (Hanoi, Haiphong, and Nam Dinh). Official development assistance differs from foreign direct investment in that the latter is money invested by a foreign enterprise, whereas official development assistance is essentially foreign aid from official agencies or countries in the form of loans, grants, or technical support. It is expected that the highways will facilitate further urban land conversion.

We conducted structured and semistructured interviews with 56 households distributed across 3 coastal districts to obtain information on household characteristics and aquaculture farm management practices. All but one household responded to the survey. In addition, we conducted interviews with regional planners in Hai Phong and Hanoi and government officials at multiple administrative levels. A majority of farmers began with no experience in shrimp farming. The availability of farm credit and low rice yields were the primary factors that led farmers to try it. Two dominant types of aquaculture farms are prevalent: those constructed in former rice paddies and those constructed in mangrove ecosystems at the mouth of the Red River. The standard of living for some aquaculture farmers has increased in the short run, but this depends on when operations began.

Recent and recurring disease outbreaks, trade barriers, and increased competition by Thai and Chinese shrimp producers have negatively impacted the productivity and profitability of shrimp farming.

Biophysical Impacts of Land Use Change

Urban growth in the Pearl River Delta has affected two key components of the terrestrial carbon cycle, net primary production and the carbon stock. Land use change, and in particular the loss of cropland, caused significant modifications to the regional carbon budget by reducing the annual net primary production and the size of the terrestrial carbon reservoir (Dye, Hinchliffe, and Woodcock, 2000). Analysis of net primary production indicates that terrestrial changes during the study period reduced the amount of annual atmospheric carbon assimilated into phytomass by approximately 1.55 million tons (7.5 percent). More than half of this reduction is due to the conversion of agricultural land. The 7.5 percent decline in annual net primary production is a measure of the reduction in total photosynthetic capacity and carbon sequestration potential of terrestrial ecosystems. The average estimate of annual carbon released due to land use and land cover change is 1.3 × 106 tons Carbon, with a total of 11.7 × 106 tons Carbon for the entire study period. While this is not an insignificant amount, it only represents 8 percent of the emissions from fossil fuels for 1996. Given the region's land use and development trajectory, it is likely that carbon sources from land use change will continue to be overshadowed by fossil fuel emissions.

Coastal changes in the Red River Delta are likely to affect biogeochemical cycling through increased methane flux from the aquaculture ponds. We combined in situ field measurements, pond management data, and remote sensing and found that all ponds were a source of methane flux, with considerably higher fluxes from the mangrove ponds than the paddy ponds (Seto et al., no date). Our results also indicate that fluxes are positively correlated with the frequency with which the ponds were cleaned as well as the age of the pond.

LESSONS LEARNED AND CHALLENGES AHEAD

We have encountered and learned from a number of challenges through incorporating multiple types of data and disciplinary foci. Specifically, we have come across issues related to integrating conceptual frameworks, data sources and limitations, and methodological challenges. In this section, we discuss each of these issues and our approach to resolving them.

Integrating Conceptual Frameworks

A recurring challenge with most interdisciplinary land use studies is how to integrate different approaches and conceptual frameworks. A related issue is how to identify the appropriate scale of analysis. In our case studies, it has been conceptually—and methodologically—difficult to develop a framework that incorporates bidirectional feedbacks between and among processes. For example, the population–land use relationships in the Pearl River and the Red River deltas operate at multiple scales and are mediated by institutions that also operate at multiple scales, often outside the domestic context. In addition, causality is difficult to assess. Does economic development drive urban growth? A compelling case can be made that urban agglomeration leads to further economic development. What is the role of foreign direct investment? Industrial estates in the Pearl River Delta often recruit workers from other provinces, thereby increasing the number of floating workers. In the Red River Delta, urban development is driven not so much by large-scale foreign direct investment as by official development assistance. Because official development assistance focuses on an economic development project (e.g., road construction) and not an export or manufacturing industry, it usually does not attract temporary workers to a region in the same manner as foreign direct investment. Nonetheless, official development assistance has a role in reshaping the landscape and migration. Developing hypotheses about the relationship among population, foreign assistance, and land use dynamics that can be tested in several contexts is a continuing challenge.

Another challenge is how to identify the decision makers or the agents who make decisions about a parcel of land. It is often assumed that command-and-control economies are characterized by top-down decrees, especially in the urban planning context. However, in reality, urban dynamics have become more the result of a mélange of uncoordinated interests (sometimes at the commune, town, or county level) than the synchronized activities of central government agencies. One challenge of working in these urban environments and, in particular, in transition economies is that land use decision making does not fall under the jurisdiction of the household. The state owns all land and there are multiple and sometimes competing—as in the case of the Pearl River Delta—land use and planning interests. Decisions made by households on how to use the land may be overturned by the state. In the Red River Delta, coastal changes are the exception, in which one of the agents is the household or the commune. Most of the conceptual frameworks developed by the land cover and land use change community pertain to "frontier" environments that are not applicable in urban settings, because the farmers are not the actors converting the land.

We have some understanding of the factors that affect urban land growth, but we need to get a better grasp of institutional processes and the role of social networks in foreign investment and migrant population movements. The actors in this case often are transnational corporations and multinational players, for which there are limited data. We understand the process at one scale, but we have a limited understanding of the larger scale processes, for example, the motivation of firms to locate in these areas. We also have very little insight into the interaction between socioeconomic processes and the pattern of land conversion. In our studies, we have been concerned primarily with the scale and rate of land conversion, and not the spatial patterns of land use change over time. We are now exploring the utility of spatial pattern analysis derived from ecology to understand the temporal and spatial patterns of land use change (Seto and Fragkias, no date), but the challenge will be understand the causal order between the patterns and the processes.

Data Sources and Limitations

Foreign direct investment will play an increasingly larger role in driving urban development in China and throughout Asia. While in frontier environments it is often the farmer or household that converts forests to pasture or agriculture, in urban environments, international capital movements play a significant role. We need better—and spatially explicit—data on domestic and foreign investments to understand patterns and trajectories of economies of agglomeration.

Urban growth in the Pearl River Delta currently occurs at a breathtaking pace, and high temporal resolution satellite and economic data are necessary to capture the temporal and spatial dynamics of change. We have annual satellite and economic data for the Pearl River Delta, but we found that during 1992-1993, the built-up area increased by nearly 700 km^2, roughly 10 times the size of Manhattan. Interannual images would have been useful to track the spatiotemporal patterns and track them with political events, such as Premier Deng Xiao Peng's visit to the region in 1992 and his affirmation that China would continue its open-door policies.

Other authors in this collection (Matson et al., Chapter 10) point to the difficulty of getting social data at appropriate scales. This has been true in our case; the social data have been more difficult to obtain than the biophysical data. Having been command-and-control economies for many decades, the Chinese and Vietnamese governments have much data on household characteristics. However, only county (China) or provincial (Vietnam) data are widely available. Limited town-level data are available in China, but they are only basic demographic indicators, like population. The 2000 census in China offers more spatially explicit data on migration flows, but the definition of migrant has changed from the 1990 census, limiting across-time comparisons.

As highlighted in the Nang Rong study (Chapter 6), long distance collaboration has its challenges. In our case, the project would not have succeeded without the assistance of Li Xiaowen and Huang Xiuhua at the Institute for Remote Sensing Applications in Beijing and Lu Jinfa the Beijing Institute of Geographical Sciences and Natural Resources Research, all of whom were invaluable for acquiring images, obtaining permission from multiple administrative units to conduct interviews, and organizing field-work. For our Chinese collaborators, traveling to the Pearl River Delta from Beijing involved not only traveling 2,000 km, but also other challenges, such as a change in language, as the local dialect in southern China is Cantonese but the national language is Mandarin, and obtaining authorization to enter special economic zones, which requires a special permit.

Methodological Challenges

Land use change tends to be conceptualized in terms of wholesale transformation of the land from one use to another (e.g., agriculture to urban or forest to agriculture). Magnitudinal changes are much more difficult to identify with remote sensing, but intensification of land use in urban environments may be as important as land cover change (e.g., low density urban to dense urban). We have begun to evaluate image processing techniques that can identify changes in the built-up environment (e.g., neural networks), but more work is needed in this area.

We also need better techniques to identify both spatial and temporal patterns of land use change, particularly in urban environments and at the urban-rural interface. Current methodologies assess change using only several satellite images, usually three points in time or fewer. Postclassification change detection remains the most common method to process longer time series, but this method is time-consuming for large data sets and has severe limitations in terms of accuracy. We need to better utilize methods from time-series analysis and apply them to high-resolution image processing. Similarly, more research is required on cross-path calibration. Our single-scene processing of the Red River Delta mosaic is inefficient and costly.

In terms of integrating remote sensing and socioeconomic data, not many remote sensing studies deal with the issue of bias. We carried out accuracy assessments to estimate the accuracy of our maps, but with time-series studies, we also need an estimate of temporal bias. For example, in linking the time series of satellite images with the time series of social data, we attribute land use observed in a particular year to social data (usually there is some lag associated with policy, migration, and land use, but we assume for simplicity there is a one-to-one relationship between land use and demographics). If the remote sensing analysis systematically biases results to attribute change to an earlier or later date, we have difficulties using these data for statistical models. There is reason to believe that this temporal bias exists because land use studies that rely on remote sensing data have a selection bias due to the availability of cloud-free or available images. The acquisition date of the imagery available may have nothing to do with socioeconomic processes on the ground, but land use change will be attributed to the dates for which images exist. In the study of the Pearl River Delta, our analysis would be quite different if we did not have images over a high temporal frequency, especially for the period before and after 1992.

A related issue is how to redistribute the pixels in space after an accuracy assessment. We have multiple methods for calculating and reporting the accuracy of maps—kappa statistics, contingency tables, etc. Because the maps are not ends in themselves but will be integrated with other data, how will the results of the accuracy assessment be incorporated? That is, do we adjust the map estimates, or do we to deal with the map errors in the integration step? Historically, remote sensing methodologies for land cover mapping aimed at producing maps as final outputs, not as data to be used with other data sets. We need accuracy in terms of space and reallocation of classes or pixels through space. For example, suppose the accuracy for a single map class, forest to urban, is 65 percent. From field-based accuracy assessments, we learn that most of the misclassified pixels should have been classified as agriculture to urban. It is common to readjust area estimates based on the accuracy assessments, but how do we reallocate the misclassified pixels spatially?

Recent developments in spatial statistics, time-series econometrics, and regional science have been applied to land use change models to overcome many conceptual and methodological constraints of the past, including improvements in modeling nonlinear relationships, spatial dependence and contagion, and temporal nonstationarity. Although methods exist that measure and correct for spatial and temporal nonstationarities, they have not been widely adopted in land use modeling. More work is necessary, especially in regard to testing for causality. Methods exist in econometrics, but they have not been widely applied or accepted in land use change studies.

Integrated Land System Science: Challenges and Opportunities

We have attempted to answer questions related to land system dynamics in rapidly changing economic and political environments in the Pearl River and Red River deltas. These case studies are continually evolving as lessons learned in one region are applied to another. The challenge ahead is to develop tools and approaches that can be applied to both regions. Although the contexts are different, we have found that the conceptual framework used in the Pearl River Delta is largely applicable to the Red River Delta. By undertaking multiple place-based case studies to draw comparisons at different spatial scales and across different political regimes, this project has sought to identify common themes about the interaction of population, institutions, and economics and land use change.

ACKNOWLEDGMENTS

This research has been supported by National Aeronautics and Space Administration Land Cover/Land Use Change Program grant no. NAG5-6214, NASA New Investigator Program grant no. NAG5-10534, and National Science Foundation CAREER Program grant no. BCS-348986. Numerous people across organizations and countries made this work possible. In particular, the author would like to thank Curtis Woodcock and Robert Kaufmann at Boston University, Michael Beman and Michail Fragkias at Stanford University, Lu Jinfa at the Beijing Geography Institute, Huang Xiuhua at the Institute of Remote Sensing Applications in Beijing, and Nguyen Dinh Duong and Dang Xuan Phong at the Vietnam National Centre for Natural Science and Technology.

REFERENCES

Boucher, A., K.C. Seto, and A.G. Journel
no   A novel method for mapping land cover changes: Incorporating time and space
date   with geostatistics. Submitted to *IEEE Transactions on Geoscience and Remote Sensing*.

Cartier, C.
2001   "Zone fever," the arable land debate, and real estate speculation: China's evolving land use regime and its geographical contradictions. *Journal of Contemporary China* 10:445-469.

Duong, N.D., L.K. Thoa, H.T. Hoan, T.A. Tuan, H.L. Thu, and K.C. Seto
2003   A study on the urban growth of Hanoi using multi-temporal and multi-sensor remote sensing data. *Asian Journal of Geoinformatics* 3(3).

Dye, D.G., T.C. Hinchliffe, and C.E. Woodcock
2000   Modeling the effects of recent land use change on the carbon cycle in the Zhu Jiang Delta region of Southern China. Presented at the 21st Asian Conference on Remote Sensing, December 4-8, Taipei, Taiwan. Available: http://www.gisdevelopment.net/aars/acrs/2000/ts11/glc003.shtml [accessed April 2005].

General Statistical Office
2001   *Vietnam Statistical Yearbook*. Hanoi, Vietnam: Statistical Publishing House.
2003   *Vietnam Statistical Yearbook*. Hanoi, Vietnam: Statistical Publishing House.

Goward, S.N., P.E. Davis, D. Fleming, L. Miller, and J.R.Townshend
2003   Empirical comparison of Landsat 7 and IKONOS multispectral measurements for selected earth observation system (EOS) validation sites. *Remote Sensing of Environment* 88:80-99.

Haertel, V., Y.E. Shimabukuro, and R. Almeida
  2004   Fraction images in multitemporal change detection. *International Journal of Remote Sensing* 25:5473-5489.
Heilig, G.K.
  1997   Anthropogenic factors in land use change in China. *Population and Development Review* 23:139-155.
Hurtt, G., X. Xiao, M. Keller, M. Palace, G.P. Asner, R. Braswell, E.S. Brondizio, M. Cardoso, C.J.R. Carvalho, M.G. Fearson, L. Guild, S. Hagen, S. Hetrick, B. Moore, C. Nobre, J.M. Read, T. Sa, A. Schloss, G. Vourlitis, and A.J. Wickel
  2003   IKONOS imagery for the large scale biosphere-atmosphere experiment in Amazonia (LBA). *Remote Sensing of Environment* 88:111-127.
Indian National Science Academy, Chinese Academy of Sciences, and U.S. National Academy of Sciences
  2001   *Growing Populations, Changing Landscapes: Studies from India, China and the United States.* Washington, DC: National Academy Press.
Kaufmann, R.K., and K.C. Seto
  2001   Change detection, accuracy, and bias in a sequential analysis of Landsat imagery in the Pearl River Delta, China: Econometric techniques. *Agriculture, Ecosystems and Environment* 85:95-105.
Le Hegarat-Mascle, S., and R. Seltz
  2004   Automatic change detection by evidential fusion of change indices. *Remote Sensing of Environment* 91:390-404.
Liang, Z.
  2001   The age of migration in China. *Population and Development Review* 27:499-524.
Lin, G.C.S.
  2002   The growth and structural change of Chinese cities: A contextual and geographic analysis. *Cities* 19:299-316.
Liu, J., M. Liu, D. Zhuang, Z. Zhang, and X. Deng
  2003   Study on spatial patterns of land use change in China during 1995-2000. *Science in China* 46:373-384.
McGee, T.G.
  1991   The emergence of desakota regions in Asia: Expanding a hypothesis. Pp. 3-25 in *The Extended Metropolis: Settlement Transitions in Asia*, N. Ginsburg, B. Koppel, and T.G. McGee, eds. Honolulu, HI: University of Hawaii Press.
Melgani, F., and S.B. Serpico
  2003   A Markov random field approach to spatio-temporal contextual image classification. *IEEE Transactions on Geoscience and Remote Sensing* 41:2478-2487.
National Research Council
  1992   *Global Environmental Change: Understanding the Human Dimensions.* Committee on the Human Dimensions of Global Change, Commission on the Behavioral and Social Sciences and Education, P.C. Stern, O.R. Young, and D. Druckman, eds. Washington, DC: National Academy Press.
Qi, Y., M. Henderson, M. Xu, J. Chen, P.J. Shi, C.Y. He, and G.W. Skinner
  2004   Evolving core-periphery interactions in a rapidly expanding urban landscape: The case of Beijing. *Landscape Ecology* 19:375-388.
Scarpaci, J.L.
  2000   On the transformation of socialist cities. *Urban Geography* 21:659-669.
Schneider, A., K.C. Seto, D. Webster, J. Cai, and B. Luo
  2003   Spatial and Temporal Patterns of Urban Development in Chengdu, 1975-2002. Stanford University Asia/Pacific Research Center Discussion Paper.

Schneider, A., K.C. Seto, and D. Webster
  1994 Urban growth in Chengdu, Western China: Application of remote sensing to assess planning and policy outcomes. *Environment and Planning B: Planning and Design* 32(3):323-345.
Schweik, C.M., K. Adhikari, and K.N. Pandit
  1997 Land-cover change and forest institutions: A comparison of two sub-basins in the southern Siwalik Hills of Nepal. *Mountain Research and Development* 17:99-116.
Seto, K.C., and M. Fragkias
  no   Quantifying Spatial and Temporal Patterns of Urban Land Use Change: A Charac-
  date terization of Four Cities with Time Series Landscape Metrics. Submitted to *Landscape Ecology*.
Seto, K.C., and R.K. Kaufmann
  2003 Modeling the drivers of urban land use change in the Pearl River Delta, China: Integrating remote sensing with socioeconomic data. *Land Economics* 79:106-121.
  2005 Using logit models to classify land use and land use change from Landsat TM. *International Journal of Remote Sensing* 26(3):563-577.
Seto, K.C., and W. Liu
  2003 Comparing artmap neural network with the maximum likelihood classifier for detecting urban change. *Photogrammetric Engineering and Remote Sensing* 69:981-990.
Seto, K.C., and D.D. Nguyen
  2002 Using a multi-sensor approach to monitoring urban growth in Hanoi: 1973-2001. *Proceedings of the International Symposium on Remote Sensing of Urban Areas.*
Seto, K.C., R.K. Kaufmann, and C.E. Woodcock
  2000 Landsat reveals China's farmland reserves, but they're vanishing fast. *Nature* 406: 121.
Seto, K.C., C.E. Woodcock, C. Song, X. Huang, J. Lu, and R.K. Kaufmann
  2002 Monitoring land use change in the Pearl River Delta using Landsat TM. *International Journal of Remote Sensing* 23:1985-2004.
Seto, K.C., J.M. Beman, W. Liu, M. Fragkias, and P.A. Matson
  no   Coastal Land Use Change in Northern Vietnam: Aquaculture Development, Mandate grove Conversion, and Methane Flux.
Shen, J.
  2002 State sponsored and spontaneous urbanisation in the Pearl River Delta of south China, 1980-1998. *Urban Geography* 23:674-694.
Sit, V.F.S., and C. Yang
  1997 Foreign-investment-induced exo-urbanisation in the Pearl River Delta, China. *Urban Studies* 34:647-677.
Song, C., C.E. Woodcock, K.C. Seto, M. Pax Lenney, and S.A. Macomber
  2001 Classification and change detection using Landsat TM data: When and how to correct atmospheric effects? *Remote Sensing of Environment* 75:230-244.
Song, F.X., and M. Timberlake
  1996 Chinese urbanization, state policy, and the world economy. *Journal of Urban Affairs* 18:285-306.
Statistical Bureau of Guangdong
  2002 *Statistical Yearbook of Guangdong.* Beijing: China Statistical Publishing House.
Tammaru, T.
  2002 Universal and specific features of urbanization in Estonia under socialism: The empirical evidence of the sources of urban and rural population growth. *Professional Geographer* 54:544-556.

Turner, B.L., and W.B. Meyer
  1991   Land use and land-cover in global environmental change: Considerations for study. *International Social Science Journal* 43:669-679.
United Nations
  2002   *World Urbanization Prospects: The 2001 Revision.* New York: United Nations.
Yang, L.M., G. Xian, J.M. Klaver, and B. Deal
  2003   Urban land-cover change detection through sub-pixel imperviousness mapping using remotely sensed data. *Photogrammetric Engineering and Remote Sensing* 69: 1003-1010.
Young, S.S., and C.Y. Wang
  2001   Land-cover change analysis of China using global-scale Pathfinder AVHRR Land-cover (PAL) data, 1982-92. *International Journal of Remote Sensing* 22:1457-1477.

9

Beyond Population Size: Examining Intricate Interactions Among Population Structure, Land Use, and Environment in Wolong Nature Reserve, China

Jianguo Liu, Li An, Sandra S. Batie, Scott L. Bearer, Xiaodong Chen, Richard E. Groop, Guangming He, Zai Liang, Marc A. Linderman, Angela G. Mertig, Zhiyun Ouyang, Jiaguo Qi, Hemin Zhan, and Shiqiang Zhou

INTRODUCTION

Human population growth influences long-term patterns of land use (Jolly and Torrey, 1993), which is a major force behind environmental changes. Many studies on human population and environment have been conducted at the aggregate level (Ehrlich and Holdren, 1971; Harrison, 1991; Thompson and Jones, 1999; Reid et al., 2000; McKee et al., 2004). For example, biodiversity loss is often related to aggregate variables, such as human population size and population density (Cincotta, Wisnewski, and Engelman, 2000). While these aggregate-level studies have generated important insights, there is an increasing recognition that focusing on aggregate variables, like population size or population growth, is not enough, because changes in population structure (e.g., age and arrangement of people into different households) are also important to the understanding of land use and environmental changes (e.g., Moran, Brondizio, and VanWey, Chapter 5; Pichon, 1997; Entwisle et al., 1998; Geoghegan et al., 2001; Perz, 2001; Fox et al., 2003). For example, age structure and sex structure affect patterns of land use and environmental conditions (Liu et al., 1999a; McCracken et al., 1999; Moran, Siqueira, and Brondizio, 2003). Also, because the household is a basic socioeconomic unit and each household occupies a specific land area, consumes natural resources, and produces wastes (e.g., CO_2), it is essential to understand the effects of household dynamics on the environment (MacKellar et al., 1995; Liu et al., 2003b; Moran et al., Chapter 5; Walsh et al., Chapter 6). Household numbers have been increasing much faster than population size has worldwide, and this trend is most likely to continue (Liu et al., 2003b). Even in areas with declining population size, household numbers are nevertheless increasing substantially. While population explosion (Ehrlich and Ehrlich, 1990) appears to be ebbing, household explosion is intensifying, elevating demands for household products and releasing more wastes, which in turn exert tremendous impacts on the environment, such as the loss and fragmentation of wildlife habitat.

Human impact on the environment is so widespread that it exists not only in nonprotected common property areas (e.g., Foster, Chapter 12; Matson et al., Chapter 10), but also in many of the world's approximately 100,000 protected areas (accounting for approximately 12 percent of the Earth's land surface) (World Conservation Union and World Commission on Protected Areas, 2003), which have been established to protect natural resources and biodiversity (Dompka, 1996; Liu, 2001). Although protected areas are believed to be the cornerstone of biological conservation (McNeely and Miller, 1983) and are often perceived as the safest preserves for nature (Armesto et al., 1998), human encroachments and threats are still very common (Dompka, 1996; Kramer et al., 1997; Liu et al., 2001). Although in some protected areas there are no local residents or land use has been restricted to designated zones, numbers of local residents have been increasing and human activities have been becoming more extensive in many protected areas. Understanding population-environment interactions in protected areas is critically important because such areas usually contain rich biodiversity that is vulnerable to human disturbances. Many ecological studies have been conducted in reserves (e.g., Schaller et al., 1985), but relatively few of those studies have explicitly investigated human dimensions, and even fewer studies have coupled ecological and human components (Hansen et al., 2002).

In this chapter, we use the Wolong Nature Reserve in China for the endangered giant panda to illustrate complex linkages among human population structure, land use, and panda habitat. We focus on two basic types of land use—agriculture and fuelwood collection. The former is the main source of human subsistence (food), whereas the latter provides energy for cooking and heating. Questions that we are particularly interested in are:

• What are the reciprocal interactions among human population structure, land use, and panda habitat (e.g., how do changes in human population structure influence land use and panda habitat)?

• How do human population structure, land use, and panda habitat as well as their interrelationships respond to changes in government policies?

STUDY AREA

Our field study was conducted in Wolong Nature Reserve (Plate 8), Sichuan Province, southwestern China (30°45' to 31°25' North, 102°52' to 103°24' East) (Schaller et al., 1985; Liu et al., 2001b). Wolong was established in 1975 as a nature reserve of 200,000 hectares (ha) (current size) and is one of the largest homes to the panda. It contains about 10 percent of the wild panda population (Zhang et al., 1997). Wolong is located between the Sichuan Basin and the Qinghai-Tibet Plateau. Its topography is very complex, with high mountains and deep valleys (elevation ranges from 1,200 to 6,525 m) (Plate 8), resulting in several climatic zones, rich habitat diversity (Schaller et al., 1985), over 2,200 animal and insect species, and about 4,000 plant species (Tan, Ouyang, and Zhang, 1995). Besides the giant panda, 12 other animal species and 47 plant species in the reserve also appear on China's national protection list. Furthermore, Wolong is part of the international Man and Biosphere Reserve Network (He, Liang, and Yin, 1996) and lies in one of the global biodiversity hot spots (Myers et al., 2000).

Along with biodiversity, there are also more than 4,000 local residents in Wolong. Although human presence inside nature reserves may surprise many people in developed countries, it is very common in China (China's National Committee on Man and Biosphere, 2000) because the vast majority of the reserves were established in the past two decades, and a large number of people had already settled in those areas before they were designated as reserves (Liu et al., 2003c). The Chinese government has tried to relocate residents from some reserves, including Wolong, but there have been many socioeconomic challenges to such relocations and the results were less than satisfactory. For example, some people who moved out of Wolong have returned to the reserve because they could not adapt to the new environment and encountered many difficulties in the new location. Local residents inside Wolong are almost exclusively farmers and are distributed in over 1,000 households. With so many people and households, human activities are diverse, including farming, fuelwood collection, house building, as well as road construction and maintenance. It is these activities that have direct impacts on the environment.

CONCEPTUAL FRAMEWORK

The interactions among human population, land use, and panda habitat are reciprocal, complex, and dynamic over time and across space and can be shaped by such contextual factors as government policies (Liu et al., 2003a, 2004) (Figure 9-1, Table 9-1). Other contextual factors include prices, technology, and institutions, but they are not considered in this chapter. Popula-

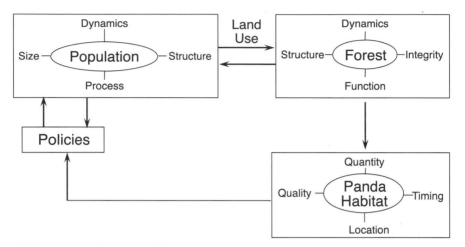

FIGURE 9-1   Conceptual framework.
SOURCE: Modified from Liu et al. (1999b).

tion factors include population size, process (e.g., birth, death, and migration), structure (e.g., age, sex, spatial distribution like household arrangement, socioeconomic conditions), and their changes over time.

Environmental factors consist of animals, plants, and physical and geographic conditions (Table 9-1). Here, we concentrate on panda habitat, the area that provides food and cover for pandas' reproduction and other activities. Suitability of panda habitat is a function of abiotic and biotic factors, as well as human impacts (Liu et al., 1999b). The main abiotic factors include slope and elevation (Schaller et al., 1985; Liu et al., 1999b, 2001b). Pandas like flat areas or gentle slopes in which they can easily move around. Bamboo and forest cover are major biotic factors. The panda uses bamboo (an understory species) as staple food and forest canopy as cover (Schaller et al., 1985; Liu et al., 1999b; Bearer et al., no date).

Land use is a direct link between population and the environment; through land use, local residents influence forests directly and panda habitat indirectly (Figure 9-1). These influences are exerted through the flows of material and energy (e.g., labor) from the residential areas to the forested areas. Along with labor is the energy and time spent in the forest to collect and transport fuelwood. As a result of fuelwood collection for cooking food (for people and pigs) and heating, a large amount of panda habitat has been lost (Liu et al., 1999b).

Changes in forest cover also affect the panda's food supply (Schaller et al., 1985) by altering the growth of understory bamboo (Table 9-1). Thus, changes in forest cover can have an important impact on panda habitat quantity, quality, location, and timing (i.e., when the habitat

TABLE 9-1 Major Variables in Each of the Components Illustrated in Plate 8

Human Component	Forest Component	Panda Habitat	Policies
Reserve Level: Number of people; Number of households; Average economic income; Percentage of ethnic groups; Population structure by age, sex, and education levels; Roads (locations, time of construction, type); Locations of trade centers, schools, administration buildings, and small hydro-power plants.	Forest cover type; Canopy coverage; Species composition; Dominant tree species; Tree heights, Tree density, Tree diameters;	Habitat type; Amount of habitat; Distribution of each habitat type; Habitat patch	Regulations on Timber Harvest and Fuelwood Collection; Contract for Forest Protection; Forest Management Act; Wildlife Protection Act;
Household Level: Number of people in a household; Household location; Household income, Household expenses, Sources of income, Aspects of expenses; Locations of fuelwood collection, Amount of fuelwood consumption, Purposes of fuelwood consumption; Amount of electricity consumption, Electricity price, Electricity quality (outage and voltage); Number and types of livestock (e.g., chicken, cattle, pigs, sheep, yaks); Amount of cropland, Types of crops; Amount of cropland returned to forest land; Amount of subsidies received; Amount of forest assigned for monitoring.	Forest stand size, Stand age; Harvesting history; Mid-story coverage; Understory coverage, Bamboo height, Bamboo species, Bamboo density, bamboo coverage, bamboo conditions (flowering or not)	Habitat patch size; Habitat patch size distribution; Elevation, Aspect, Slope	Regulations on Nature Reserve Management in Sichuan Province; Natural Forest Conservation Program; Grain-to-Green Program; Hydro-power Plant Program; Master Plan of Wolong Nature Reserve; Master Plan on Ecotourism Development in Wolong Nature Reserve
Individual Level: Migration, Birth, Death; Marital status, Time of marriage, Education level, Age, Sex, Occupation; Attitudes, Perception, Concerns, Needs, Wants.			

becomes available) (Liu et al., 1999b). Because slopes in some regions of Wolong are too steep or elevations too high, about half of the reserve is not suitable for the panda even in the absence of human impacts (Liu et al., 1999b).

Government policies directly affect population and indirectly affect forest and panda habitat through flow of information (e.g., government regulations) and material (e.g., financial support) from upper level government agencies (China's State Forestry Administration and Sichuan Province's Department of Forestry) to the Wolong Nature Reserve Administration Bureau and ultimately to the local residents (Table 9-1). The effectiveness of policies, however, can be influenced by local residents. For example, local residents may not follow government policies because financial supports may not be high enough to meet their needs and wants, including electric appliances for cooking. In addition, the majority of local residents belong to minority ethnic groups (mainly Tibetans), who add another layer of complexity to government policies because minority ethnic groups receive some preferential treatments (e.g., exemption from China's one-child policy). Deteriorated habitat conditions (Liu et al., 1999b, 2001a; Liu, 2001) have prompted the government to develop and implement more effective policies for conservation. Furthermore, population and land use may be constrained by feedback from the forest system. As forests used for fuelwood collection shrink and are more distant from households, fuelwood collection becomes more difficult (He et al., no date). After all the trees in a forest are harvested, local residents must adopt a different lifestyle without the use of fuelwood (Liu et al., 2004).

APPROACHES

Systems Approach: We consider ecological and demographic factors as well as socioeconomic and behavioral factors; factors inside the reserve and those outside the reserve; what happened in the past, what is happening now, and what may happen in the future. The reserve is an open system and has inflows (e.g., in-migration through marriage, organisms moving into the reserve, commercial or nonmarket products brought into the reserve) and outflows (e.g., out-migration through marriage or seeking higher education in cities, organisms moving out of the reserve, and local products purchased by tourists visiting the reserve). The interactions among various components of the reserve are accomplished by exchanging matter, energy, and information; they vary over time; and they are influenced by a combination of interacting factors.

Interdisciplinary Approach: To understand population, land use, and panda habitat as well as their interrelationships, we integrate ecology, conservation biology, forestry, demography, sociology, geography, economics, behavioral science, and advanced technologies (remote sensing, geographic information systems, and systems modeling and simulation). These disciplines are complementary to each other and provide different perspectives, methods, and theories.

Collaborative Approach: Our international team consists of reserve managers and experts in the disciplines mentioned above. We have built close relationships among team members; have accumulated experience dealing with demographic, socioeconomic, behavioral, institutional, and ecological issues; have enjoyed good cooperation and support from local residents; and have become very familiar with the local conditions, as well as data collection methods and analytical tools.

Multiscale Approach: Our research and interactions among population, land use, and environment take place at several spatial, temporal, and organizational scales. Spatial scales range from plots or pixels (1 by 1 m, ..., 80 by 80 m), patches (e.g., forest stand, agricultural land parcel), to the entire reserve landscape. The time span of our research is from daily to decadal. For population, the organizational scale ranges from individuals, households, villages, and townships to the entire reserve community.

Integrated Approach: We have developed and taken an integrated approach to data collection, management, analysis, and integration. Data were collected using various methods (Table 9-2), such as field studies, interviews, analysis of government statistics and documents, review of literature, remote sensing (satellite imagery and aerial photographs), and global positioning systems (GPS). To understand detailed forest structure and composition, we have taken random samples (plot sizes were from 1 by 1 to 60 by 60 m) in areas with different forest conditions (e.g., with and without fuelwood collection). We chose large plots for assessing conditions of large trees and forest canopy, and we sampled smaller plots for shrubs (5 by 5 m, three in each plot) and herbaceous plants (1 by 1 m) (Liu et al., 1999b). To measure spatial and temporal patterns of forest and panda habitat changes, we have acquired a number of remote sensing imagery (Table 9-2): Corona data from 1965; Landsat Multi-Spectral Scanner (MSS) data from 1974; Landsat Thematic Mapper (TM) data from 1987 and 1997; Landsat 7 (data from 1999, 2001, 2002); SPOT data from 1998 and 1999; and IKONOS data from 2000 (Liu et al., 2001b, 2003a; Linderman et al., 2004).

We began collecting socioeconomic, demographic, and behavioral data in 1996 (Liu et al., 1999b, 2001b; An et al., 2001, 2002; An, Mertig, and Liu, 2003; Tables 9-1 and 9-2), and the most recent survey was conducted in summer 2004. The surveys include household interviews regarding fuelwood consumption, socioeconomic conditions, and demographic conditions (For more detailed information on survey data, see Liu et al. (2003a). We also interviewed more than 300 people regarding their time allocation

TABLE 9-2 Major Variables According to Data Sources

Field Studies	Interviews	Government Agencies	Remotely Sensed Data	Estimated or Derived from Other Sources
Forest types; Tree height, diameters, density; Stand age, size, and harvest history; Canopy coverage; Bamboo species, cover, height, and density; Panda feces distribution; Ground control points; Ground truthing plot data; Locations of human activities; Household locations; Road locations; Elevation, aspect, slope; Electricity price; Fuelwood log: species, length, weight, and diameter	Attitudes, perceptions, concerns, needs, and wants; Amount of fuelwood consumed for different purposes (heating, cooking human food and fodders); Location of fuelwood collection; Origins of local residents; Number of people and relationships in a household; Age, sex, occupation, ethnic group, marital status, education level; Human activities; Livestock; Amount of cropland; Income sources and expenses	Total number of people; Total number of people died, Total number of born; Total number of households; Electricity prices; Age, sex, occupation, education level; Policies; Forest parcel maps for the natural forest conservation program; Amount of crop land returned to forest land	Corona data from 1965; Landsat Multi-Spectral Scanner (MSS) data from 1974; Landsat Thematic Mapper (TM) data from 1987 and 1997; Landsat 7 (1999, 2001, 2002); SPOT data from 1998 and 1999; IKONOS data from 2000	Amount of panda habitat; Degree of forest and habitat fragmentation; Digital elevation models; Human population structure; Household locations; Locations of schools and major buildings; Distances between households and locations of fuelwood collection; Distances between household locations and panda habitat

for different activities (e.g., fuelwood, agriculture, road construction, and herbal medicine collection). Sample size for particular portions of the data collection depended on specific research objectives, for example, for household fuelwood consumption, we surveyed 220 households (An et al., 2002). In our household surveys, we selected respondents using simple or stratified random designs (Liu et al., 2003a). We used face-to-face interviews with local residents because this method has proven to be the best and most feasible approach for Wolong (An et al., 2001) and almost everyone who was asked to be interviewed did participate in the interviews.

At the household level, we collected a variety of data, such as household size, structure, location, time of formation and dissolution (e.g., through divorce and marriage); amount of annual income; sources of income; amount of expenses; aspects of expenses (e.g., schooling); labor force; land area; area of the house; crop production; number of livestock (e.g., pigs); types of land use (e.g., fuelwood collection); and amount of electricity for cooking, heating, and electronic appliances (such as TVs and radios).

Individual information includes age; sex; marital status; time of marriage, separation or divorce if applicable; occupation; years of schooling; and attitudes towards out-migration and childbearing. Besides these first-hand data, we have also obtained some secondary data (Table 9-2), including those of Wolong Administration Bureau (e.g., annual population reports with records on birth, death, age, sex, in-migration, and out-migration), national population census data in 1982 (Wenchuan County, 1983), the 1996 Agricultural Census (Wolong Nature Reserve, 1996), and national population census data in 2000 (Wolong Nature Reserve, 2000). Population census data were collected based on a de jure approach, which counts people who are usually in a household.

Macro-level socioeconomic factors (contextual factors beyond the household level, such as roads, trade centers, administration buildings, bridges, dams, and schools) also influence population–land use–environment interactions because their relationships with households (e.g., households' distances to major roads or trade centers) are different. The measurements include these factors' locations and timing of occurrence. We obtained the information regarding the timing of occurrence from the records of the Wolong Administration Bureau, or by interviewing local residents, officials, and other stakeholders (Table 9-2). The locations of these factors were measured using GPS receivers, from remote sensing imagery (IKONOS), or from topographic maps (Liu et al., 2003a) (Table 9-1).

All the data were entered into and are managed in a relational database program (i.e., ACCESS) and geographic information systems (GIS, including both Arc/Info and ArcView) for analysis. Remotely sensed data were classified using ERDAS Imagine software or visual classification. We georeferenced the remotely sensed data using highly accurate data (1-5 m) from

GPS receivers (Trimble Pathfinder) and used data from ground-based observations for training and validating supervised classifications of the remotely sensed data (Table 9-2). The accuracy of classification ranged from 80 to 87 percent (Liu et al., 2001b). We analyzed various data using spatial statistics, GIS, and statistical packages such as SAS, SPSS, and LISREL (An et al., 2001, 2002, An, Mertig, and Liu, 2003), depending on types of data and questions.

We developed several systems simulation models to synthesize information from various sources (Liu et al., 1999b; An et al., 2001, 2005a, 2005b; Linderman et al., in press, 2005). The models fall into three major types: at the household level (An et al., 2001), at the reserve level (Liu et al., 1999b; Linderman et al., in press, 2005), and at the multiple levels ranging from individuals and households to the entire reserve (An et al., 2005a, 2005b). The household-level model integrates household demography (e.g., household size and age and schooling years of each family member), household economy (land use activities, income and expense sources, etc.), attitudes toward issues of interest (e.g., childbearing), and fuelwood consumption. The reserve-level models consider the collective impact of all households (Liu et al., 1999b; Linderman et al., in press, 2005). The multilevel model is agent-based, (treating individuals and households as agents and simulating the interactions among individuals and households, land use, and panda habitat at multiple levels (An et al., 2005a, 2005b). Both the reserve-level and multilevel models are linked with a GIS to project demographic and ecological consequences of policy scenarios in a spatially explicit manner.

Our models differ from those discussed in Fischer and O'Neill (Chapter 3) in several aspects. First, their models use aggregated population size rather than households. Second, our multilevel model and household-level model are process-based, whereas their models are regression-based. Third, their models treat population change as an exogenous variable to land use change and environmental impact. In our models, population (e.g., locations of new households) not only may affect the environment but also may be affected by the environment and policy changes.

FINDINGS

Population size in Wolong increased by over 70 percent and the number of households more than doubled (125 percent) between 1975 (the year the reserve of current size was established) and 1999 (Figure 9-2). As in many other places around the world (Liu et al., 2003b), the reason for this more rapid increase in household numbers is household division or the continued reduction in household size (the number of people in a household) (Figure 9-3) due to such factors as declines in multigeneration families, an increase in the divorce rate, and population aging. Land use deci-

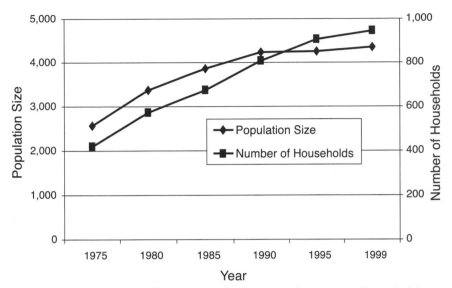

FIGURE 9-2   Dynamics of human population size and numbers of households.

sions are affected by the transition from fewer to more households. The increase in the number of households means more land is used for house construction as well as for farming, and more timber is needed for house construction and furniture. Also, as household size declines, the amount of fuelwood use per capita increases (Figure 9-4), the total amount of fuelwood

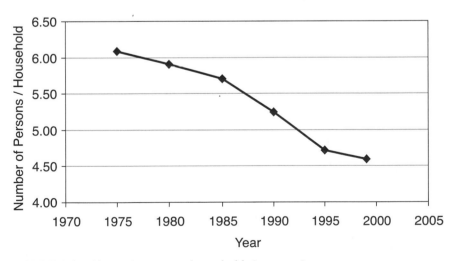

FIGURE 9-3   Change in average household size over time.

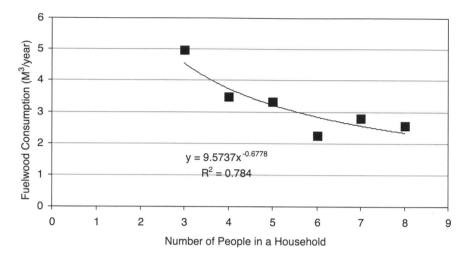

FIGURE 9-4 Average per capita use of fuelwood as a function of average household size.

consumption increases, and more forest needs to be harvested. As the demand for fuelwood increases and the forests near households become exhausted, people spend more time collecting fuelwood in areas farther away from their residences. The average distance between household locations and locations of fuelwood collection has increased, and the elevation of fuelwood collection has also increased over time (from the 1970s to the 1990s) (He et al., no date). Because those forested areas farther from the households and at higher elevations happen to be better panda habitat, fuelwood collection in those areas has done more damage to it.

Population structure has changed dramatically (Figure 9-5). The rise in the proportions and numbers of adults, particularly males, increased the labor force involved in fuelwood collection and farming. Through interviews with 328 people in the reserve about their activities in 1997 (Liu et al., unpublished data), we found that the number of days that local residents participated in fuelwood collection increased with age, reached its peak in the age group of 25-59, and decreased sharply after age 60 (Figure 9-6a). Furthermore, men spent more time in collecting fuelwood than women (Figure 9-6b). Although farming (Figure 9-6c, 9-6d) showed similar general patterns to those of fuelwood collection, there are two major differences between fuelwood collection and farming labor forces. First, the average numbers of days that people participated in farming (Figure 9-6c) was much larger than those for fuelwood collection (Figure 9-6a) across age and gender groups. Second, on average, women spent 75 more days on

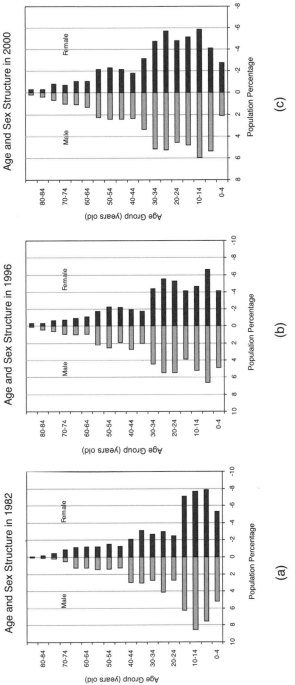

FIGURE 9-5 Variations in population structure over time.
SOURCE: An et al. (2005b).

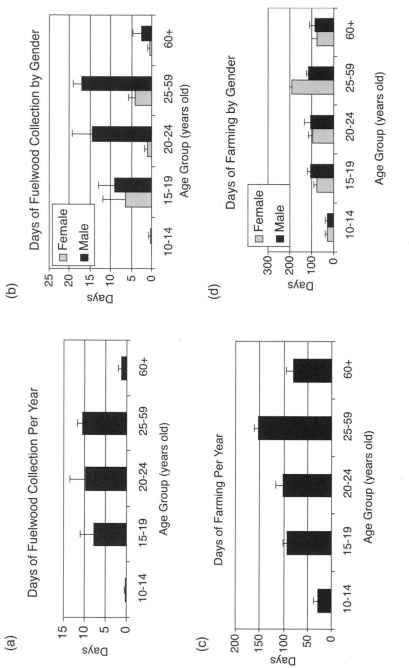

FIGURE 9-6 Fuelwood collection and farming activity by age and gender. An error bar indicates one standard error.

farming than men in the age group of 25-59, whereas in the other age groups, men spent equal or greater amounts of time in farming than women (Figure 9-6d).

Fuelwood consumption is influenced by household size as well as age structure (An et al., 2001) (Figure 9-7). On average, more fuelwood is needed in a large household because more food needs to be cooked for more people, although household size does not affect the amount of fuelwood needed for heating that much. However, households with one or more senior residents consume more fuelwood than those without seniors, because the heating season for the elderly is longer (starting earlier and ending later) (An et al., 2001).

Land use has contributed to the significant changes in panda habitat in Wolong. We found that forest cover in Wolong had been dramatically reduced from 1965 to 1997 (Liu et al., 2001b) and high-quality panda habitat has been lost more rapidly after the reserve's establishment than before it was created (Liu et al., 2001b). Furthermore, fragmentation of high-quality habitat became more severe.

Our models, validated through comparisons between independent empirical data and model results (Liu et al., 1999b; An et al., 2001, 2005a, 2005b; Linderman et al., in press, 2005), helped us to gain better insights into the mechanisms of population–land use–habitat interactions and to understand the long-term consequences of altering various components.

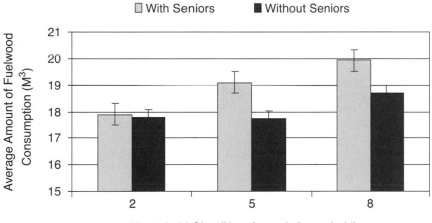

FIGURE 9-7 Fuelwood consumption as a function of age structure and household size.
SOURCE: An et al. (2001).

For example, if one of every five young people left the reserve, the population size would decline by more than 80 percent (from about 4,320 in 1997 to 760 in 2047) over a period of 50 years (Liu et al., 1999b). However, under the status quo, population size would increase by nearly 40 percent (to 5,960 in 2047). If fuelwood consumption were replaced by electricity, panda habitat would gradually recover (Liu et al., 1999b).

Government policies have profound impacts on population, land use, and forest and panda habitat. A sudden and unexpected increase of 65 households occurred in 2001, approximately three times higher than the average annual rate of household increase during the past 25 years (about 21 new households a year from 1975 to 1999, Figure 9-2). Based on our interviews with local residents (He et al., unpublished data), at least two-thirds of those new households were formed to take advantage of the subsidies from the Natural Forest Conservation Program, whose aim is to prevent natural forests from illegal harvesting. Households monitor forest parcels assigned by the government and receive subsidies from the government on a household basis. The subsidies provide significant household revenue, as it may account for about 20-25 percent of total annual income for most of the households involved (Sichuan Forestry Survey Institute and Wolong Nature Reserve, 2000). The impact of the Grain to Green Program on agriculture land use is another example. Its goal is to restore hillside agricultural land to forested area over a period of five to eight years. Farmers are given grain and cash subsidies according to the amount of cropland converted to forests. So far, trees or bamboo have been planted on approximately 450 ha of cropland since 2000 (Wolong Nature Reserve, 2000).

CONCLUDING REMARKS

Integrating natural and social sciences was essential for us to understand the patterns and mechanisms of changes in population, land use, and panda habitat as well as their interactions. Through this integration process we were able to determine the reasons for the unexpected higher rate of loss of high-quality panda habitat after the reserve was established (Liu et al., 2001b). Our integrated study enabled us to evaluate the reasons for policy failures and successes, develop recommendations for more feasible and effective policies, and assess long-term consequences of policy scenarios. The emigration policy serves as an example. In the past, the government tried to move local residents out of the reserve on a household basis to reduce population pressure on panda habitat (Liu et al., 1999b). However, the success of the program was very limited, despite economic incentives. We found that middle-aged and senior residents did not want to relocate because they were accustomed to the local conditions. However, young people were more than willing to relocate, especially if they could attain higher education and find jobs elsewhere. Thus, relocating young people out of the reserve would be not only socially acceptable, but also more ecologically effective and economically efficient, compared with relocating senior and middle-aged people (Liu et al., 1999b, 2001b, 2003c). In addition to enhancing school education so that more children can go to college and find jobs elsewhere (Liu et al., 2003c), perhaps there is something that Wolong can do to facilitate temporary labor migration of more young people. In fact, there is such a precedent, also in Sichuan Province. In Jintang County (about 60 kilometers from Chengdu, the capital of Sichuan Province, approximately 150 kilometers from Wolong), the county government has been actively involved in facilitating labor migration. They do so by helping migrants get jobs in specific destinations, running bus lines on frequently traveled routes for them, and protecting their labor rights in the places to which they travel (Jintang County Government, 2004). The experience of Jintang has been very successful.

Our research in the reserve has generated many ideas that have been applied and scaled up to the national and global levels. The understanding of interrelationships among population, land use, and panda habitat in Wolong (e.g., Liu et al., 2001a, 2001b) helped us to examine the status and challenges in designing and managing the entire nature reserve system (with a total of 1,757 reserves) in China (Liu et al., 2003c) as well as China's environment in the context of globalization (Liu and Diamond, no date). It also enabled us to link wildlife management with global human health (Liu, 2003). The higher growth rate of household numbers versus population growth in Wolong prompted us to compare household growth and population growth at the global scale (Liu et al., 2003b).

While the benefits of integrating social and natural sciences are enormous, it is also challenging throughout the integration process (Liu, 2001). Our research indicates land use and panda habitat were affected not only by population size, but also by population structure. However, going beyond population size was more challenging than considering population size alone, because more detailed and more comprehensive data were needed, and more time and effort were also spent to analyze and interpret the data. Despite this challenge, population structure provides many unique insights and thus should be integrated into more studies at the local as well as national and global scales.

ACKNOWLEDGMENTS

We thank the logistic support of Michigan State University and Wolong Nature Reserve, especially the helpful assistance of Jayson Eageler, Jinyan Huang, Yingchun Tan, William W. Taylor, Julie Traver, and Jian Yang. Constructive comments and suggestions from Barbara Entwisle and Paul Stern as well as two anonymous reviewers are greatly appreciated. We gratefully acknowledge the financial support from the National Science Foundation (CAREER Award and Biocomplexity Grant), the National Institute of Child Health and Human Development (R01 HD39789), the National Aeronautics and Space Administration, the American Association for the Advancement of Sciences, The John D. and Catherine T. MacArthur Foundation, the National Natural Science Foundation of China, the Ministry of Science and Technology of China (G2000046807), and China Bridges International.

REFERENCES

An, L., J. Liu, Z. Ouyang, M. Linderman, S. Zhou, and H. Zhang
   2001   Simulating demographic and socioeconomic processes on household level and implications for giant panda habitats. *Ecological Modeling* 140:31-50.
An, L., F. Lupi, J. Liu, M. Linderman, and J. Huang
   2002   Modeling the choice to switch from fuelwood to electricity. *Ecological Economics* 42:445-457.
An, L., A.G. Mertig, and J. Liu
   2003   Adolescents leaving parental home—Psychosocial correlates and implications for conservation. *Population and Environment* 24:415-444.
An, L., G. He, Z. Liang, and J. Liu
   2005a Impacts of demographic and socioeconomic factors on spatio-temporal dynamics of panda habitats. Submitted to *Biodiversity and Conservation.*
   2005b Exploring complexity in a human-environment system: An agent-based spatial model for multidisciplinary and multi-scale integration. Submitted to *Annals of Association of American Geographers.*
Armesto, J.J, R Rozzi, C. Smith-Ramirez, and M.T.K. Arroyo
   1998   Conservation targets in South American temperate forests. *Science* 282:1271-1272.
Bearer, S.L., J. Huang, M. Linderman, L. An, G. He, Z. Ouyang, and J. Liu
   no   Effects of Timber Harvesting and Fuelwood Collection on Giant Panda Habitat
   date   Use. Unpublished manuscript, Michigan State University, East Lansing.
China's National Committee on Man and Biosphere
   2000   Study of Sustainable Management Policies for China's Nature Reserves *(in Chinese)*. Beijing: Scientific and Technical Documents Publishing House.
Cincotta, R.P., J. Wisnewski, and R. Engelman
   2000   Human population in the biodiversity hotspots. *Nature* 404:990-992.
Dompka, V., ed.
   1996   *Human Population, Biodiversity and Protected Areas: Science and Policy Issues.* Washington, DC: American Association for the Advancement of Science.
Ehrlich, P.R., and A.H. Ehrlich
   1990   *The Population Explosion.* New York: Simon and Schuster.
Ehrlich, P.R., and J.P. Holdren
   1971   Impact of population growth. *Science* 171:1212-1216.
Entwisle, B., S.J. Walsh, R.R. Rindfuss, and A. Chamratrithrong
   1998   Land use/land-cover and population dynamics, Nang Rong, Thailand. Pp. 121-144 in National Research Council, *People and Pixels: Linking Remote Sensing and Social Science.* Committee on the Human Dimensions of Global Change, D. Liverman, E.F. Moran, R.R. Rindfuss, and P.C. Stern, eds. Washington, DC: National Academy Press.

Fox, J., V. Mishra, R. Rindfuss, and S. Walsh
  2003   *People and the Environment: Approaches for Linking Household and Community Surveys to Remote Sensing and GIS*. Boston, MA: Kluwer Academic Publishers.
Geoghegan, J., S.C. Villar, P. Klepeis, P.M. Mendoza, Y. Ogneva-Himmelberger, R.R. Chowdhury, B.L. Turner, and C. Vance
  2001   Modeling tropical deforestation in the southern Yucatan peninsular region: Comparing survey and satellite data. *Agriculture Ecosystems and Environment* 85: 25-46.
Hansen, A.J., R. Rasker, B. Maxwell, J.J. Rotella, J.D. Johnson, A.W. Parmenter, L. Langner, W.B. Cohen, R.L. Lawrence, and M.P. Kraska
  2002   Ecological causes and consequences of demographic change in the new west. *Bioscience* 52:151-162.
Harrison, S.
  1991   Population growth, land use and deforestation in Costa Rica, 1950-1984. *Interciencia* 16.
He, G., M. Colunga, S. Bearer, L. An, M. Linderman, S. Zhou, J. Huang, S. Gage, Z. Ouyang, and J. Liu
  no   Spatial and Temporal Patterns of Fuelwood Collection in a Nature Reserve.
  date   Unpublished manuscript, Michigan State University, East Lansing.
He, N., C. Liang, and X. Yin
  1996   Sustainable community development in Wolong Nature reserve. *Ecological Economy* 1:15-23.
Jintang County Government
  2004   Document on Labor Exporting from Jintang County. Unpublished internal document.
Jolly, C.L., and B.B. Torrey
  1993   Introduction. Pp. 1-14 in National Research Council, *Population and Land Use in Developing Countries: Report of a Workshop*. Committee on Population. C.L. Jolly and B.B. Torrey, eds. Washington, DC: National Academy Press.
Kramer, R.C., C. van Schaik, and J. Johnson, eds.
  1997   *Last Stand: Protected Areas and the Defense of Tropical Biodiversity*. New York: Oxford University Press.
Linderman, M., J. Liu, J. Qi, L. An, Z. Ouyang, J. Yang, and Y. Tan
  2004   Using artificial neural networks to map the spatial distribution of understory bamboo from remote sensing data. *International Journal of Remote Sensing* 25:1685-1700.
Linderman, M., L. An, S. Bearer, G. He, Z. Ouyang, and J. Liu
  2005   The effects of understory bamboo on broad-scale estimates of giant panda habitat. *Biological Conservation* 121:383-390.
  in   Modeling the spatio-temporal dynamics and interactions of households, landscape,
  press   and giant panda habitat. *Ecological Modeling*.
Liu, J.
  2001   Integrating ecology with human demography, behavior, and socioeconomics: Needs and approaches. *Ecological Modeling* 140:1-8.
  2003   SARS, wildlife, and human health. *Science* 302:53.
Liu, J., and J. Diamond
  no   China's Environment in a Globalizing World. Submitted to *Nature*.
  date
Liu, J., Z. Ouyang, Y. Tan, J. Yang, and S. Zhou
  1999a   Changes in human population structure and implications for biodiversity conservation. *Population and Environment* 21:45-58.

Liu, J., Z. Ouyang, W.W. Taylor, R. Groop, Y. Tan, and H. Zhang
  1999b A framework for evaluating effects of human factors on wildlife habitat: The case
         of the giant pandas. *Conservation Biology* 13:1360-1370.
Liu, J., M. Linderman, Z. Ouyang, and L. An
  2001a The pandas' habitat at Wolong Nature Reserve—response. *Science* 293:603-604.
Liu, J., M. Linderman, Z. Ouyang, L. An, J. Yang, and H. Zhang
  2001b Ecological degradation in protected areas: The case of Wolong Nature Reserve for
         giant pandas. *Science* 292:98-101.
Liu, J., L. An, S. Batie, R. Groop, Z. Liang, M. Linderman, A. Mertig, Z. Ouyang, and J. Qi
  2003a Human impacts on land cover and panda habitat in Wolong Nature Reserve: Link-
         ing ecological, socioeconomic, demographic, and behavioral data. Pp. 241-263 in
         People and the Environment: Approaches for Linking Household and Community.
         Surveys to Remote Sensing and GIS, J. Fox, V. Mishra, R. Rindfuss, and S. Walsh,
         eds. Boston: Kluwer Academic Publishers.
Liu, J., G. Daily, P. Ehrlich, and G. Luck
  2003b Effects of household dynamics on resource consumption and biodiversity. *Nature*
         421:530-533.
Liu, J., Z. Ouyang, S.L. Pimm, P.H. Raven, X. Wang, H. Miao, and N. Han
  2003c Protecting China's biodiversity. *Science* 300:1240-1241.
Liu, J., Z. Ouyang, H. Zhang, M. Linderman, L. An, S. Bearer, and G. He
  2004   A new paradigm for panda research and conservation: Integrating ecology with
         human demography, behavior, and socioeconomics. In *Giant Panda: Conservation*
         Priorities for the 21st Century, D. Lindburg and K. Baragona, eds. Berkeley, CA:
         University of California Press.
MacKellar, F.L., W. Lutz, C. Prinz, and A. Goujon
  1995   Population, households, and CO_2 emissions. *Population and Development Review*
         21:849-865.
McCracken, S.D., E.S. Brondizio, D. Nelson, E.F. Moran, A.D. Siqueira, and C. Rodriguez-
Pedraza
  1999   Remote sensing and GIS at farm property level: Demography and deforestation in
         the Brazilian Amazon. *Photogrammetric Engineering and Remote Sensing* 65:1311-
         1320.
McKee, J.K., P.W. Sciulli, C.D. Fooce, and T.A. Waite
  2004   Forecasting global biodiversity threats associated with human population growth.
         Biological Conservation 115:161-164.
McNeely, J.A., and K.R. Miller
  1983   *National Parks and Protected Areas.* Bangkok, Thailand: United Nations Economic
         and Social Commission for Asia and the Pacific.
Moran, E.F., E. Brondizio, P. Mausel, and Y. Wu
  1994   Integrating Amazonian vegetation, land-use, and satellite data. *Bioscience* 44:329-
         338.
Moran, E.F., A. Siqueira, and E. Brondizio
  2003   Household demographic Structure and its relationship to the Amazon Basin. Pp.
         1-30 in *People and the Environment: Approaches to Linking Household and Com-*
         munity Surveys to Remote Sensing and GIS, J. Fox, V. Mishra, R. Rindfuss, and S.
         Walsh, eds. Boston: Kluwer Academic Publishers.
Myers, N., R.A. Mittermeier, C.G. Mittermeier, G.A.B. da Fonseca, and J. Kent
  2000   Biodiversity hotspots for conservation priorities. *Nature* 403:853-858.
Perz, S.G.
  2001   Household demographic factors as life cycle determinants of land use in the Ama-
         zon. *Population Research and Policy Review* 20:159-186.

Pichon, F.J.
  1997   Settler households and land-use patterns in the Amazon frontier: Farm-level evidence from Ecuador. *World Development* 25:67-91.
Reid, R.S., R.L. Kruska, U. Deichmann, and P.K. Thornton
  2000   Human population growth and the extinction of the tsetse fly. *Agriculture, Ecosystem and Environment* 77:227-236.
Schaller, G.B., J. Hu, W. Pan, and J. Zhu
  1985   *The Giant Pandas of Wolong*. Chicago: University of Chicago Press.
Sichuan Forestry Survey Institute and Wolong Nature Reserve
  2000   Forest Monitoring for Natural Forest Conservation Program in Wolong Nature Reserve. Chengdu.
Tan, Y., Z. Ouyang, and H. Zhang
  1995   Spatial characteristics of biodiversity in Wolong Nature Reserve. *China's Biosphere Reserve* 3:19-24.
Thompson, K., and A. Jones
  1999   Human population density and prediction of local plant extinction in Britain. *Conservation Biology* 13:185-189.
Wenchuan County
  1983   Statistics of Population Census of 1982. Sichuan Province, China.
Wolong Nature Reserve
  1996   *Agricultural Survey Data*. Sichuan Province, China.
  2000   2000 National Population Census. Sichuan Province, China.
World Conservation Union and World Commission on Protected Areas
  2003   *United Nations List of Protected Areas*. Gland, Switzerland: UNEP World Conservation Monitoring Centre.
Zhang, H., D. Li, R. Wei, C. Tang, and J. Tu
  1997   Advances in conservation and studies on reproductivity of giant pandas in Wolong. *Sichuan Journal of Zoology* 16:31-33.

10

People, Land Use, and Environment in the Yaqui Valley, Sonora, Mexico

Pamela Matson, Amy L. Luers, Karen C. Seto,
Rosamond L. Naylor, and Ivan Ortiz-Monasterio

This chapter describes ongoing research that integrates social and natural science approaches to the study of interactions between development and environment in the Yaqui Valley region of southern Sonora, Mexico. While the focus of this project has evolved over the past 10 years, much of our research addresses three broad questions: (1) What drives land use and land management decisions? (2) What are the implications of these decisions for the people and ecosystems in the region, and for the regional and global environment? (3) What alternatives are available to the people of the region in order to harmonize development and environment? Our analysis draws from various disciplines, including agronomy, biogeochemistry, ecology, economics, geography, hydrology, international policy analysis, remote sensing science, and water resources engineering to address these questions at multiple points across the landscape.

In this chapter, we first present an introduction to the Yaqui Valley study region. We then outline several of the conceptual themes or frameworks that we have used to organize our study of the Yaqui system, all of which focus on the interaction of social and biophysical factors in the human-environment system. We briefly describe three broad studies—on agriculture–environment interactions, land use dynamics at the regional scale, and vulnerability—discussing the motivation for and results of the work as well as the multiple data sources and analytical techniques used in each. We include at the end of this section a brief discussion of the potential insights that could be gained from a more specific and focused analysis of human population dynamics. Finally, we discuss the lessons learned about integrative studies of the human-environment systems.

THE YAQUI VALLEY

The Yaqui Valley is located on the northwest coast of mainland Mexico in the state of Sonora (Plate 9). Situated on a coastal strip along the Gulf of California, the valley consists of an intensively managed agricultural region amidst a desert scrub forest and is bordered by estuarine ecosystems that provide critical habitat for migratory and resident water birds, marine mammals, fish, and shellfish populations (Flores-Verdugo, Gonzalez-Farias, and Zaragoza-Araujo, 1992). These coastal waters have long been an important center for both subsistence and the export fishing industry. The Yaqui Valley region is of vital economic importance to Mexico both in terms of its agricultural production and fish production. Today the Yaqui Valley consists of 225,000 hectares (ha) of irrigated wheat-based agriculture, and it is one of the country's most productive breadbaskets (Naylor, Falcon, and Puente-González, 2001). Using a combination of irrigation, high fertilizer rates, and modern cultivars (Matson, Naylor, and Ortiz-Monasterio, 1998), valley farmers produce some of the highest wheat yields in the world (Food and Agriculture Organization, 1997). The region also maintains the most productive fisheries in Mexico, with sardines and shrimp among the most important species (CONAPESCA, 2002). In recent years the region has also developed the second-largest shrimp aquaculture industries in Mexico (CONAPESCA, 2002). However, in a world of globalized markets, reduced subsidies and price supports, drought, hurricanes, and other forces, many farmers and fishers in the region are concerned about maintaining production and household incomes.

Like many developing regions, the Yaqui Valley is undergoing rapid socioeconomic and ecological changes. Population growth, urbanization, agricultural intensification, expanded livestock operations, and coastal aquaculture development are just some of the major developments in the area.

People and Land: A Brief History

In the early 1900s the land in the Yaqui Valley was primarily under the control of large landholders (Lewis, 2002). However, the land tenure in the region began to change in the aftermath of the 1910 Mexican Revolution, when Article 27 of the Mexican Constitution established the *ejido* land reform program and declared all land ultimately the property of the nation. While private property was allowed in principle under the new system, Article 27 established a legal limit on private landholdings of 100 irrigated hectares or the "non-irrigated equivalent."[1] Furthermore, Article 27 man-

---

[1]Article 27 defines "non-irrigated equivalent" as follows: one hectare of irrigated land is assumed to be equal to two hectares of rain-fed agricultural land, four hectares of pasture land and eight hectares of grazing land.

dated that the state reserved the right to expropriate private landholdings when they exceeded the legal limit and to reclaim *ejido* lands when they were improperly managed.

The first major land distribution in southern Sonora was in the 1930s under President Lazaro Cardenas. The Cardenas administration expropriated nearly 120,000 ha and distributed it to over 5,000 *ejidatario*s (collectives of peasants) (Hernandez, Quiñónez, and Naranjo, 1981). The vast majority of the redistributed land was managed collectively for grazing and rain-fed agriculture (Dabdoub, 1980). However, by the mid-1900s, land use and management began to rapidly change.

The Agriculture System

In the mid-twentieth century, the Mexican government and the international development community identified the Yaqui Valley as an appropriate center for agricultural development. In 1943, Normal Borlag, working for the Mexican government and the Rockefeller Foundation, launched a wheat research program that was the forerunner of the International Maize and Wheat Improvement Center (CIMMYT), located in Ciudad Obregon, which remains in the region today (Naylor et al., 2001). Later, a national agricultural experiment center (CIANO) was also established in the valley. Because the region is agroclimatically representative of 40 percent of the developing world's wheat-growing areas, it was selected as an ideal place for the early wheat improvement program.

The climate of the region is semiarid, with variable precipitation rates averaging 317 mm yr-1, which made the development of irrigation reservoirs essential for agricultural intensification. By 1963, three dams had been constructed, supplying irrigation water to 233,000 ha (Naylor et al., 2001). However, the construction of these reservoirs did not eliminate the region's sensitivity to climatic extremes. Prolonged droughts, such as the one that has persisted in the region since 1994, have led to dramatic declines in total reservoir volume, increases in well pumping, and reduced water allocations to farmers, resulting in less than 50,000 ha in production in 2003. Meanwhile, recent studies have pointed to the concerns that increasing temperatures resulting from global warming may lead to decreased wheat yields (e.g., Lobell et al., 2002).

The use of fertilizer nitrogen has increased markedly in the past three decades; between 1968 and 1995, fertilizer application rates for wheat production increased from 80 to 250 kg N ha–1. Today the most common agronomic practice for wheat production in the valley is a preplanting broadcast application of urea or injection of anhydrous ammonium (at the rate of 150-200 kg N ha–1), followed by irrigation (the preplanting irrigation is intended to aid in weed control by causing germination of weeds that can then be plowed under prior to planting). As we discuss later, the causes and consequences of these management approaches have been one focus of our studies in the region.

As agricultural development and intensification have proceeded, concerns about the quality of agricultural soils have increased. Approximately one-third of the soils of the valley are thought to be vulnerable to salinization. Today, approximately 19,000 ha have salinity levels high enough to reduce productivity. Management approaches that reduce groundwater tables and improve drainage, along with the use of large amounts of relatively low-salt freshwater in irrigation, prevent much broader salinization problems. However, as the availability of high-quality freshwater from the reservoirs has declined drastically due to long-term drought, dependence on groundwater from wells has increased. In areas in which high salinity well water is present, vulnerability to salinization will increase.

Although agricultural management practices have changed during the past three decades, wheat has remained the dominant crop. Harvested winter wheat averaged 130,000 ha in the late 1970s, ranging up to 190,000 ha currently. Other crops, however, have increased or decreased in area planted over the same time frame. Planted hectares of cotton have declined since the 1950s, whereas alfalfa, garbanzo beans, vegetables, and fruit crops have increased (Naylor et al., 2001). The proportion of vegetables planted has increased eight-fold since the early 1980s, while the proportion of fruit trees has quadrupled in the past decade.

This growth in agriculture was accompanied by an increase in population in the region, at an annual rate of 7 percent between 1950 and 1960. Most of the growth in population in the region in recent years has occurred in the two major population centers, Ciudad Obregon (population approximately 250,000) and Navajoa (population approximately 100,000). While high growth in these urban centers continues, over the last two decades the populations in the rural areas have remained remarkably stable (Figure 10-1). We currently have very little information on the source of the increase, whether it is from immigration or internal growth. Nor can we say with complete certainty that the increase is a result of the government's purposeful development of agriculture in the region (discussed below). It seems likely, however, that the development of the irrigation district, which provides water to both agricultural and nonagricultural (urban) users, as well as the influx of technological assistance in the form of national and international agricultural experiment stations, allowed the support of many more people than the arid region was earlier able to support.

Coastal Zone

Between 1940 and the 1970s, during the peak of agricultural intensification and expansion, land redistributions to *ejidos* were minimal, as gov-

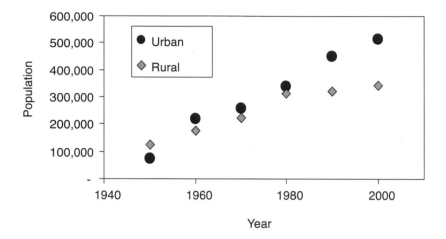

FIGURE 10-1   Population changes in the urban and rural sectors in the Yaqui region. Urban defined by the five largest cities in the region: Cuidad Obregon, Empalme, Guaymas, Huatabampo, and Navajoa (these are population centers that currently have populations of 25,000 or greater).
SOURCE: From Instituto Nacional de Estadistica, Geografía, y Informáticancy (INEGI) census years 1950-2000.

ernment support moved away from the *ejido* sector toward the private sector.   Finally, in 1976, in response to continued peasant rebellions demanding land, the Luis Echeverria administration redistributed almost 100,000 ha to local peasants and formed 62 new *ejidos* in the region (Cristiani, 1984). Only about one-third of these lands was irrigated, and most of the other two-thirds was made up of near coastal lands that were seen to have little or no productive use at the time (Dabdoub, 1980). However, by the early to mid-1990s, with the rise of shrimp farming in the region, these coastal lands that were once seen as wastelands began to be perceived as potential gold mines.

Shrimp farming, part of the Blue Revolution (similar to the Green Revolution), was first introduced to the region as a government-supported program.   In the late-1980s, the administration of President Carlos Salinas distributed over 5,000 ha of nonarable coastal lands in southern Sonora to approximately 2,000 new *ejidatarios* as part of a state program that provided technical and financial assistance to the *ejido* sector for shrimp farm development.   Despite these initial efforts, the industry did not begin to grow rapidly until almost a decade later, when a series of policy reforms opened the region to private investors (Luers, 2003).

Recent Policy Changes

During the 1990s the use and management of lands in both the upland and coastal regions began to rapidly change, as did the individuals who operated the lands (as noted below, one important result has been the transfer of lands from the *ejido* to private sector). These changes were driven in large part by a series of legal, economic, and institutional reforms promulgated in the 1980s and 1990s by the Mexican government to integrate rural Mexico into the global economy. The most important of these policy reforms included (1) the development of a 15-year program of direct income payments to farmers (PROCAMPO), linked to the abolition of input subsidies and price supports; (2) the reduction in the government's institutional involvement in agriculture, including privatizing the Mexican Fertilizer Company (FERTIMEX) and the reduction in government credit subsidies (BANRURAL); (3) the decentralization of operating authority and funding responsibilities for irrigation systems to local water user groups via the Water Laws of 1992 and 1994; (4) the amendment of Article 27 of the Constitution of Mexico, which made possible the legal sale, rental, and mortgage of previously inalienable *ejido* land (the amendment created a process that provided *ejidos* for the first time transferable titles to their land); (5) the adoption of the North American Free Trade Agreement (NAFTA), which led to large changes in prices of many agricultural inputs and outputs; (6) modifications to the fisheries law, which legalized the direct private investment in the shrimp industry and removed long-standing rules that restricted the capture and cultivation of shrimp to the *ejido* and cooperative sectors; and (7) modifications to the foreign investment laws, which allowed up to 100 percent foreign ownership of industries in Mexico. Many of these political-economic liberalization policies parallel those in Vietnam and China with similar impacts on land use (see Seto, Chapter 8).

Prior to these changes, the government was the primary investor in the nascent shrimp farming industry. In addition, government involvement in the Mexican agricultural sector provided price supports for agricultural products and input subsidies on water, credit, and fertilizer that by 1990 represented about 13 percent of the Mexican federal budget (Naylor et al., 2001). The planned reforms replaced these policies and, in effect, shifted responsibility for agriculture and aquaculture from government to the private and *ejido* sectors, leading to many changes regarding how and by whom land and water resources are being used. Prior to the reforms, in the Yaqui Valley region, 56 percent of the total agricultural area and 72 percent of producers were *ejidatarios* (Puente-González, 1999; Comisión Nacional del Agua, 1998), whereas 40 percent of the total aquaculture area was controlled by *ejidos* (Luers, 2003); however, changes in the *ejido* land reform program have led to the transfer of both ownership and management of lands throughout the region from *ejido* back to the private sector (Lewis, 2002; Luers, 2003).

A focus of our research has been to understand how these and other policy reforms coupled with biophysical variability and change have influenced land use decisions, environmental conditions, and the sustainability and vulnerability of people and ecosystems in the region.

CONCEPTUAL THEMES AND RESEARCH FRAMEWORKS

Our research on the drivers and consequences of changes in land use and resource use has followed several related themes. In a sense, these themes track the evolutionary thinking and perspectives that our team experienced during 10 years of research in the valley. Indeed, the conceptual framework that we are applying now in most of our studies (described in the vulnerability section) is a product of our prior experience in the valley, as well as the experiences of our collaborators in other places. All of these themes deal with sustainability issues in one form or another; all of them address interactions in human-environment systems, although population dynamics have been very inadequately evaluated. In the following sections, we discuss research questions and results; research participants; approaches, methods, and data sources; and plans for continued research on (1) integrating ecological and economic perspectives in agriculture, (2) land use change and interactions on the landscape, and (3) vulnerability and resilience. Although work is ongoing in all three areas, we present them in the chronological order in which they were initiated. We conclude this section with a short discussion of critical aspects of these themes related to population dynamics, some of which we are currently exploring in our research.

Linking Ecological and Economic Perspectives in Intensive Agriculture

Beginning in 1993, we evaluated questions about nitrogen (N) fertilizer use and efficiency in the Yaqui Valley, asking how farmers managed fertilizer and why, what the consequences of their fertilizer practices were for crop yields and also for environmentally important losses of nitrate and trace gases, and what alternatives were available to them to reduce fertilizer losses to the environment. Our research was driven not only by broad issues related to agriculture and global environmental change, but also by concerns about plant nutrient use efficiency and farmer economic well-being. Three principal investigators—an economist, an agronomist, and a biogeochemist-ecologist—initiated the project.

Worldwide, inputs of nitrogen in agriculture have been increasing rapidly and represent an enormous change in the global nitrogen cycle (Vitousek and Matson, 1993; Vitousek et al., 1997). Production of fertilizer nitrogen and the planting of legume crops together fix more nitrogen annually than is fixed by biological nitrogen fixation in all natural terrestrial ecosystems. These enhanced inputs of nitrogen are critical to crop yield, but they also affect losses of nitrogen from soils to freshwater and marine systems and greenhouse gases and air pollutants to the atmosphere. When we began our study, the consequences of fertilizer management for emission of trace gases and nitrate losses in developing world agricultural systems had not yet been evaluated; it was one of several outstanding questions related to global atmospheric change as defined by the international global change research community (the International Geosphere-Biosphere Program—Matson and Ojima, 1990). Had only a biogeochemist been involved in this work, the analysis might have stopped there. However, we also were motivated by the growing dialogue focused on reconciling the needs for food with the needs of the environment (Naylor and Matson, 1993; Conway, 1997), and, importantly, we were concerned about the welfare of the farmers and their crops in the Yaqui Valley. Ultimately, we wanted to understand how and why farmers made their fertilizer management decisions and to evaluate management alternatives in terms of their ability to reduce nitrogen losses and yet to be agronomically feasible and economically attractive. The combination of researchers allowed this integrated concern to be addressed.

Using daily to weekly sampling frequencies during the six-month wheat season in two consecutive years, we measured changes in soil nutrients, soil gas fluxes, and nitrate leaching prior to and following fertilizer additions in farmers' fields and also in experimental plots (in a randomized block design with four-block replicates), in which fertilizer additions simulated farmers' practice in comparison to alternatives. This biogeochemical research involved the use of gas chromatography, chemoluminescence detection, lysimetry, isotopic labeling, and many other lab and field analytical approaches, ultimately resulting in the analysis of more than 10,000 gas and soil samples. In sites using the farmers' practice, gas fluxes were among the highest ever reported (Matson et al., 1998). We concluded that, if fluxes of nitrous oxide and nitric oxide in other intensive agricultural systems in the developing world are similarly high, agriculture is likely to be a more important source of atmosphere change than currently thought, and it will become even more critical in the future. We evaluated several alternative management practices that added less nitrogen fertilizer or added it later in the crop cycle, in closer synchrony with plant uptake. Although all of our alternatives resulted in some reduction in losses, the "best" alternative, which applied 20 percent less nitrogen per hectare and applied it during and after planting, lost less trace nitrogen gas over the entire cycle than the simulated farmers' treatment lost in just the first month.

Fertilizer use and loss are but one component of farm budgets, and farmers typically focus not only on costs, but also on the balance between costs and expected income under some degree of price and production uncertainty. For wheat farmers in the Yaqui Valley, yield of good-quality wheat provides the essential income. In our integrated analysis, when we measured yields and grain quality in the experimental plots and farmers' fields using standard agronomic measurement approaches, we found that the more nitrogen-conserving alternatives were not significantly different from the farmers' practice.

We carried out an economic analysis of farmers' costs and returns for both 1994-1995 and 1995-1996 wheat seasons, using farm-based socioeconomic survey techniques. The surveys were conducted in person by our team members as well as by Mexican collaborators who had long histories of research with farmers in the Valley. Our surveys consisted of a random sample of 58 farmers in 1994-1995 and 31 farmers in 1995-1996, stratified by farm operating size and land tenure (private versus collective landholders). Farm owners or managers relied on recorded input, yield, and price data to answer questions. The survey results indicated that fertilization was the highest direct production cost in the Yaqui Valley farm budgets and the single most important cost component in the entire budget. Given the importance of fertilizer in the valley farm budgets, we evaluated the extent to which savings in terms of increased fertilizer efficiency represented a significant budgetary savings to the farmers. In contrasting the farmers' practice with our "best" alternative in terms of reduced trace gas losses and total nitrogen losses, we found that the alternative resulted in a savings equivalent to 12-17 percent savings of after-tax profits from wheat farming in the valley.

We are currently working on social and private profitability in the valley, especially critical in the current policy and global market environment, and conducting similar farm-based surveys. This earlier work also led to a series of studies by Ortiz-Monasterio, in his role as an agronomist at CIMMYT on reliable nitrogen diagnostic tests and other metrics that provide information to farmers that they can use to reduce overfertilization. It also led to studies by David Lobell and Greg Asner (a Stanford Ph.D. student and research scientist at the Carnegie Institution, respectively) on new remote sensing–based techniques to estimate yield and the factors that regulate variation in yields over space and time at the regional scale. One Ph.D. thesis (Avalos Sartorio, 1997) and one undergraduate honors thesis (Harris, 1997) at Stanford originated from this area of research.

Land Use Decisions and the Provision of Ecosystem Services

Our early work on agriculture and environment in the Yaqui region demonstrated to us some of the tight linkages between the agricultural sector and other components of resource use and development in the valley. For example, it became clear that agricultural land use and management decisions were highly related to the availability of water as well as input subsidies, and that policy changes that affected both needed to be evaluated. Likewise, we realized that fertilizer management decisions were likely to influence the marine systems adjacent to the valley. Starting in 1996, with an expanded team that included remote sensing scientists, geographers, and hydrologists as well as ecologists, economists, and agronomists, we evaluated the causes and consequences of land use change and land management decisions across the valley. Land use issues had become a central focus for many disciplines in the global change and geography research communities, and the mid-1990s were a period of intense analysis on drivers and consequences (for people and environment) of land use change (see Lambin, Geist, and Lepers, 2003, for a review). In our analysis of land use changes in the Yaqui Valley, we contributed to the body of research attempting to draw general understanding about land use dynamics. In doing so, we also joined the discussion and debate around the topic of agricultural intensification and its role in "sparing land for nature" (Waggoner, 1994). We hypothesized that the intensification of agriculture over the decades of the Green Revolution in the Yaqui Valley would be related to many off-site consequences, including those related to urbanization, nutrient transfers downwind and downstream, and extensive land use changes in surrounding areas.

Much of this research (funded by the National Aeronautics and Space Administration) used time-series remote sensing data to examine land cover changes inside and outside the intensive irrigation district. We accumulated information on such things as the valley-wide irrigation systems, land ownership, and population using municipal, state, and national databases, and we used a database of farm-scale and *ejido*-scale socioeconomic survey information from our own work (see the earlier section for details on typical survey sampling) and from the long-term CIMMYT surveys to track changes in agricultural yields, varieties, and fertilizer use over the past 40 years.

We found that intensive, irrigated agriculture increased in area by only 6.5 percent over the past 30 years, but that dramatic increases in wheat yields and fertilizer use, as well as rapid adoption of new varieties of wheat, characterized a rapidly changing agricultural region. During this period, land owners diversified by changing summer crops and increasing tree crops. In addition, during the decades of the 1980s, there was an estimated 15-fold increase in pigs and poultry in the valley. By 1996, production was approximately 350,000 head and 6 million birds (Naylor et al., 2001).

Some of these changes can be explained by policies put in place by the Mexican national government. In the 1970s and 1980s, a set of domestic policies that included price supports, input subsidies, and consumer subsidies, adding up to 18 percent of federal budget, supported intensification and livestock diversification (Naylor et al., 2001). According to our analysis, approximately 33 percent of gross farm income came from subsidies in the 1980s and encouraged continued increase in inputs. During the 1990s, these and other subsidies changed with the suite of liberalization policies we have described. In 2000, price supports for wheat were reintroduced due to falling farm incomes and heightened competition from the United States, where farm supports are much higher. We are still trying to understand the consequences of these earlier and more recent and dramatic policy changes.

Other dramatic changes in cropping systems occurred during this time frame as well, not because of planned policy changes but due to unplanned shocks. Until 1993, the most consistent cropping pattern in the valley was wheat as the winter crop and soybeans as the summer crop. Between 1993 and 1996, whitefly outbreaks decreased soybean area from 69,000 ha in 1991 to 0 ha in 1996. One response by farmers was to increase the area of sorghum and summer maize, both of which receive much more nitrogen fertilizer than the previous soybean crops. As noted later, this unplanned change has consequences for off-site effects.

While the land area under intensive agriculture remained constant over our study period, intensification in the form of increasing fertilizer inputs influenced off-site ecosystems through their effects on nutrient use and loss. We estimated nitrogen loss from current fertilization practices in comparison with earlier practices (using the NLoSS simulation model developed by Bill Riley as part of our earlier project; Riley and Matson, 2000), and found that the typical farmer practice results in very large losses of nitrogen relative to losses of just 10 years ago. These losses influence the functioning of both the surface water systems draining the valley as well as the coastal ecosystems of the Sea of Cortez. Two Ph.D. dissertations in terrestrial biogeochemistry (Harrison, 2002; Harrison and Matson, in press) and marine biogeochemistry (Beman et al., 2005) and one undergraduate honors thesis (Rice, 1995) have focused on the processing of agricultural and urban effluents in the surface waters and coastal marine system adjacent to the valley. In addition, Esther Cruz from the Center for Conservation and Use of Natural Resources (CECARENA) in Guaymas, Mexico, and several Stanford professors in engineering and earth sciences have begun a focused study of estuarine and open ocean circulation, ultimately to be tied to ocean biogeochemical processes that link to activities on land.

Water resource issues related to the intensive and nonefficient use of water in irrigation also characterized the period of study. Although we have not examined the off-site consequences of water diversions from the Yaqui and other rivers, we recently have examined the components of decision making in the irrigation district that have led to severe overdraw of reservoir water during the recent five years of drought. An additional Ph.D. dissertation in water resource engineering and policy modeling (Addams, 2004), plus considerable research by collaborator Jose Luis Minjares in the

Mexican National Water Commission have detailed the structure, function, and constraints in the water sector, leading to policy changes in the way water allocation decisions are made.

In addition to the off-site biogeochemical and hydrologic consequences, we evaluated the extent to which land use changes in the surrounding natural coastal lands accompanied and could be related to intensification in the irrigation district. Our assessment of coastal land use dynamics was based on the analysis of satellite time-series data and formal interviews with *ejido* households and shrimp farm managers. Using a combination of supervised and unsupervised maximum likelihood classification, we produced thematic land use and land cover maps of subscenes from two mosaicked Landsat images from 1973 (MSS), 1992 (MSS), and 2001 (ETM) for change detection and modeling. In addition, we conducted 131 formal household interviews with 41 different coastal *ejidos* (controlling approximately 70 percent of coastal *ejido* land) and 88 formal interviews with private and *ejido* shrimp farms. We set out to conduct interviews in all the coastal *ejidos* and operating shrimp farms in our study region. However, we had to reduce the sample size slightly due to difficulties with locating households of members for several *ejidos* and making successful contacts with a few *ejido* farms. We conducted 2-5 household interviews in each *ejido* we included. One interview was with a member of the *ejido* governing committee, and the others were randomly selected.

Our results indicated a very rapid and relatively recent expansion of land use changes in the coastal zone, with coastal wetlands and mud flats being converted to aquaculture ponds at an increasing rate (Luers, 2003). Our analyses suggest that this expansion has been facilitated by reforms in the fisheries and foreign investment laws, changes in the rural credit system, and the constitutional reform of land tenure laws (Article 27), which allows *ejidos* for the first time to rent and sell their land (a significant share of which is coastal land) (Naylor et al., 2001; Lewis, 2002; Luers, 2003). These policy reforms and their impacts on coastal aquaculture development mirror similar processes and land use changes in the Red River Delta in Vietnam, discussed in this volume (Seto, Chapter 8).

Our surveys further suggest that a large part of the private shrimp farm development has been carried out by private agricultural farmers from the irrigation district who have had the capital or access to credit to allow them to diversify their production activities. Thus, agricultural intensification in the irrigation district and the expansion of aquaculture appear to be directly linked. Our findings highlight the importance of looking beyond simplistic single-cause explanations of land use and land cover dynamics and toward explanations that incorporate both endogenous and exogenous factors that lead to different opportunities and constraints on land use and land cover changes (Lambin et al., 2003).

Taken together, our analyses suggest managed and natural ecosystems in the Yaqui region are linked biogeochemically, hydrologically, ecologically, and economically (Matson et al., no date-a, no date-b). Decisions made in the intensive agricultural area affect off-site areas in a number of ways, many of which may negatively affect natural ecosystems and the services (clean water, healthy fisheries, conservation of species) that they provide.

Vulnerability and Resilience

As we studied a place undergoing rapid change through changes in national and international policies, the globalization of markets, and variations in climate (including drought), we identified dramatic differences in the way individuals could respond. This concern about vulnerability and response has likewise become a focal point in the international realm. As policy makers shift their attention from broad assessments of potential global change impacts to specific preventive and mitigative action, the global change research community is increasingly focusing on questions about the vulnerability and resilience of people and ecosystems to environmental change (Liverman, 1994; Dow, 1992; Cutter, 1996; Kelly and Adger, 2000; Bohle, 2001). This focus on vulnerability is particularly evident in the climate change assessments. The latest publications of the Intergovernmental Panel on Climate Change are dedicated to questions of vulnerability, which they define as "the degree to which a system is susceptible to, or unable to cope with, adverse effects of climate change, including climate variability and extremes" (Intergovernmental Panel on Climate Change, 2001).

Much of the vulnerability literature focuses on either the biophysical hazards or social aspects of vulnerability separately. However, in recent years, there have been efforts to integrate these approaches (Folke et al., 2002; Downing et al., 2000; Turner et al., 2003a). Members of the Yaqui Valley research team, working in collaboration with scientists from Clark University, Harvard University, and the Stockholm Environmental Institute, developed a conceptual framework for integrating social and biophysical processes to address questions of vulnerability (Turner et al., 2003a, 2003b). We extended this work to explore quantitative approaches of analyzing vulnerability in the Yaqui Valley (Luers et al., 2003).

In our multidimensional framework, vulnerability, defined as a function of exposure, sensitivity, and adaptive capacity, is manifested in the interactions of social and ecological systems (Figure 10-2). In our analysis of the agricultural region of the Yaqui Valley, we used this framework to identify the critical interactions and feedbacks that mediate the responses of

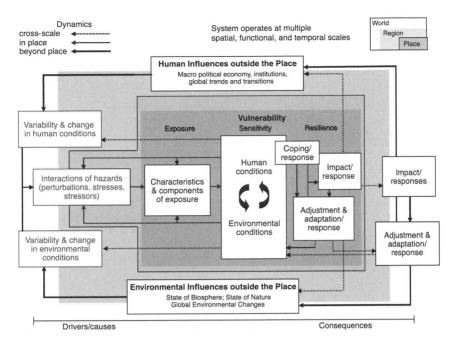

FIGURE 10-2 A framework for evaluating the vulnerability of a linked human-environmental system subjected to multiple and interacting forces. Compenents of the vulnerability framework are identified and inked to factors beyond the system of study and operating a various aptial scales. Temporal dimensions are omitted. SOURCE: Turner et al. (2003a).

both social and biophysical parts of the system to external and internal stresses and shocks.

In the valley, the changes in the suite of national policies in the 1990s related to farm and fishing commodities (see above) are external forces that have removed significant financial support and exposed land owners and managers to the vagaries of the international market. Biological shocks such as whitefly invasion, continue to force farmers to respond through changes in management and in production patterns. Climate shocks and the ongoing drought are forcing farmers to consider alternate crops and changes in irrigation management, at the same time that policy changes with respect to water resource allocation are potentially opening new opportunities for efficient use of water. And on top of these changes themselves, the uncertainties associated with some of them (e.g., drought, commodity prices, exchange rates) have made planning and decision making very difficult (Naylor et al., 2001). The ability of farmers to respond to these and other stresses is likely to depend on both their social and bio-physical resources, as well as how those resources are changing in response to the stresses. If so, the vulnerability of farmers in the valley may be very heterogeneous, potentially leading to winners and losers. We have begun to explore these issues using various analytical techniques.

One approach we have taken is to estimate the vulnerability of selected outcome variables of concern (e.g., agricultural yield) to identified stresses (e.g., climate change) as a function of the state of the variables of concern relative to a threshold of damage, the sensitivity of the variables to the stresses, and the magnitude and frequency of the stressors to which the system is exposed. Our proposed metric of vulnerability is distinct from many previous efforts to quantify vulnerability, which have focused more generally on identifying sets of proxy vulnerability indicators for a place or population of interest (Downing et al., 2000).

We used this metric of vulnerability to begin to evaluate the relative vulnerability of wheat yields to temperature variability and change, as well as market fluctuations. The data on wheat yields for this analysis were based on yield estimates derived from Landsat Thematic Mapping (TM) and ETM+ data for four years, 1994, 2000, 2001, and 2002, as described in detail by Lobell et al. (2003). Building on this analysis, we developed a linear least-squares regression model of yield with average nighttime temperature for January-April (Luers et al., 2003) to define the sensitivity. We then calculated the vulnerability using a threshold value of 4 tons/ha, which is the approximate average minimum yield required for farmers to break even (i.e., zero net profit) based on average management practices.

Our analysis suggests a skewed distribution of vulnerability to temperature variability and change in the study region, with most farmers exhibiting low vulnerabilities and a few farmers with high vulnerability. In addition, our method revealed that valley farmers, without adaptations, are on average more vulnerable to a 10 percent decrease in wheat prices than a 1 degree (C) increase in average minimum temperature. Finally, we found that soils and management both contributed to relative vulnerabilities in the region; however, it appears that the some constraints imposed by poor soil types can be overcome by improved management practices.

A recent focus of our work in the valley has been to examine the relative vulnerability of farmers and their agricultural ecosystems to long-term drought. As noted earlier, Yaqui Valley agriculture relies on irrigation, with the water largely derived from surface reservoirs draining the Yaqui watershed, with an additional small contribution pumped from private and public wells in the valley. Now in its ninth year of drought, reservoir levels are at less than a third of their long-term values, and water allocations have been reduced throughout the valley, resulting in less than 20 percent of the valley's agricultural area in production. Our research team is exploring the social and biophysical factors that created the current crisis and the alternatives and constraints that the valley farmers face today.

Switching crops from wheat to less water-intensive crops like garbanzo and safflower is one alternative being considered (Naylor et al., 2001), although such changes are highly influenced by global markets and the skewed subsidy–price support environment that the farmers find themselves in, with wheat being more strongly supported than other crops. In addition, crop choice is influenced by the emergence of new diseases in the alternatives. An additional option that farmers are considering is increasing the pumping of water from aquifers. However, aquifer water is often too saline to apply directly to fields. Most wells pump water directly to canals, so that mixing with the less saline surface water reduces the salinity to acceptable levels. In the 2003-2004 crop cycle, most farmers did not have access to reservoir water and the very limited planted area received water directly from the wells to fields. If water from the reservoir continues to be limited, this practice will create salinity problems for at least some of the valley's soils. However, analyses by team members suggest that the energy-related costs of pumping are themselves prohibitive, and thus groundwater, whatever its salinity, is not a profitable approach at this time (Addams, 2004).

Our analysis of the region's vulnerability to drought draws on a combination of hydrologic modeling, remote sensing analysis, and household surveys. Lee Addams and Jose Luis Minjares from our team have developed a model of the water basin and water distribution system that we are using to assess alternative management plans. Meanwhile, David Lobell and Greg Asner are using Landsat TM and MODIS satellite images to assess the effect of water stress on yield for different crops under different management regimes. Farmers' responses to the drought and reservoir draw-down are also being analyzed in a masters thesis (McCulloch, 2004). These studies are being coordinated with household interviews that focus on management practices, risk perception, and responses to the drought crisis. Of particular interest is how the prolonged drought will influence the relocation of people and resources in the region.

Population Dynamics in the Yaqui Valley: Critical Missing Pieces in the Analyses

As our work evolved over the past decade, it became increasingly clear that we needed an explicit focus on population dynamics if we were to succeed in understanding the social and human dynamics associated with land use in this region. We began to incorporate population data through two sources: census data and household surveys. Although the census data provide general information, such as age structure, gender, and household size, they lack detailed household-level information about income, migration, and health of the population. What we do know from the census data is that urban populations are increasing and rural populations are remaining relatively stable at the municipality level. For example, the population of the municipality of Cajeme has increased by nearly seven-fold since 1950. Most of this increase has occurred in the city of Obregon, where the official population has increased from 31,000 in 1950 to 251,000 in 2000.

One of the current research activities is to examine demographic dynamics at the locality level by combining data from demographic surveys and census into a spatial context using a geographic information system. Our preliminary results indicate that there are huge variations in population structure and growth rates over space and time. Of the 31 localities in Cajeme for which we have a comprehensive data set spanning 1950 to 2000, 12 have experienced a decline in population since 1950. In the most extreme case, the locality of Daniel Leyva Higuera has seen a decline in population from 299 in 1950 to 6 in 2000. Yet this pattern of population decline is not limited to localities in Cajeme. Other such municipalities as Guaymas, Etchojoa, and Navajoa also have localities with shrinking populations. Thus, throughout the Yaqui Valley, larger towns are growing faster than smaller ones, and, in many cases, smaller localities are disappearing. We lack an understanding of why these changes are occurring and their direct role in land use changes in the Yaqui Valley. Our household surveys provided detailed information about household characteristics, but the surveys were designed to collect information about different sectors of the population (e.g., aquaculture households, farmers) and not of the entire population. We were unable to extrapolate our survey data to characterize household dynamics for the entire region.

A second missing piece of information that is critical to analyses of land use change is spatially disaggregated data on migration. These data can be obtained through household surveys or estimated via the "residual method," whereby the rate of natural increase is estimated (births minus deaths) and then deducted from the total population increase. The result is then attributed to emigration or immigration. We hypothesize that many of the population changes have occurred in the region as a response to exogenous shocks. For example, it is likely that purposeful economic and technological development of the region during the early years of the Green Revolution encouraged in-migration. Over time, however, improving mechanization and increasing sizes of lands being managed by single owners may have resulted in surplus agricultural workers. Whether these workers migrated out of the region or were absorbed by local urban or rural economies is unclear from the available census data. Ciudad Obregon and Navajoa experienced significant economic and urban growth over the last three decades, but population data aggregated at the city level make it difficult to answer questions about inter- and intracity socioeconomic differentiation and income and welfare dynamics. Furthermore, the census data classify population based on residence; a household is labeled rural if the home structure is located in a nonurban place. As it becomes more common for rural residents to work in the city, this urban-rural dichotomy may not be sufficient to fully describe the demographic characteristics of the area, nor for accounting for the role of population on land use change. How significant is rural nonfarm employment and incomes to rural households, and how has this contributed to out-migration? Likewise, have changes in Article 27 that allow *ejido* land to be rented and sold resulted in significant alteration of ownership patterns and out-migration, and, if so, what are the consequences for land uses?

Information on population and household dynamics are even more important in the study of vulnerability. Our conceptual vulnerability framework directs us to examine the access of individuals and groups to human and social resources as well as biophysical capital. We know that access to credit and information varies among communities and individuals (Naylor et al., 2001), but we can only surmise that differential access is influenced by population dynamics. Are different components of the population differentially at risk under external pressures resulting from policy changes or climate change? As the land tenure law changes lead to changes in ownership, will they decrease or increase the vulnerability of the *ejido* population? Does the level of education, household size, age structure, or other population variables influence the ability of people to respond to external stresses? How have neighborhoods and place-based community ties influenced information sharing and risk management?

While it is easy to state such questions, access to and development of appropriate data that allow their answers are more difficult. As we discuss later, such information is surprisingly unavailable at desired scales of analysis. Thus, it is apparent that addressing them will require focused on-the-ground research at a level that our team has not yet engaged in.

LESSONS LEARNED: CHALLENGES FOR INTEGRATING NATURAL AND SOCIAL SCIENCES

Our work in the Yaqui Valley incorporates multiple data sources and types, including social surveys, annual compendium, archival maps, remote sensing imagery, administrative boundaries, and soil, water, and plant data collected in situ and analyzed at multiple institutions. From our efforts to integrate these data emerged a number of challenges related to the scale, availability, compatibility, and integration of biophysical and social data. Likewise, our research integrates the perspectives and knowledge of many disciplines and ranges across a knowledge-action continuum. These interactions have resulted in significant complexities in collaboration and funding issues. In the following sections, we discuss some of those challenges and how we addressed them.

Scale Issues

We encountered two specific scale-related issues related to the unit of analysis and temporal dynamics. One of the objectives of the Yaqui project as it has evolved today is to make the research results available to farmers and policy makers in order to influence and assist in decision making. Toward this end, our analysis must be conducted at a unit that is policy relevant. Where we have integrated remote sensing with household-level data, we have defined the "farm unit" as a Landsat TM pixel. Although the pixel does not correspond with either the operational or the management unit, it is the smallest observational scale and thus could be aggregated to correspond with the decision-making unit. Alternatively, the analysis could be conducted at the management unit and resampled to be consistent with the scale of the imagery. Which unit of analysis is most appropriate and how should the data be integrated?

In addition, we are studying farm management and land use change at the substate level, whereas most policy decisions are made at the federal or state level. Do environmental changes at the local level warrant policy action at the federal level? Similarly, are incentive structures set by federal and state policy compatible with the constraints and development goals of the southern Sonoran region? Scale issues in the policy domain pose particularly difficult problems in analyzing sustainability challenges.

A related issue is that of temporal dynamics. In a rapidly changing region like the Yaqui Valley, what is the temporal scale (study period) and temporal resolution (frequency of observation) required to capture land system dynamics? Data acquired in decadal cycles may not provide a complete picture of the fluctuations and interannual variability of the coupled human-environment system.

Availability of Biophysical Data

We have used a suite of field methods to monitor ecosystem dynamics and their responses to multiple external forcings. In part due to the composition of our research team and in part due to our research questions, one of the strengths of this project is the wealth of biophysical data collected over the life of the project. There have been significant challenges and difficulties with collecting biophysical data, including setting up and maintaining analytical instrumentation, transporting samples across international borders, and managing tremendous amounts of data being collected at fine temporal resolution and analyzed at different places. The collaboration with CIMMYT researchers and the use of the CIMMYT labs in Ciudad Obregon considerably reduced these difficulties. Such research would not have been possible without a well-established and well-protected laboratory in situ, and without the relationships between principal investigator Ortiz-Monasterio and the local farmers who allowed us access to their fields.

Availability of Social Data

Social scientists have a long tradition of studying human behavior with the use of data on the individual or some aggregation thereof (e.g., household, administrative units, firms). Two methods to obtain these data include conducting a survey designed for the research project and using figures published by a government statistics bureau. We used both approaches in Yaqui and encountered different challenges in each case.

Over the course of our project, we carried out three farm-level surveys on general agricultural conditions, with each survey focused on a particular topic: nitrogen fertilizer applications (1994, 1996, 2001, 2003), farm management practices (1996, 2001, 2003), and land ownership and rental agreements (1999) (Naylor et al., 2001; Lewis, 2002; Lobell et al., 2005). Using structured and in-depth interviews, we developed a rich data set on farm characteristics, with much less information at the household level. A principal advantage with conducting surveys is the ability to acquire exact (or proxy) variables of interest (e.g., farm profits, household income, management practices). However, surveys are time- and labor-intensive, and their temporal and spatial extents are limited to the duration and budget, respectively, of the project. If the sample size is large or the distances between samples great, the cost of a survey can quickly become prohibitive. We greatly benefited from the longer term set of survey data acquired by economists at CIMMYT, in which they carried out valley-wide surveys of farmer practice and budgets starting in 1981.

We also used socioeconomic data from INEGI (Instituto Nacional de Estadística Geografía e Informática or the National Institute of Statistics, Geography, and Informatics) to provide a regular snapshot of demographic and economic trends. INEGI is an organization of the federal government of Mexico that is responsible for the collection of data on national accounts, prices, socioeconomics, and geography. Like most other government statistical bureaus, INEGI collects detailed census statistics every 10 years, as well as at higher temporal frequency for select data. These data are available at multiple spatial scales, subdivided along administrative units (e.g., state, municipality, and locality). However, while these data provide information for a large area over a long time period, they are not available with enough temporal frequency to present a detailed picture of the dynamics of the system.

Compatibility and Integration of Biophysical and Social Data

Our experience in the Yaqui Valley has shown that both social and biophysical data need to be collected via fieldwork, and that only limited information about demographic dynamics can be obtained from such sources as statistical bureaus. Critical social data have been difficult to obtain because we rely on the availability of such data from INEGI. For example, human migration patterns at a fine spatially disaggregated level are wholly absent from their database. In order to collect these data, we will have to embark on extensive household surveys. However, integrating the socioeconomic and biophysical data will be challenging due to inconsistent data and a mismatch of temporal and spatial scales. While conceptually simple, the incompatibility of data makes integration a methodological challenge.

Understanding How the World Works Versus Solution-Oriented Research: Project Evolution

The long-term nature of this project allows us to think about project evolution and issues related to knowledge production and use. Our early interactions were among only three investigators—Matson (ecologist), Naylor (economist), and Ortiz-Monasterio (agronomist)—and their research groups. Our research was driven by broader issues related to agriculture and environmental change; our funding for the scientific work was from the U.S. Department of Agriculture, and for the economic analysis from the Ford Foundation and the Pew Charitable Trusts. The process of bringing our perspectives together in our research design was enlightening—and it is fair to say that the kinds of questions that we ultimately asked together, and the kinds of measurements that we made, were different from what any one of us would have made alone. In this first study, we did not involve stakeholders, although Ortiz-Monasterio's close connection with farmers of the Yaqui Valley provided considerable real-life perspective to our work. Ultimately, that project expressed our desire to help farmers as well as the environment, and luckily our results indicated that win-win opportunities were possible with respect to fertilizer use. Even with win-win outcomes, however, adoption of new practices is not necessarily widespread (Manning, 2002). This first project, motivated by a simple but nonetheless integrative interest, was to date the most easily funded piece of Yaqui Valley research.

The perspective of concern for people and the environment established in this first study laid the groundwork for all research to follow. It was impossible to work in the Yaqui region and ignore the broader set of issues that were influencing farmer decision making: resource availability, information availability, global markets, national and international agricultural policies, etc. Likewise, it was impossible to overlook the strong possibility that decisions made in isolation by farmers were not only influencing their well-being, but also were in fact influencing people and ecosystems far away, as well as the long-term sustainability of agriculture itself. We began to think of the Yaqui Valley as a microcosm for the developing world, and we began to use it as a place to pursue questions about land use change, and the responses of human-environment systems to interacting local, regional, and global forcings.

Not surprisingly, these new perspectives attracted and demanded new kinds of participants with different expertise. Moreover, the work from the first Yaqui studies provided a base from which graduate students and undergraduate honors students could launch their research; while some of these students remained quite disciplinary in their approach to their research, others completed truly interdisciplinary research and training and have carried that perspective and knowledge base to their subsequent positions. With the support of Stanford University seed money (from the Institute of International Studies Bechtel Initiative funds) and relatively small amounts from the Packard and MacArthur foundations, our research group rapidly grew to include agricultural policy, international development policy, mathematical modeling (engineering), and remote sensing, along with economics, agronomy, and biogeochemistry. With a grant from the National Aeronautics and Space Administration Land Use/Land Cover Change program, we focused on the history of land use in the area, and the consequences of landuse decisions for the broader region. As our group and resources grew, we also increased our connections with regional nongovernmental organizations and other researchers working in the broader Sea of Cortez area. Over time, influenced by our principal investigators' interactions with the international global change research programs and the nascent international sustainability science community, we began to think about what it would take for this place to move toward sustainable resource use. With a grant from the Packard Foundation providing "matrix money" that allowed the coming together of many more researchers in the region, we expanded our project to include water resources, conservation, and marine researchers from Mexico. Importantly, we began to identify ways in which local stakeholders (including local farmers and the local research community) could be included, and we confirmed our role as one of information providers to the people of the area, as well as international researchers striving to identify generalizations in research tools and approaches that could be useful well beyond the Yaqui Valley.

Study of the Yaqui Valley has been useful in terms of identifying the dynamics of change in human-environment systems and providing tools and approaches that can help the people of the Yaqui Valley in decision making for human and environmental well-being. We did not intentionally design it to be thus, at least not in its early years. Had we done so, we probably would have included additional members of the research team, and certainly more local stakeholders. Still, thanks to the involvement of principal investigators who have practical, place-based interests, the research is probably more directly useful than many such studies by academic researchers might be. Our additional intent, however, is to contribute information and knowledge that is useful beyond the valley, in terms both of understanding global changes and developing sustainability approaches. Our best hopes for more general learning are through a comparative approach with other such case studies and through the development of tools and metrics, many of which use remote sensing and modeling, that can be applied in many places.

ACKNOWLEDGMENTS

The work of a great many researchers has made this paper possible. We thank Lee Addams, Toby Ahrens, Kevin Arrigo, Gregory Asner, David Battisti, Michael Beman, Kim Bonine, Esther Cruz, Robert Dunbar, Dagoberto Flores, Steve Gorelick, John Harrison, Peter Jewett, Jeff Koseff, Jessa Lewis, David Lobell, Ellen McCullough, José Luis Minjares, Stephen Monismith, Jane Panek, Bill Riley, and Peter Vitousek. We particularly thank Walter Falcon for his insight, advice, and assistance in all areas of this research, and Yaqui coordinator Ashley Dean, along with Mary Smith and Lori McVay, for facilitating the research of so many researchers in the valley and at Stanford.

REFERENCES

Addams, L.
   2004   Water Policy Evaluation Through Combined Hydrological-Agronomic-Economic Modeling Framework: Yaqui Valley, Sonora, Mexico. Ph.D. dissertation thesis, Stanford University.
Avalos Sartorio, B.
   1997   Modeling Nitrogen Fertilization Practices of Wheat Farmers in Mexico's Yaqui Valley. Ph.D. dissertation, Stanford University.
Beman, M., K.R. Arrigo, and P.A. Matson
   2005   Agricultural runoff fuels large phytoplankton blooms in vulnerable areas of the ocean. *Nature* 434(7030):211-213.
Blaikie, P., T. Cannon, I. Davis, and B. Wisner
   1994   *At Risk: Natural Hazards, People's Vulnerability and Disaster.* London, England: Routledge.

Bohle, H.G.
2001   Vulnerability and Criticality. Perspectives from social geography. *IHDP Newsletter of the International Human Dimension Programme on Global Environmental Change* 2:1-4.

Comisión Nacional del Agua (CNA)
1998   Clasificación de la Propiedad Agrícola de los Usuarios Ejidales y Números Ejidales en el Distrito de Riego No. 41, Río Yaqui, Sonora. Working Paper. Cd. Comisión Nacional del Agua, Obregón, Mexico.

CONAPESCA
2002   Comisión Nacional de Acuacultura y Pesca home page. Available: http://www.sagarpa.gob.mx/conapesca [accessed February 10, 2005].

Conway, G.
1997   *The Doubly Green Revolution.* Ithaca, NY: Cornell University Press.

Cristiani, B.C.
1984   *Hoy Luchamos por la Tierra.* Xochimilco, Mexico: Universidad Nacional Autonoma de Mexico.

Cutter, S.
1996   Vulnerability to environmental hazards. *Progress in Human Geography* 20(4):529-539.

Dabdoub, C.
1980   *Breve Historia del Valle del Yaqui.* Mexico City: Editores Asociades Mexicana, S.A.

Dow, K.
1992   Exploring differences in our common future(s): The meaning of vulnerability to global environmental change. *Geoforum* 23(3):417-436.

Downing, T.E., A.A. Alsthoorn, and R.S.J. Tol, eds.
1999   *Climate, Change and Risk.* London, England: Routledge.

Downing, T.E., with R. Butterfield, S. Cohen, S. Huq, R. Moss, A. Rahman, Y. Sokona, and L. Stephen
2000   Climate Change Vulnerability: Linking Impacts and Adaptation. Report to the Governing Council of the United National Environment Program. United Nations Environment Programme (UNEP), Nairobi and Environmental Change Institute, University of Oxford, Oxford.

Flores Verdugo, F., F. Gonzalez-Farias, and U. Zaragoza-Araujo
1992   Mangrove ecosystems of the Pacific Coast of Mexico: Distribution, structure, litterfall, and detritus dynamics. Pp. 269-288 in *Coastal Plant Communities of Latin America,* U. Seeliger, ed. Boston, MA: Academic Press.

Folke, C., S. Carpenter, T. Elmquist, L. Gunderson, C.S. Holling, B. Walker, J. Bengtsson, F. Berkes, J. Colding, K. Danell, M. Falkenmark, L. Gordon, R. Kasperson, N. Kautsky, A. Kinzig, S. Levin, K.-G. Möler, F. Moberg, L. Ohlsson, P. Olsson, E. Ostrom, W. Reid, J. Rockström, H. Savenije, and U. Svedin
2002   Resilience and Sustainable Development. Scientific Background Paper commissioned by the Environmental Advisory Council of the Swedish Government. International Council for Science (ICSU) Series on Science and Sustainable Development No. 3. Available: http://www.icsu.org [accessed February 5, 2005].

Food and Agriculture Organization
1997   FAOSTAT. On-line and Multilingual Database Time-Series Records Covering International Statistics. Rome, Italy: Food and Agriculture Organization, United Nations. Available: http://www.apps.fao.org/.

Harris, J.
1997   Conservation Tillage: A Viable Solution for Sustainable Agriculture in the Yaqui Valley, Mexico. Senior honors thesis, Stanford University.

Harrison, J.A.
  2002   Nitrogen Dynamics and Greenhouse Gas Production in Yaqui Valley Surface Drain-
          age Waters. Ph.D. dissertation thesis, Stanford University.
Harrison, J.A., and P.A. Matson
  in   Patterns and controls of nitrous oxide (N_2O) emissions from drainage waters of the
  press   Yaqui Valley, Sonora, Mexico. Global Biogeochemical Cycles.
Hernandez, G., R. Quiñónez, and V. Naranjo
  1981   Ejido Collectivo, Revolution Verde, y La Lucha de Classes en el Sur de Sonora.
          Xochimilco, Mexico: Universidad Nacional Autonoma de Mexico.
Intergovernmental Panel on Climate Change (IPCC)
  2001   Climate Change 2001: Impacts, Adaptation, and Vulnerability. Third Assessment
          Report of the IPCC, Cambridge, England: Cambridge University Press.
Kates, R.W., W.C. Clark, R. Corell, J.M. Hall, C.C. Jaeger, I. Lowe, J.J. McCarthy, H.J.
Schellnhuber, B. Bolin, N.M. Dickson, S. Faucheux, G.C. Gallopin, A. Grübler, B. Huntley, J.
Jäger, N.S. Jodha, R.E. Kasperson, A. Mabogunje, P. Matson, H. Mooney, B. Moore III, T.
O'Riordan, and U. Svedin
  2001   Environment and development: Sustainability science. Science 292(5517):641-642.
Kelly, P.M., and W.N. Adger
  2000   Theory and practice in assessing vulnerability to climate change and facilitating
          adaptation. Climatic Change 47:325-352.
Lambin E.F., H. Geist, and E. Lepers
  2003   Dynamics of land use and cover change in tropical regions. Annual Review of
          Environment and Resources 28:205-241.
Lewis, J.
  2002   Agrarian change and privitization of ejido land in northern Mexico. Journal of
          Agrarian Change 2(3):402-420.
Liverman, D.
  1994   Vulnerability to global environmental change. Pp. 201-216 in Global Environmen-
          tal Risk, J.X. Kasperson and R.E. Kasperson, eds. Tokyo, Japan: United Nations
          University Press.
Lobell, D.B., and G.P. Asner
  2003   Comparison of earth observing-1 ALI and Landsat ETM+ for crop identification
          and yield prediction in Mexico. IEEE Transactions on Geoscience and Remote
          Sensing 41(6):1277-1282.
Lobell, D.B., J.I. Ortiz-Monasterio, C.L. Addams, and G.P. Asner
  2002   Soil, climate, and management impacts on regional wheat productivity in Mexico
          from remote sensing. Agricultural and Forest Meteorology 114:31-43.
Lobell, D.B., G.P. Asner, J.I. Ortiz-Monasterio, and Y. Benning
  2003   Remote sensing of regional crop production in the Yaqui Valley, Mexico: Estimates
          and uncertainties. Agricultural, Ecosystems, and Environment 114:31-43.
Lobell, D.B., I. Ortiz-Monasterio, G.P. Asner, R.L. Naylor, and W.P. Falcon
  2005   Combining field surveys, remote sensing, and regression trees to understand yield
          variations in an irrigated wheat landscape. Agronomy Journal 97:241-249.
Luers, A.L.
  2003   From Theory to Practice; Vulnerability Analysis in the Yaqui Valley Region of
          Sonora, Mexico. Ph.D. dissertation thesis, Stanford University.
Luers, A.L., D.B. Lobell, L.S. Sklar, C.L. Addams, and P.A. Matson
  2003   A method for quantifying vulnerability, applied to the agricultural system of the
          Yaqui Valley, Mexico. Global Environmental Change 13:255-267.
Manning, R.
  2002   Agriculture versus biodiversity: Will market solutions suffice? Conservation in Prac-
          tice 3(2):18-27.

Matson, P.A
    2001   Environmental challenges for the 21st century: Interacting challenges and integra-
            tive solutions. *Environmental Law Quarterly* 27(4):1179-1190.
Matson, P.A., and D.S. Ojima, eds.
    1990   *Terrestrial Biosphere Exchange with Global Atmospheric Chemistry.* (IGBP Report
            No. 13.) Stockholm, Sweden: International Geosphere-Biosphere Programme.
Matson, P.A., W.J. Parton, A.G. Power, and M. Swift
    1997   Agricultural intensification and ecosystem properties. *Science* 277:504-509.
Matson, P.A., R.L. Naylor, and I. Ortiz-Monasterio
    1998   Integration of environmental, agronomic, and economic aspects of fertilizer man-
            agement. *Science* 280:112-115.
Matson, P.A., R.L. Naylor, I. Ortiz-Monasterio, W.P. Falcon, A. Luers, and G. Asner
    no   Agricultural Intensification in the Yaqui Valley, Sonora, Mexico: Does It Save Land
    date-a for Nature? Unpublished paper, Stanford University.
Matson, P.A., R.L. Naylor, I. Ortiz-Monasterio, G. Asner, M. Beman, W.P. Falcon, J.
Harrison, D. Lobell, A. Luers, K. Seto, and W. Riley
    no   Does Agricultural Intensification "Save Land For Nature"? Analysis from the Yaqui
    date-b Valley, Sonora, Mexico. Unpublished paper, Stanford University.
McCullough, E.
    2004   Coping with Drought: An Analysis of Crisis Responses in the Yaqui Valley. Mas-
            ters Thesis, Stanford University.
Naylor, R., and P.A. Matson
    1993   Food, conservation, and global environmental change: Is compromise possible?
            EOS Transactions 74(15):178-179.
Naylor, R.L., W.P. Falcon, and A. Puente-González
    2001   *Policy Reforms and Mexican Agriculture: Views from the Yaqui Valley.* (CIMMYT
            Economics Program Paper No. 01-01.) Distrito Federal, Mexico: International
            Maize and Wheat Improvement Center.
Naylor, R.L., R. Goldburg, J. Primavera, N. Kautsky, M. Beveridge, J. Clay, C. Folke, J.
Lubchenco, H. Mooney, and M. Troell
    2000   Effect of aquaculture on world fish supplies. *Nature* 405:1017-1024.
Panek, J., P.A. Matson, I. Ortiz-Monasterio, and P. Brooks
    2000   Distinguishing nitrification and denitrification sources of N_2O in a Mexican wheat
            system using 15N as a tracer. *Ecological Applications* 10(2):506-514.
Perez, T., S.E. Trumbore, S.C. Tyler, P.A. Matson, I. Ortiz-Monasterio, T. Rahn, and D.W.T.
Griffith
    2001   Identifying the agricultural imprint on the global N_2O budget using stable isotopes.
            Journal of Geophysical Research-Atmospheres 106(D9):9869-9878.
Puente-González, A.
    1999   Agricultural, Financial, and Economic Data of Mexico and the Yaqui Valley. Work-
            ing Paper. Center for Environmental Science and Policy, Stanford University.
Rice, E.
    1995   Nitrate, Development, and Trade Liberalization: A Case Study of the Yaqui Valley,
            Mexico. Senior honors thesis, Stanford University.
Riley, W.J., and P.A. Matson
    2000   NLOSS: A mechanistic model of denitrified N_2O and N_2 evolution from soil. *Soil
            Science* 165(3):237-249.
Riley, W.J., I. Ortiz-Monasterio, and P.A. Matson
    2001   Nitrogen leaching and soil nitrate, nitrite, and ammonium levels under differing
            fertilizer management in an irrigated wheat system in northern Mexico. *Nutrient
            Cycling in Agroecosystems* 61:223-236.

Turner, B.L. II, R.E. Kasperson, P.A. Matson, J.J. McCarthy, R.W. Corell, L. Christensen, N. Eckley, J.X. Kasperson, A. Luers, M.L. Martello, C. Polsky, A. Pulsipher, and A. Schiller
   2003a A framework for vulnerability analysis in sustainability science. *Proceedings of the National Academy of Sciences* 100(14):8074-8079.

Turner, B.L. II, P.A. Matson, J.J. McCarthy, R.W. Corell, L. Christensen, N. Eckley, G.K. Hovelsrud-Broda, J.X. Kasperson, R.E. Kasperson, A. Luers, M.L. Martello, S. Mathiesen, R. Naylor, C. Polsky, A. Pulsipher, A. Schiller, H. Selin, and N. Tyler
   2003b Illustrating the coupled human-environment system for vulnerability analysis: Three case studies. *Proceedings of the National Academy of Sciences* 100(14):8080-8085.

Vitousek, P.M., and P.A. Matson
   1993 Agriculture, the global nitrogen cycle, and trace gas flux. Pp. 193-208 in *Biogeochemistry of Global Change: Radiatively Active Trace Gases,* R. Oremland, ed. New York: Chapman and Hall.

Vitousek, P.M., J. Aber, R. Howarth, G.E. Likens, P. Matson, D. Schindler, W. Schlesinger, and G.D. Tilman
   1997 Human alteration of the global nitrogen cycle: Causes and consequences. *Ecological Applications* 7(3):737-750.

Waggoner, P.E.
   1994 *How Much Land Can Ten Billion People Spare for Nature?* (Report No. 121.) Ames, IA: Council for Agricultural Science and Technology. Available: http://www. formal.stanford.edu/jmc/nature/nature.html [accessed February 10, 2005].

11

Patterns of Urban Land Use as Assessed by Satellite Imagery: An Application to Cairo, Egypt

John R. Weeks, Dennis P. Larson, and Debbie L. Fugate

INTRODUCTION

At the beginning of the nineteenth century, almost everyone in the world lived in rural places. Cities like London and Paris were islands of urbanness in a sea of rurality. Even at the beginning of the twentieth century the vast majority (nearly 90 percent) of people lived in rural places. But, at the beginning of the twenty-first century, we find that almost one in two humans is living in an urban place, with the tipping date estimated to be within the first decade of the century (United Nations Population Division, 2004). This urban transition—the shift of humans from being predominantly rural to being predominantly urban—is an integral part of the demographic transition and is moving along in concert with the other parts of the demographic transition (see Weeks, 2005, for a discussion of the interrelationships). We have in fact reached the point in history at which we can envision the end of the urban transition. This is already happening in the more developed nations, where nearly everyone lives in or very close to an urban environment. However, the end of the urban transition does not necessarily signal the end of urban evolution (Pumain, 2004). Evolutionary processes include patterns of suburbanization, exurbanization, peri-urbanization (the shift of urban populations from more dense to less dense regions), multinucleation (the clustering of population around several centers, rather than just one, in the same region) and even counterurbanization (a return of some people back to more urban places; see, for example, Champion, 1989).

There is almost certainly more variability among urban places, and in the populations in urban places, than ever before in human history. This variability has important consequences for the relationship between human populations and the environment, because places (and thus the populations in those places) become urban through the transformation of the land into a built environment, and, as urban places evolve, the subsequent changes in the built environment may well have forward-linking influences on human behavior. In concert with Redman (Chapter 7) and Seto (Chapter 8), we posit a fundamental ecological relationship between urban places and human behavior: humans transform the environment and are then transformed by the new environment.

Evolutionary ecological processes such as this cannot be captured by the standard distinctions of urban and rural or urban and nonurban. The concept of urbanness, as we use it here, implies that the rural/urban distinction is a continuum, rather than a dichotomy. Humans increasingly live not simply in urban, but in highly differentiated urban, settings. This means that there is an ever-increasing variability in population-environment interactions because a majority of people live in an environment that is substantially and differentially transformed by human invention and intervention, with the exact nature of that transformation varying considerably from place to place. The ecological perspective suggests that this variability will be associated with variability in human behavior—in how people organize their lives, interact with each other, and utilize the resources of nature. Although we could extend this idea to the entire range of human settlements, in this chapter we focus more specifically on the variability *within* an urban area. As dramatic as human behavioral differences may be between rural and urban areas, there are nonetheless very large intraurban differences in demographic processes (Weeks et al., 2004), and it is probable that these differences will become more important over time as increasing fractions of the world's population come to live in urban places.

Our conceptual framework is thus based on the ecological principle that human behavior is shaped by a combination of the natural, built, and social environments in which people live. Most social science literature that describes the nature and character of urban populations focuses almost exclusively on the measurement of the social environment, often drawing on census data to describe this milieu. But variations in the social environment depend in part on variability in the built environment. For example, high population density—an index that is often used as a measure of urbanness—can be achieved with some kinds of physical structures, but not others. In order to put a lot of people in a relatively small amount of space, buildings must be very high above ground or very far below ground or both. The technology to build such structures is relatively new in human history and the expense of doing so limits its uses, adding to the spatial variability in the application of the techniques that permit very high density.

Cities, or urban places more generally, are defined in terms of the way humans have converted the land to largely "unnatural" and nonagricultural uses. But the creation of a built environment that we define as an urban place is itself a representation of the culture of the people living in that place, if we define culture to mean "the manifestation of the way in which we humans solve the problems of everyday life and transmit those solutions to other people and subsequent generations through the teaching and learning process. What do we eat and how do we eat it? How and with what do we protect ourselves from nature and predators? How do we organize our lives to minimize risk and maximize satisfaction?" (Weeks et al., 2004:75). But this is not a one-way street. The built environment, in its turn, can have an influence on the way in which people pattern their social lives. Social science literature is rich with examples of how high-rise apartments and streets crowded with cars create different social worlds for people than do low-rise buildings and spacious pedestrian walkways.

Taken together, the ideas that people create an urban place and then are influenced by the place that has been created lead us to the hypothesis that an important component of variability in human behavior may be captured in surrogate form by knowledge of the variability of the built environment. In this conceptualization, the built and social environments are intimately entwined, but not completely dependent on one another. The same built environment can host variation in the social environment, and the same social environment can exist in a range of built environments, but we hypothesize that a relatively narrow range of combined values of the built and social environments would describe a unique set of urban populations.

We typically measure the social environment by the responses to questions on surveys and censuses. Some aspects of the built environment can be captured by census data related to housing characteristics, but one of the difficulties of using only census data to define this aspect of urbanness is that people are almost always enumerated at their place of residence and are asked only about the characteristics of the home in which they live. Little or no information is gathered about the environmental context—Do you live next door to the shopping center or to a forest?

There is a variety of data sources that might be employed to describe (and thus measure the variability in) the urban built environments that humans create for themselves. Censuses of buildings and their uses, cadastral maps that tell what categories of things on a piece of property are being taxed, and even maps of such urban infrastructure as water, sewer, and power lines would be candidates for use. Traffic counts and censuses of businesses can generate data from which can be inferred something about daytime populations. In this research, we propose to use a more universally available set of data—remotely sensed satellite imagery. We suggest that the modification of the physical environment that is characteristic of urban places can be inferred by quantifying data derived from multispectral satellite images.

URBAN PLACE METRICS DERIVED FROM IMAGERY

In order to appreciate the value of remotely sensed imagery for the analysis of urban places, it is crucial to understand exactly what information can be extracted from such images. The image itself is composed of a two-dimensional array of pixels (picture elements) from which radiant energy has been captured for an area on the ground that is equal to the spatial resolution of the image. A basic premise of remote sensing is that earth surface features and landscapes can be discriminated, categorized, and mapped according to their spectral-radiometric characteristics (Lillesand and Kiefer, 2000). The information recorded for each image depends on the particular sensor, but the brightness or reflectance within a given band is assigned a digital number. The combination of digital numbers representing relative reflectance across the different bands of light yields the spectral signature of that pixel.

Images are generally characterized according to spatial, spectral, radiometric, and temporal resolution. Spatial resolution refers to the characteristic length of a ground element represented by the image pixel. The highest resolution data available from commercial satellites (such as Quickbird or Ikonos) are, at the time of this writing, 0.6 m for panchromatic and 2.4 m for multispectral imagery. More detailed imagery typically requires the use of airborne platforms, such as light aircraft or helicopters to capture aerial digital images. High spatial resolution imagery tends to be quite expensive, so most academic research focuses on moderate resolution data. In the research reported here, we are using Indian Remote Sensing (IRS) images that have a spatial resolution of 5 m in panchromatic format, and 24 m in multispectral format. This means that in the multispectral bands, one pixel in the imagery covers an area on the ground that is 24 meters square. We also make use of a Landsat Thematic Mapper (TM) multispectral image that has a spatial resolution of 30 m.

As already alluded to, images vary according to the spectral bandwidth of energy captured by the image, ranging from panchromatic (one broad waveband mostly in the visible portion of the spectrum) to multispectral (red, green, blue, near-infrared short-wave, and thermal infrared bands). Radiometric resolution pertains to the number of radiant energy levels that can be quantified by a digital remote sensing instrument, which tend to range from 64 to 2,048 levels. In general, the greater the number of different bands that are identified, the more finely detailed the numeric distinctions that can be made about the data in the image. The possible combinations of numbers from 6 bands is geometrically larger than can be derived from 3 bands, and for this reason a more precise spectral signature of something on the ground can be determined with a higher spectral resolution.

Finally, we note that the repeat imaging capability of a remote sensing system is characterized by its temporal resolution. Satellites that capture images of the same place on the ground several times a year, for example, have higher temporal resolution than satellites capturing data only once a year.

Satellite optical imagery is obviously capable of capturing only what can be seen on the ground, and for this reason the data from the imagery refer to land cover classes, such as vegetation (or even different types of plants), bare soil, water, and impervious surfaces (things that are impervious to water, such as a cement road or parking lot, or a tin or tile roof). It is up to the researcher to infer the land use that is associated with each land cover class, so there is a certain amount of semantic subjectivity in the entire process. We use a semantic classification (such as "impervious surface") to denote a set of spectral signatures that are known to be associated with those kinds of land covers. We then infer land use (e.g., built area) based on the land cover classification, on the assumption that impervious surfaces, for example, are especially likely to be associated with the human transformation of the environment characteristic of roads and buildings and other aspects of the urban area.

The classification of an image is done at the level of the individual pixel, but we are especially interested in the *composition* and *configuration* of all of the pixels in a defined geographic region, such as a census tract or enumeration area, because we want to use the data from the imagery in conjunction with census and survey data to better understand the relationship between people (whose characteristics are measured from census and survey data) and the environments in which they live (measured in this instance from the imagery). There are two types of geographic features that are captured by the imagery: continuous features (such as land cover and land use types) and discrete objects (such as buildings) that are distinguishable from the background surface. Continuous features represent the compositional aspect of the scene under investigation, whereas discrete objects represent the configurational aspect. Much more attention has been paid thus far to composition than to configuration (Bian and Xie, 2004), so our ability to quantify composition is superior to our ability to quantify configuration.

Composition refers to the proportional abundance in a region of particular land cover classes that are of interest to the researcher. In our research, the semantic classification of pixels is guided by Ridd's (1995) V-I-S (vegetation, impervious surface, soil) model. Each pixel is analyzed according to its spectral properties and is assigned to one of three land cover classes (vegetation, impervious surface, or bare soil). The V-I-S model views the urban scene as being composed of combinations of these three distinct land cover classes. An area that is composed entirely of bare soil would be characteristic of desert wilderness, whereas an area composed entirely of vegetation would be dense forest, lawn, or intensive fields of crops. Areas composed of combinations of these land cover classes are the least urban of environments and are represented as lying along the base of a pyramid. At the top of the pyramid is impervious surface, an abundance of which is characteristic of central business districts, which are conceptualized as the most urban of the built environments. Places that fall between these extremes are, in essence, relatively more or less urban than would be found at the extremes.

These compositional metrics build on the qualitative sense that each of us has about what an urban place "looks like." Even today in highly urbanized countries in Europe and North America it is visually very evident when you move from a largely rural to a predominantly urban place and, of course, the change in the built environment is the principal index of that. Even in nonurban areas it is usually quite evident when you have passed from a wilderness area into a largely agriculture area. Once again, it is the composition of the environment that provides the clue. Figure 11-1 shows this in a schematic way. Wilderness areas can, at the extreme, be expected to be composed especially of bare soil, since deserts tend to be the places least habitable by humans. As the fraction of vegetation increases, there is an implicit increase in the availability of water, and where there is sufficient water the possibility of agricultural increases, and agriculture creates a

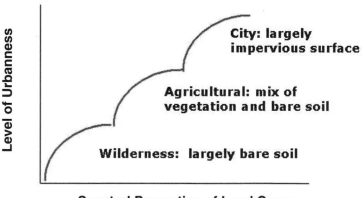

FIGURE 11-1   The urban gradient may be discontinuous.

signature on the ground that is typically distinct from areas that have not
been modified by humans. However, the nature of urban places is that the
built environment is dominant, and so cities are distinctly noticeable from
the air because vegetation gives way immediately, discontinuously, to impervious surfaces.

The most commonly used method of classifying a pixel is what can be
called a hard classification, in which the entire surface area is assumed to be
represented by a single land cover class. However, when using moderate
spatial resolution imagery (such as imagery in the 10 to 24 m range) it is
very unlikely that an entire pixel will be completely undifferentiated, especially in urban areas in which humans have modified the environment in a
variety of ways. Thus, the use of hard classification schemes with moderate
resolution data has led to questions about the ability of researchers to
accurately discern the characteristics of urban places from such imagery.
These problems can be particularly acute in urban settings with considerable amounts of vegetation that may distort the interpretation of the classification of the ground cover underneath the vegetation canopy (Small,
2002).

To deal with this problem, the techniques of spectral mixture analysis
and multiple end-member spectral mixture analysis have been developed
that use a procedure somewhat analogous to principal components analysis
to "unmix" each pixel into its constituent components of land cover classes.
Thus, in a hard classification, the decision may have been made to assign
the land cover class "impervious surface" to a particular pixel. However,
the spectral mixture analysis or multiple end-member spectral mixture
analysis may lead instead to the decision that 70 percent of the surface area
of that pixel was covered by impervious surface, 20 percent by vegetation,
and 10 percent by bare soil. We would call this a soft classification, and it
allows us to infer more about a pixel than is the case with a hard classification. The details of these classification methods are described elsewhere
(Rashed and Weeks, 2003; Rashed et al., 2001, 2003, 2005; Roberts et al.,
1998a, 1998b, 1998c), but the important point is that the soft classification
offers a potentially more accurate representation of the surface area covered by each land cover class when the data are aggregated into areal units,
such as census tracts or enumeration areas. Thus far the accuracy assessments have come largely from comparing the results of spectral mixture
analysis of moderate spatial resolution imagery with the classification of
data from higher spatial resolution imagery, such as the comparison with
Ikonos imagery (Small, 2003) or with Quickbird imagery (Stow et al.,
2004).

We also made one modification to the Ridd V-I-S model by adding
another component—shade/water—following the work of Ward, Phinn,
and Murray (2000), suggesting that this fourth physical component im-

proves the model in settings outside the United States. When combined with impervious surfaces in urban areas, it becomes a measure of the height of buildings (based on the shadows cast by buildings). Our spectral mixture analysis then permits a soft classification of a pixel into the likely fraction that is composed of each of the four physical elements of interest to us: vegetation, impervious surface, soil, and shade. By summing up these fractions over all pixels contained in each area of interest, we have a composite measure of the fraction (the "proportional abundance") of the area that is covered by each of the four land cover types.

The proportional abundance of impervious surface is the baseline measure of urbanness, as suggested by the Ridd model, but shade is also a factor, especially in areas dominated by tall buildings creating shade that is then radiated to the sensor, essentially in the place of the underlying impervious surface. Thus, in areas that are generally urban, such as greater Cairo, the simple addition of the impervious surface and shade fractions should provide an appropriate measure of the proportional abundance of land cover most associated with an urban place.

Measures of proportional abundance capture the land cover composition of the scene that we are analyzing. The other aspect of landscape metrics is the quantification of the spatial configuration of each land cover class. The most widely used measures of configuration employ a fractal approach, which examines the spatial relationships among pixels of the same land cover class (Herold, Scepan, and Clarke, 2002; Lam and Cola, 1993; McGarigal, 2002). We may know that 60 percent of a given area is covered by impervious surface (the measure of composition), but we would also like to know how those pixels are arranged in the area under observation. For example, if the pixels identified as being of impervious surface are clustered together, we may infer that we are "seeing" a large building or other large urban surface. A low level of clustering of impervious surface pixels might represent a greater number of smaller buildings in the scene, suggesting a less intensely urban use of the land. Such a measure of spatial configuration should provide a somewhat more nuanced index of urbanness, when folded into the measure of composition.

McGarigal (2002) notes that configuration is much more difficult to assess than composition and, although several measures have been developed in an attempt to capture the essence of configuration, it is important to keep in mind that most measures of landscape configuration were developed for the purpose of describing landscape ecology and have only recently been shown to have an adaptation to the measurement of the urban environment (Herold et al., 2002). The most specific problem confronting us in the quantification of these measures is that all such measures require that each pixel in the scene be identified as a member of a single land cover class—a hard classification. This required us to essentially remix each pixel from our soft classification back into a hard classification. We did this with an algorithm that assigned each pixel to the land cover class that represented the majority proportional abundance based on the spectral mixture analysis. If no land cover class represented a majority, then the classification was based on an average of the highest proportional abundances among near neighbors.

We have used the Fragstats software (McGarigal, 2002) to calculate the contiguity index as a measure of spatial configuration of impervious surfaces in each census area. The contiguity index assesses the spatial connectedness (contiguity) of cells of a given land cover class. A value of 0 indicates that no pixel classified as impervious surface is contiguous to any other pixel classified as impervious surface. At the other extreme, a value of 1 indicates that all pixels classified as impervious surface are contiguous to one another. The contiguity index is blind to the composition of the area with respect to each land cover class—it looks at whatever number of pixels there are of a given class and examines their spatial relationship to one another. For this reason, this (and the other) measures of configuration do not provide a baseline of urbanness. Rather, they add to our knowledge of urbanness derived from the compositional measures, giving us a more nuanced index.

Our measure of urbanness is thus based first on the proportional abundance of the impervious surface (I) and shade (S) land cover classes. If those percentages are high, an area can be interpreted as being very urban, and, if they are low, the area is not very urban. However, for any given proportional abundance of impervious surface and shade, we think that a high contiguity index (C) will indicate a slightly more urban place (a greater density of urban material) than would a low contiguity index. In general, we would expect that city centers would have the highest abundance of impervious surface and shade and also the highest level of contiguity of that impervious surface. At the other extreme, a place that is not very urban will have a low proportion of impervious surface, but that surface may be highly contiguous (one small building) or only moderately so (three small buildings); the degree of contiguity would matter less than it would when the proportion of impervious surface is high. This suggests that the configuration of the pixels increases in importance as the proportional abundance of impervious surface increases, implying a conditional relationship such that the value (a coefficient that we label as a) assigned to the contiguity index would increase as the sum of I and S increased.

On the basis of these considerations, our proposed measure of urbanness (U) is the sum of the proportional abundance of impervious surface (I) and shade (S), plus the contiguity index (C) times a coefficient (a). The coefficient (a) should have a value that permits the contiguity index to add no more than 10 percentage points to a measure (U) that would otherwise range between 0 (completely nonurban) and 100 (completely urban). Furthermore, its size should be proportional to the proportional abundance of I and S. Since the contiguity index ranges from 0 to 1, this would imply that the coefficient (a) should be as follows:

$$a = (I + S)/10$$

and the urban index (U) is calculated as:

$$U = (I + S) + (a \times C).$$

APPLYING THE URBAN INDEX

We now apply the urban index to the study site of Cairo, Egypt. The urban area of greater Cairo represents the governorate of Cairo on the east side of the Nile River as it travels through the metropolitan region, the portion of the governorate of Giza that is along the west bank of the Nile River within the metropolitan region, and the southern tip of the governorate of Qalyubia—which currently represents the northernmost reach of greater Cairo. The area's location is shown in Figure 11-2. Nearly one in

FIGURE 11-2 The study site of Cairo, Egypt.

five Egyptians lives in the greater Cairo region, and for centuries it has been a quintessentially primate city, dominating the social, economic, and political life of the region. The United Nations Population Division lists the population of Cairo to be 10.4 million as of 2000 (the 15th most populous city in the world), with a projected population of 13.1 million in 2015 (when it would be the 13th most populous) (United Nations Population Division, 2004). Note that these latest data reflect a significant upward revision of the current and projected population of Cairo, signaling the importance of knowing more about the dynamics of the region.

Two multispectral images have been utilized in this study. The earlier image is a Landsat TM image acquired in June 1987 and the more recent is an Indian Remote Sensing Satellite 1C image acquired in August 1996. The acquisition dates correspond as closely as possible to the 1986 and 1996 Egyptian censuses. Both images were acquired at approximately the same time of year (midsummer) in order to minimize any effects of seasonality. In the interest of brevity, we focus our attention especially on the latter image, which covers three bands in visible the visible ranges of (520-590) and (620-690) and near-infrared (770-860 nm) at 23.6 m spatial resolution and one band in short-wave infrared (1,550-1,700 nm) at 70.8 m spatial resolution.

Cairo is divided administratively into *shiakhas,* a word that literally means places controlled by a sheikh, but in modern times they represent areas controlled by a police station and, more importantly for our purposes, are the bounded areas for which census data are collected by the Central Agency for Public Mobilisation and Statistics (CAPMAS). These areas are thus equivalent to a census tract in the United States or an enumeration area in the United Kingdom. We have census data for 298 *shiakhas* from the 1986 and 1996 censuses, and the goal is to characterize each of these in terms of their urbanness as measured quantitatively from the imagery.

The urban index as defined above is comprised of two components—the proportional abundance of impervious surface and shade and the spatial configuration of the pixels identified as representing impervious surface. The spatial patterning of each of these components is shown in Figures 11-3 and 11-4, respectively. Figure 11-3 shows the percentage of surface area in each *shiakha* that is composed of either impervious surface or shade. The pattern is for the older, more central parts of Cairo to the east of the Nile (in the Cairo governorate and in the more industrial governorate of Qalyubia to the north of downtown Cairo) to have higher proportional abundances of these land cover classes, whereas in the more suburban western portion (in the governorate of Giza), the fractions tend to be lower. This is the pattern we would expect to find.

Figure 11-4 shows the spatial pattern in the spatial configuration of pixels that are classified as impervious surface. Low values indicate the

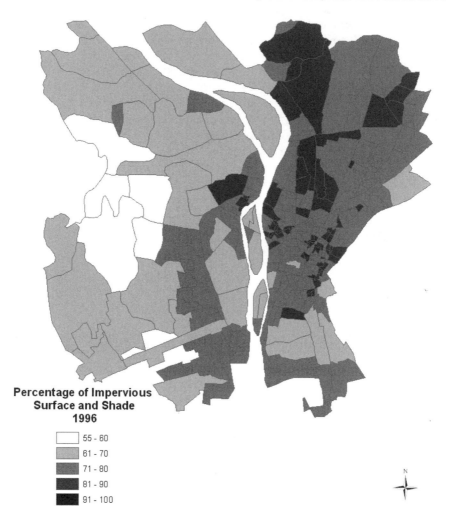

**Percentage of Impervious
Surface and Shade
1996**

☐	55 - 60
▨	61 - 70
▨	71 - 80
▨	81 - 90
■	91 - 100

FIGURE 11-3   Percentage of area in each *shiakha* of greater Cairo that is composed of impervious surface or shade, 1996.

such pixels are not highly contiguous to one another in a given *shiakha*, which we interpret to be characteristic of a lower density, more suburban area; higher values indicate a high degree of contiguity, which we interpret to be more likely to occur in more dense, central city areas—at least when it occurs in the presence of a high proportional abundance of impervious surface. The data appear visually to support this expectation. Note as well that the measures of composition and configuration are not simple overlays of one another—they exhibit somewhat different spatial patterns. This supports our view that configuration provides a more nuanced index of urbanness than we would obtain from using only the composition measure.

The combination of composition and configuration makes up our urban index and the spatial pattern of the index in Cairo in 1996 is shown in Figure 11-5. The pattern is consistent with the qualitative assessment of urbanness in Cairo. The old center is very urban, as is the more industrial area in the northern part of the city. The suburbs of Giza are generally less urban, with the notable exception of the Imbaba area (in the northeastern

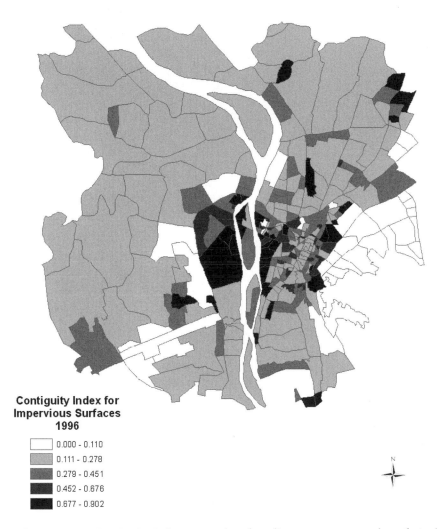

**Contiguity Index for
Impervious Surfaces
1996**

□	0.000 - 0.110
▨	0.111 - 0.278
▨	0.279 - 0.451
■	0.452 - 0.676
■	0.677 - 0.902

FIGURE 11-4   Contiguity index measuring the adjacency to one another of pixels classified as being impervious surface, 1996.

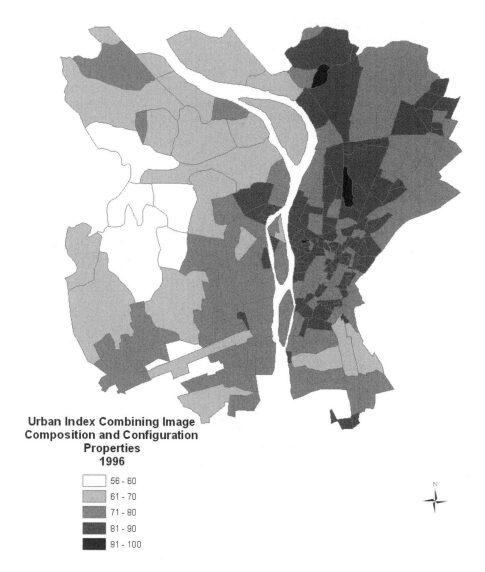

FIGURE 11-5   Urban index, Cairo, 1996.

part of Giza, near the Nile River) which is a well-known high-density slum area.

Figure 11-6 zooms in on several neighborhoods near central Cairo so that the numbers from the urban index for 1996 are displayed at the center of each neighborhood with a high resolution DigitalGlobe Quickbird image

FIGURE 11-6 The urban index for 1996 overlaid on a high-resolution image of central Cairo.

in the background. This allows for a qualitative visualization of what the quantification of that neighborhood (the urban index) stands for. In particular, it is easier to see in this figure that the values on the eastern side of the river, in the central part of old Cairo, are higher than in the more

TABLE 11-1   Urban Index for Cairo, 1987 and 1996

		1987	1996
N of shiakhas		276	276
Mean		80.84	78.81
Median		82.08	80.06
Standard deviation		8.50	6.30
Kurtosis		0.50	1.08
Minimum		52.94	56.48
Maximum		100.27	91.50
Percentiles	25	76.37	75.63
	50	82.08	80.06
	75	86.65	82.81

suburban areas on the western side of the river in Giza. In the older part of Cairo, buildings are more closely spaced together, whereas in Giza there is somewhat less impervious surface (because there is more vegetation) and the buildings show some spacing between them.

Table 11-1 compares the distribution of the urban index in 1996 (based on the Indian Remote Sensing image) with that derived from the 1987 Landsat image. The two images were obtained from different sensors (with similar but not identical spatial and spectral resolution), so some of the observed difference may be due to these technical differences, even though both images were subjected to identical methods of semantically classifying the imagery. The data show that Cairo was, on average, slightly less urban in 1996 than in 1987. That is, in fact, consistent with other evidence that during this time there was a general movement out of the central city and toward the suburbs, accompanied by a pattern of new migrants to the city eschewing the center of the city for the suburbs. The changes in the central city are potentially detectable from the imagery because between 1987 and 1996 the government bulldozed several slum areas near the central city. And, of course, in the more suburban areas, the expansion of roads and homes was clearly observable and measurable from the imagery. The census data for 1986 show an average density in the greater Cairo area of 50,000 persons per square kilometer, and that had dropped to an average of 45,000 by 1996. The population of greater Cairo was increasing during this time from 7.5 million in our study area in 1986 to 8.2 million in 1996. Thus, the drop in density represented a decline in the central city at the same time that there was a rise in the suburbs.

The potential utility of the index lies in its ability to measure some aspect of the physical context in which social lives are being played out. In a previously published analysis of intraurban fertility in Cairo, Weeks and his colleagues (2004) demonstrated that a less sophisticated set of measures from the imagery were statistically significantly related to the proportion of young women who were married in a given neighborhood in Cairo, which in turn was the predominant predictor of the neighborhood's total fertility rate. We now substitute the urban index that we have just created into that prior analysis to see the extent to which the total fertility rates in Cairo's neighborhoods are a function of the social environment (measured by variables derived from the census) and the built environment (assessed with these imagery derived variables).

From the censuses in both 1986 and 1996 we were able to derive several variables that measure the social class characteristics of a *shiakha*. We summarized educational status by calculating the percentage of the population age 15 and older that had at least an intermediate level of education (equivalent to at least some high school). We calculated these percentages separately for men and women. The participation of women in the paid labor force is a well-known correlate of the status of women, and we were able to measure that for women age 15 and older. Probably the single best measure of social status is the occupational status of the householder. The census does not ask for characteristics specific to the householder, but we know from other sources that in Cairo, as in most places, the householder tends to be male, and we are able to calculate the percentage of economically active men age 15 and older whose occupation was in the highest occupational status categories, which include technical, professional, administrative, and managerial occupations. Not surprisingly, all of these variables were highly intercorrelated. In 1996, for example, the lowest correlation coefficient among any two of these four variables was .851, and in 1986 it was .888. For this reason, we were able to combine them into a single index using principal components analysis. In both 1986 and 1996 the combined index weights each variable roughly equally into a measure that we call STATUS. This of course refers to a value for the *shiakha*, not individuals.

We know that neither built nor social environments can have a direct effect on fertility. Rather, they can influence one or more of the proximate determinants of fertility, which include especially age at marriage, breast-feeding, abortion, and contraception (Bongaarts, 1982). There is strong evidence from the Demographic and Health Surveys that age at marriage is by far the most important determinant of current fertility trends in Cairo (and possibly in other Arab nations as well) (Weeks et al., 2004), and we were able to derive a proxy for age at marriage from the census data on marital status. This measure calculates the percentage of women ages 15-29 who are single.

Our model suggests that the social environment and the built environment will have independent, but potentially overlapping, effects on the age at marriage in a neighborhood, which in turn will directly affect the neighborhood's total fertility rate. This calls for a structural equation model (path analysis) and the results for 1996 are shown in Figure 11-7. It can be seen first that the expectation of overlap between the social and built environments is not met. These two variables are almost completely independent of one another, evidenced by the correlation coefficient of .01. This suggests that if we are to understand the behavior of individuals in a neighborhood, we are going to have to know something about both the built and social environments, and that different combinations of each will produce unique patterns of social behavior. Of these two factors, the social environment appears, not surprisingly, to be somewhat more important than the built environment in its influence on the proportion of women who are single. The standardized beta coefficient for social status in 1996 was .66, whereas the coefficient for the urban index was .43. However, both measures are strong and statistically significant predictors, and together they explain 63 percent of the variability in the proportion of women who are single, which in turn explains 71 percent of the variation in neighborhood fertility rates.

The results for 1986 are similar to those for 1996, as can be seen in Figure 11-8. In 1986 there was only a low correlation between social status and the urban index, but once again these two measures combined to explain a high fraction (69 percent) of the variability in the proportion of young women who were single. And, once again, the status variable was more important a predictor than the urban index, but both variables were strongly correlated with the age at marriage. And, once again, the variability in the proportion of young women who were married explained a high fraction (88 percent) of the variability in neighborhood fertility levels.

Finally, we ask whether observed changes in either the social or built

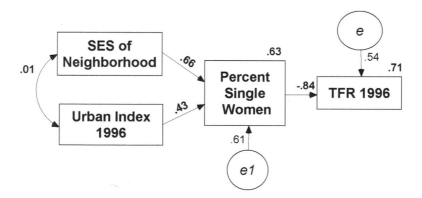

FIGURE 11-7 Path model showing the indirect effects of the social and built environments on neighborhood fertility levels: Cairo, 1996.

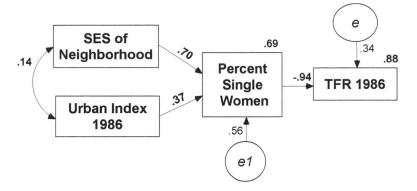

FIGURE 11-8 Path model showing the indirect effects of the social and built environments on neighborhood fertility levels: Cairo, 1986.

environments are related to changes in neighborhood fertility levels. The results in Figure 11-9 suggest not. There is essentially no impact of changes in either the social status of a neighborhood or its urban index on the neighborhood proportions of women who are single. Almost the entire effect comes from the endogenous effect of the fertility level in 1986. In other words, the decline in fertility occurred in those places where fertility was highest in 1986, regardless of what other changes might have been occurring in the neighborhood. Yet we know from Figures 11-7 and 11-8

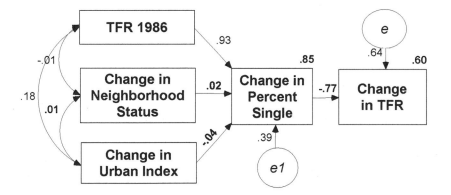

FIGURE 11-9 Path model showing the indirect effects of the change in social and built environments on the change in neighborhood fertility levels: Cairo, 1986 to 1996.

that much of our knowledge of whether fertility was high or low in a neighborhood in 1986 (and again in 1996) was based on information derived about the social environment and the built environment. Neither one of those neighborhood characteristics told us as much individually as did both in combination with each other.

DISCUSSION AND CONCLUSION

The basic premise of this research is that information gleaned from satellite imagery is a proxy for the built environment of urban places, complementing data obtained from a census, which represent surrogate measures of the social environment. The underlying theory of our work is that the built environment reflects aspects of the social environment that will be reflected in the attitudes and behaviors of people. The urban environment creates a difference in people's lives by increasing the volume and intensity of social interaction and by increasing the opportunities that exist for educational and occupational specialization and differentiation. By developing a quantitative measure that is potentially comparable over time in the same region, we should be able to quantify the urban evolution taking place in different contexts throughout the world. Our goal in this chapter, then, has been to create and apply an index that could be measured at different time periods to see if the characteristics of places (and thus potentially of the people in those places) are changing over time or varying across space. Such an index has the potential to help us assess both the quantum (the amount) and the tempo (the timing) of urban change and evolution, and thus it should increase our predictive power and understanding of what is actually happening as nations transition to being largely urban, and as they continue to evolve in their urbanness.

ACKNOWLEDGMENTS

This research was supported by a grant from the National Science Foundation (grant BCS-0095641). The author would like to thank Tarek Rashed, Anna Carla Lopez, and Tony Marca for invaluable assistance with the remote sensing and geographic information system work used in this research. Barbara Entwisle, Arthur Getis, Douglas Stow, Stuart Sweeney, and two anonymous reviewers provided useful comments on earlier versions of the chapter.

REFERENCES

Bian, L., and Z. Xie
  2004   A spatial dependence approach to retrieving industrial complexes from digital images. *The Professional Geographer* 56:381-393.
Bongaarts, J.
  1982   The fertility-inhibiting effects of the intermediate fertility variables. *Studies in Family Planning* 13:179-189.
Champion, A.G.
  1989   Counterurbanization: The conceptual and methodological challenge. In *Counterurbanization: The Changing Pace and Nature of Population Deconcentration,* A.G. Champion, ed. London, England: Edward Arnold.
Herold, M., J. Scepan, and K.C. Clarke
  2002   The use of remote sensing and landscape metrics to describe structures and changes in urban land uses. *Environment and Planning A* 34:1443-1458.
Lam, N., and L.D. Cola
  1993   *Fractals in Geography.* Englewood Cliffs, NJ: Prentice-Hall.
Lillesand, T.M., and R.W. Kiefer
  2000   *Remote Sensing and Image Interpretation* (4th ed.) New York: John Wiley & Sons, Inc.
McGarigal, K.
  2002   FRAGSTATS Documentation, Background Material. Available: http://www.umass.edu/landeco/research/fragstats/fragstats.html.
Pumain, D.
  2004   An evolutionary approach to settlement systems. In *New Forms of Urbanization: Beyond the Urban-Rural Dichotomy,* A.G. Champion and G. Hugo, eds. London, England: Ashgate Publishing Company.
Rashed, T., and J.R. Weeks
  2003   Assessing vulnerability to earthquake hazards through spatial multicriteria analysis of urban areas. *International Journal of Geographical Information Science* 17:549-578.
Rashed, T., J.R. Weeks, M. Saad Gadalla, and A.G. Hill
  2001   Revealing the anatomy of cities through spectral mixture analysis of multispectral imagery: A case study of the greater Cairo region, Egypt. *Geocarto International* 16:5-16.
Rashed, T., J.R. Weeks, D.A. Roberts, J. Rogan, and R. Powell
  2003   Measuring the physical composition of urban morphology using multiple endmember spectral mixture analysis. *Photogrammetric Engineering and Remote Sensing* 69:1111-1120.
Rashed, T., J.R. Weeks, D.A. Stow, and D. Fugate
  2005   Measuring temporal compositions of urban morphology through spectral mixture analysis: Toward a soft approach to change analysis in crowded cities. *International Journal of Remote Sensing* 26(4):699-718.
Ridd, M.
  1995   Exploring a V-I-S (vegetation-imperious surface-soil) model or urban ecosystem analysis through remote sensing: Comparative anatomy of cities. *International Journal of Remote Sensing* 16:2165-2185.
Roberts, D.A., G.T. Batista, J.L.G. Pereira, E.K. Waller, and B.W. Nelson
  1998a   Change identification using multitemporal spectral mixture analysis: Applications in Eastern Amazonia. In *Remote Sensing Change Detection: Environmental Monitoring Applications and Methods,* C.M. Elvidge and R.S. Lunetta, eds. Ann Arbor, MI: Ann Arbor Press.

Roberts, D.A., M. Gardner, R. Church, S. Ustin, G. Scheer, and R.O. Green
  1998b   Mapping chaparral in the Santa Monica mountains using multiple end-member
          spectral mixture models. *Remote Sensing of the Environment* 65:267-279.
Roberts, D, G.T. Batista, J.L.G. Pereira, E.K. Waller, and B.W. Nelson
  1998c   Change identification using multitemporal spectral mixture analysis: Applications
          in eastern Amazonia. Pp. 137-161 in *Remote Sensing Change Detection: Environ-
          mental Monitoring Applications and Methods,* R. Lunetta and C. Elvidge, eds. Ann
          Arbor, MI: Ann Arbor Press.
Small, C.
  2002   Multitemporal analysis of urban reflectance. *Remote Sensing of Environment* 81:
          427-442.
  2003   High spatial resolution spectral mixture analysis of urban reflectance. *Remote Sens-
          ing of Environment* 88:170-186.
Stow, D.A., D. Fugate, T. Rashed, J. Weeks, and A. Getis
  2004   Validation of Satellite Derived End-Member Fraction Maps of Cairo, Egypt Using
          Quickbird Imagery. Paper presented at the Annual Meeting of the Association of
          American Geographers, Philadelphia, PA.
United Nations Population Division
  2004   *World Urbanization Prospects: The 2003 Revision.* New York: United Nations.
Ward, D., S.R. Phinn, and A.T. Murray
  2000   Monitoring growth in rapidly urbanizing areas using remotely sensed data. *The
          Professional Geographer* 52:371-385.
Weeks, J.R.
  2005   *Population: Introduction to Concepts and Issues* (9th ed.) Belmont, CA: Wadsworth
          Thomson Learning.
Weeks, J.R., A. Getis, A.G. Hill, M. Saad Gadalla, and T. Rashed
  2004   The fertility transition in Egypt: Intra-urban patterns in Cairo. *Annals of the Asso-
          ciation of American Geographers* 94:74-93.

12

A Review of 10 Years of Work on Economic Growth and Population Change in Rural India

Andrew Foster

INTRODUCTION

While there is an extensive literature in the field of natural resource economics arguing that population growth and economic development can adversely affect renewable environmental resources,[1] there have been few comprehensive attempts to empirically explore these relationships at the scale of the country or over a sufficient interval of time so that these multifaceted interlinkages can play out. In this chapter I discuss one such study, an examination of forest change and its interaction with population and economic growth in India over a 30-year period, that I have undertaken with two collaborators, a number of research assistants, and with the input of experts from a variety of different fields. The project has evolved over almost a decade, requiring the development and adaptation of new methodologies, and has yielded a number of new insights into these relationships.

This chapter summarizes the project as a whole and assesses more general insights into population environment linkages that stem from this work. I have organized the chapter into five sections. The first section addresses the role of theory in this work and gives particular consideration to the issue of how one establishes the presence of environmental externalities to population growth. This section also highlights how the model

---

[1]A recent textbook on natural resource economics by Harris (2002) provides a good summary of the relevant issue. For a useful characterization of the microfoundations of this literature, see Pender (1999).

provides a framework for thinking about the different ways that population growth and technology change affect forest cover. This section is followed by a discussion of the key features of the data that have been used in the analysis and then a characterization of the primary results to date. Finally, I examine a central theme that has governed the work, the identification of the appropriate set of scales of analysis.

THEORY

While a variety of global economic forces affect the trends in deforestation in developing countries, recent research in development economics has emphasized the importance of local-level processes, such as agricultural encroachment and product extraction through firewood collection and animal grazing that are themselves importantly influenced by the fact that forest resources in most developing countries are not privately owned (e.g., Dasgupta, 1995; Filmer and Pritchett, 1986). The nonprivate ownership of forests lands, as well as of grazing and wastelands, has raised two questions: (1) whether there has been historically or currently is a "tragedy of the commons" (Hardin, 1968) that characterizes forest operations and (2) whether this tragedy is or is not exacerbated or a cause of excess population growth (Lee, 1991). Although, as popularly conceived, depletion of such resources is a straightforward consequence of rapid population growth, these studies suggest that traditionally many common property resources have been well managed by local institutions so that historically the effects of rapid population growth have been, in Jodha's (1985:247) words, "mediated by institutional factors and often overshadowed by pressures arising from changing market conditions."

In the substantial economic literature concerned with the question of the efficiency with which common areas, such as forest areas, are managed in developing countries, however, there is surprisingly little discussion of the process by which forest area is chosen. The primary difficulty with this literature, with its emphasis on the tree management, is that it neglects factors determining the demand for forest products inclusive of population growth and does not allow for the possibility that forest area will be importantly determined by the relative returns to forest and other uses of land. These omissions would seem difficult to justify in terms of current patterns of forestation and deforestation in both developed and developing countries. In particular, growth in forests in the developed world in recent years can be attributed in part to investment decisions on the part of private owners in certain regions (such as the northwest United States) and to decreases in the returns to agriculture in others (such as New England) that reflect the changing costs of labor, an important input in forest extraction, and changes in the demand for forest products (Sedjo, 1995). An investigation of the determinants of deforestation thus needs to pay attention to the markets for land, labor, and forest products as well as to land management practices.

The initial motivation of our forest study was to examine the extent to which forest resources are efficiently managed and to consider potential implications of failures in the management of forest resources for population change. At the heart of the issue is a long-standing debate regarding the importance of environmental resources as a source of externalities to child-bearing—that is, whether, in choosing the number of children to have, a couple fully accounts for the consequences of their childbearing on environmental resources and thus on the well-being of other couples. The answer to this question is important because it has a direct implication for population and environmental policy. In the case that couples do not fully account for these consequences, there is a basis for public subsidy of family planning services, for example.[2] Alternatively, identification of the key failures in the management of environmental resources that create these external effects may help in the design of environmental policies.

The basic insight here is that if there are open-access environmental resources and the cost of raising children or ultimate economic prospects of children are importantly related to the presence of open access environmental resources, then one might anticipate childbearing to be greater than it would be if these resources were rationed through the market. Moreover, depending on the ability of households to substitute away from the use of environmental resources as they become more scarce, it has been argued that incentives for childbearing may actually increase with environmental degradation, yielding a vicious circle in which higher rates of environmental degradation promote higher population growth, and higher population growth increases environmental degradation (Nerlove, 1991).

It is clear that establishing that there is an impact of population on forest cover or that forest cover has an impact on populations, even if done in a manner in which the obvious problems of reverse causality are addressed, is not a basis for asserting an externality that would then serve as a basis for justifying fertility interventions on efficiency grounds. One must further establish that these effects are not directly mediated by markets or other mechanisms that serve the same purpose. Even in cases in which formal markets are in place, this can be complex, due to the difficulty of collecting price data in a setting in which many market transactions are subject to negotiation. In other cases, the costs of particular types of behav-

---

[2]Lee (1990) provides an excellent summary description of the economics of childbearing externalities, including an attempt to obtain rough estimates of key externalities in a number of countries. It is notable that the one source of externality that he does not try to benchmark is that due to environmental resources.

ior may not be fully monetized. It may nonetheless be the case under such circumstances that social controls result in outcomes that mimic those that would arise in the context of the market. Indeed, as noted, there is an extensive literature arguing that, in fact, local institutions often do an excellent job of regulating the use of these common resources without direct use of monetary pricing or state intervention (Jodha, 1985; Ostrom, 1990).

An early and important decision in the context of this research was to set up, as a kind of benchmark, a simple model based on the premise that forest land could be treated in much the same way as land devoted to more traditional agricultural products. This was not done because we thought that this model would necessarily characterize forest land allocation, but because we thought a structure was needed within which one could isolate the different mechanisms that link population size, technology change, and forest cover. In particular, the model highlights how population and technological change affect both the demand for forest products and the cost of labor used to extract forest resources, suggesting an empirical approach that allows one to isolate these components. Morevoer, the model provides a point of comparison by which to evaluate other more sophisticated models that formally incorporate market failures or policy objectives other than revenue maximization.

A key feature of the benchmark model is the assumption that many types of forest products are primarily distinguished from other agricultural commodities because of their relative nontradability across villages.[3] The idea is that many forest products (fodder, kindling) have relatively high volume relative to value and thus are likely not be transported across village lines. Otherwise the model is fairly standard for a model of agricultural products and quite distinct from traditional models of the economics of forestry, which tend to be focused on the dynamics of forest growth and management, given the underlying biophysical constraints.[4]

An important implication of the nontradability assumption is that changes in population will impact the demand for forest products as well as their supply. From the perspective of supply, an increase in population, whether through an increase in household size or the number of households, will expand labor supply. This expansion in labor supply will tend to

---

[3]The importance of transportation costs and thus the relative degree of economic integration also plays an important role in the agent-based models used by Fischer and O'Neill (Chapter 3) to examine population–environment interactions in China.

[4]The fact that this model is essentially static is, of course, an important simplification. The basic trade-offs captured by the model between prices of land and labor and the economic return to forest products would be preserved in a more complex dynamic model. Moreover, dynamic considerations are likely in practice to play a minor role in terms of our empirical analysis, given the rough correspondence between the observations in our empirical analysis (10 years) and typical tree ages in plantation forests in India (6-10 years; Brown, 2000).

decrease wages and increase land rents, as there are more workers available for given land. The changes in the economic returns to land and labor will, in turn, tend to cause land to be reallocated between forest goods and agricultural goods, depending on the relative labor intensity of agricultural and forest products. But an increase in population size will also generally expand total village income and thus increase the demand for forest products.

While distinguishing supply and demand effects is, of course, difficult, it is worth doing. Through separation of these effects, one can gain insight into the question of whether forest resources are efficiently managed. If forests are efficiently managed and produce local nontradables such as fodder and fuel, then an expansion in local demand should result in an expansion in local supply and thus greater forest area. By contrast, if forests are not efficiently managed, then an increase in demand for forest products can have the opposite effect, because higher demand for the product may be met by the nonsustainable extraction of forest resources.

If the per capita demand for forest products at the level of the household is importantly affected by household size, then some purchase on this issue may be gained through a comparison of the effects of expansion in household size for a given population and an expansion in the total population for given household size. If, for example, heating or cooking needs grow less than proportionately with household size, as one might expect, then an increase in household size for given total population (and thus a decline in the number of households) should result in lower firewood consumption. Thus a comparison of how household size affects the demand for forest products and how household size affects forest area, given equilibrium land prices, wages, household income, and the number of households, provides an indirect test of whether forest area is managed efficiently.

Using this model as a starting point, we considered a number of alternative assumptions about the management of forest resources. One model assumed that forest labor could not be monitored but that forest area was otherwise selected to maximize village welfare, subject to the constraint created by this market failure. A key implication of this model was that no private individual would want to hold forest land (because he or she could not extract any rents from that land), and thus public ownership (or regulation) of forest land was essential to ensure the availability of forest products in the village at all. A second model considered the use of forest land as an indirect mechanism for the transfer of resources to poor households. The idea of this model was that the size of the forest will in general affect the wages and forest-good prices that prevail in a particular village. Given that the poor are net suppliers of labor and may also be differential consumers of forest products, an increase in forest area may effectively transfer economic resources to or from poor households. These models yielded some differences in prediction relationships between population and environmental resources and established that the test proposed above for efficient management of commons resources has power against interesting alternatives. It was striking, however, that under a variety of conditions the qualitative predictions of the perfect markets model were likely to obtain, even in the context of models with far from perfect markets.

DATA

While, as noted, exploration of the mechanisms underlying population-forest interaction provided the initial motivation for this project, it became clear in the course of the analysis that even basic descriptive analyses had yet to be carried out on a data set with the geographic and temporal scale of the one developed in this project. In particular, much of what was known about relationships between economic well-being and forest cover (e.g., Cropper and Griffiths, 1984) has been gleaned from cross-national studies and thus could not account for spatial differences in, among other things, land quality, which might affect both forest cover and economic well-being. As such it is unclear whether correlations between forest cover, population density, and income simply reflect differences in, for example, soil quality or other agroclimatic conditions. Moreover, given variation in the economic systems and economic integration across countries, it is not clear that the underlying mechanisms relating these variables are stable across countries. At a lower level of analysis, those few detailed longitudinal maps of forest cover that exist have either little spatial heterogeneity or could not be linked to underlying representative household survey data. Our analysis uses a panel data set that covers a period of 30 years in a sample that is representative of rural India and can be linked to local-level measures of forest cover and thus addresses all of these issues.

India seems to be an especially useful setting in which to examine the relationship between population growth and forest change. First, India is a setting in which there are low levels of primary forest and therefore one in which forest change has a great deal of salience as a national policy issue. There is particular concern about the role that forests have traditionally played in poverty alleviation, through allowing a basic livelihood to be earned in the form of firewood or fodder collection during periods of economic stress (Dasgupta, 1995). India is also recognized by such organizations as the World Bank to be an important test case for policy initiatives such as joint forest management, in which local villages are given some control over nearby national forest reserves (Kumar et al., 2000).

India is also an area of considerable ecological, population, and economic diversity. A key implication of the ecological diversity is that there is substantial spatial and temporal variation across India in the extent of agricultural productivity growth. This is of value because it provides a basis for examining the relationship between productivity growth in agriculture and forest cover. This ecological diversity, however, also creates a potential problem for inference. While 95 percent of India's forests are considered tropical, they span the gamut from rain forests to scrub forests in arid areas to mangrove forests in coastal areas. There is thus substantial variation in the biological constraints to forest growth in different areas. At the very least, this suggests that cross-sectional relationships between forest cover, population, and economic well-being are likely to be quite misleading. There is also considerable variation in population and economic change, reflecting substantial differences across regions in cultural attitudes, such as the status of women, that may impact fertility decline (e.g., Dyson and Moore, 1983) as well as state-level differences in economic policy that have led to different levels of income growth in different parts of the country. Despite these differences, however, there is also a substantial degree of economic integration across India, with different states facing roughly similar constraints with regard to trade across national boarders and tradable prices (such as those of grains) within the country being well equilibrated. Thus underlying mechanisms relating agricultural productivity to forest cover are not likely to differ substantially across villages in the country.

The survey data that formed the basis of the analysis consists of a 30-year panel collected by the National Council of Applied Economic Research (NCAER) in Delhi, India. The first round of the survey was introduced in the 1968-1969 crop year, with the specific purpose of evaluating the consequences of this focused attempt at agricultural productivity enhancement on agricultural incomes. The survey was a clustered stratified random sample of rural households in India. The original sample consisted of 5,115 households drawn from 259 villages in 100 districts in the 17 major states of India. It oversampled villages in districts or parts of districts that were participants in two programs (International Associate Development Program and Intensive Agricultural Areas Programme) targeting areas thought to be particularly well suited to the productions of high-yielding varieties. In each village, a census was taken that included information on household income. Households were divided into three strata based on income, and the top two strata were oversampled. Follow-up surveys were collected in the subsequent two crop years. The first year for which complete village and household level information is currently available is 1971.

Due to sample attrition and nonresponse, there were 4,527 households interviewed in this round. In 1982, 250 of the original villages were revisited (the state of Assam was excluded) and 4,979 household surveyed, approximately two-thirds of which were the same households as in the 1971 round. The criteria for reinterviewing the households were that either the original household was intact or that the original household head was alive. In cases in which the household had divided, only that household in which the original household head was currently residing was interviewed. The remaining one-third of households was drawn from the village so that the 1982 sample would again be representative of rural households.

In 1999, 251 of the original villages were interviewed (the state of Jammu and Kashmir was excluded). In this case, both the original and any split-off households of the 1982 households currently resident in the village were surveyed, as were five additional randomly selected households, for a total sample of 7,474 households. Given that a full census was constructed in each survey year and these censuses can be linked using names and relationships over time, there is good reason to believe that the interviewers have successfully tracked all splitoff households in the villages and can identify households that have left the study villages. However, full computation of follow-up rates awaits the computerization of the census lists, which is currently under way. We also have proxy responses on the relatives of current household residents, which provide information on out-migrant households. In all rounds, weights are available so that summary measures are representative at the level of the village and, with the exception of any new villages, representative of the rural population as a whole.

The data set provides comprehensive information on sources of income and expenditure, detailed attributes and activities of household members, and a demographic module covering issues of fertility, health, and mortality. Particularly detailed information is available in terms of inputs and outputs of agricultural products by seed type and crop. A village-level module provides detailed information on village programs, average yields, infrastructure, employment, industry, wages, and prices.

We also appended to the data information on rainfall, obtained from the monthly time series available from 40 Indian weather stations, using our geocoding of the villages and weather stations to compute nearest-station rainfall measures for the villages. Plate 10 displays the locations of sample villages as well as the weather station locations used to obtain the rainfall data.

The original data incorporated some information on village forest area, which is also reported in the census. At the early stages of the project, however, it became clear that this information was incomplete. In particular, the measure was restricted to the administrative area of the village rather than some fixed catchment area, and it was unclear whether the standards by which forest cover were being reported were comparable across areas, whether forest area included areas that were designated as forest reserves but did not necessarily have standing trees, and whether reported forest area included plantation forest. While district-level data on forest cover are available in India, these data are based on administrative records of land devoted to forest, and it was again unclear whether these were measures of the actual stock of trees. Moreover, the district-level variation would not permit us to take advantage of important village-level variation in economic conditions. We thus explored the use of satellite images for recovery of forest area.

The process of constructing geographically and temporally consistent measures of forest cover at the village level by compiling remote sensing images over this scale and time period proved to be time-consuming and difficult. Most importantly, the nature of satellite images has changed substantially over the years. Our earliest set of images, from Landsat I, contained only four bands of the spectrum, began in 1974, and were not available digitally. Given image size and the locations of our villages, we determined that we would need approximately 70 distinct scenes. Each of the relevant images needed to be scanned and registered by hand. Data storage, given available technology at the time, was also a major challenge. Availability of these images, particularly in the early 1980s, was spotty. In principle, Landsat images were also available from the early 1990s, but at the time they were prohibitively expensive, so lower resolution images had to be substituted. The Landsat 7 images we collected for use in 1999 were, by contrast, available digitally, relatively inexpensive, and very high resolution. All images were resampled to a resolution of approximately 500 meters, so that a comparable time series could be constructed.

Ideally the measures of forest collected from these series would have involved supervised classification and verification. However, given the relatively diverse ecological variation across India and the number of images involved, we elected to use, as a basis for measuring forest density, a standard measure of vegetative cover, the Normalized Differentiated Vegetation Index (NDVI) (Rouse et al., 1974), obtained during periods in which there are few standing crops in the field as a basis of forest cover. Our primary analysis was conducted using two summary measures of NDVI. The first was the share of pixels within a 10 kilometer radius of the village center that exceeded the value of 0.2. The second was the average value of the NDVI within that radius among pixels exceeding 0.2. While the NDVI is commonly used in studies of forest cover, concerns have been raised that the relationship between NDVI and forest cover need not be monotonic (Wulder, 1998). A detailed attempt to compare NDVI in one part of the study area with more sophisticated and robust measures of forest cover in that region suggested, however, that this was not a major issue, given the focus and context of our project (Firestone, 2000).

RESULTS

Our principal results are presented in two papers, one published (Foster and Rosenzweig, 2003) and one under review (Foster, Rosenzweig, and

Behrman, 2003). The first paper focuses on a surprising result that has emerged from this analysis—that forest cover in rural areas of India has grown appreciably over the last 30 years. When we first began this work we had assumed, as much of the literature seemed to suggest, that India, as with much of the developing world, was in the process of forest decline. While early on we discovered published statistics suggesting that forest area in India had increased, we understood this to be a result of administrative classification of lands rather than real growth of trees, as discussed above. Our first two rounds of satellite imagery also provided some evidence of increases in forest cover, but we largely ignored this given that we were primarily interested in differential change in forest cover across regions. We were also concerned that the differences in measured forest cover might reflect the differences in the satellite and storage medium of the first two rounds. By the time we put together the third round of satellite imagery, it became evident that this positive trend was real. Recalibration of the 1974-1982 data to address possible concerns about differences in image quality also confirmed that the earlier trend was not an artifact. Upon more detailed examination of the literature, we found substantial support for this conclusion of rising forest cover from other unrelated sources.

Long-term trends in forest cover (1880 and 1999) are illustrated in Figure 12-1. Estimates of forest cover between 1880 and 1950 from

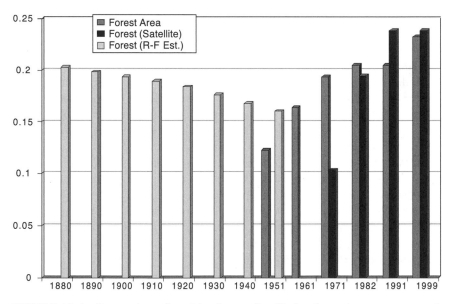

FIGURE 12-1   Proportion of total land area classified as forest (government statistics) and proportion of land forested, India, 1880-1999.
SOURCES: Richards and Flint (1994) and satellite data.

Richards and Flint (1994) indicate that forest cover declined from 20 percent of total land in India in 1880 to about 16 percent in 1950.[5] Figure 12-1 also shows, however, that the proportion of land designated by the Indian government as forest land (Department of Agriculture and Cooperation, 1997; Food and Agriculture Organization, 2000) increased from 12 percent in 1951 to over 23 percent in 1999. The time series of tree coverage for India based on satellite imagery that we carried out, which are also presented in the figure, indicate that the increase in officially designated forest land has been accompanied, with a lag, by increases in the proportion of land covered by forests, from just over 10 percent in 1971 to over 24 percent in 1999.

This sustained increased in forest cover is remarkable when set in the context of overall rates of economic and population growth in the study villages. Basic statistics derived from the household surveys as well as the 1990 census are presented in Table 12-1. Average population size in the study villages almost doubled over the 1971-1999 period, from 2,033 to 3,877, a 90 percent increase. There was a similar expansion in household income, which rose from 2,846 to 5,214 *rupees* (in 1982 *rupees*), an increase of 83 percent. There was also substantial real wage growth from 6.7 to 16.7 1982 *rupees*, an increase of 150 percent. Evidently growth in forest cover, at least at the national level, is not inconsistent with substantial rates of growth in population and economic activity.

To address possible mechanisms underlying these changes, we examined a number of hypotheses as to why forest area might be increasing in India. The statistical analyses for this work consisted primarily of estimation of a series of equations relating forest cover at the village level to agricultural productivity, household size, population size, and measures of infrastructure. To account for unmeasured differences across villages in climatic conditions and biophysical constraints, we used fixed effects,[6] relating changes over time in forest cover to changes over time in economic and population conditions. The issue here is that conditions that increase the propensity for forest growth in a particular area may be correlated, in the cross-section, with both agricultural productivity and population: more favorable soil conditions will promote forest growth but will also raise agricultural productivity and support higher population densities. Thus the cross-sectional correlation between agricultural productivity and forest cover may be positive, even if an increase in agricultural productivity, for given soil conditions, will tend to decrease forest cover. Indeed, this is

---

[5]Richards and Flint provide estimates of forest cover for 1880, 1920, and 1950. The intervening years are interpolated in the figure.

[6]Seto (Chapter 8) uses a fixed-effects estimator to examine land cover change in China for similar reasons.

TABLE 12-1   Village Characteristics (Mean and SD), by Survey and
Census Year

Variable	1971	1982	1991	1999
Proportion of land forested (NDP)	.105[a]	.210[b]	.239[c]	.239[d]
	(.176)	(.264)	(.198)	(.294)
Proportion of biomass attributable	.0271[a]	.0579[b]	.0462[c]	.0842[d]
to forests	(.0487)	(.0790)	(.0235)	(.1195)
Mean net cultivated area (acres)	1,344[f]	1,564[g]	NA	1,541[h]
	(1,575)	(1,579)		(1,641)
Village population size	2,033[e]	2,642[e]	3,311[e]	3,877[h]
	(3,121)	(3,466)	(4,948)	(5,510)
Household size	5.88	6.12	6.05	6.51
	(1.24)	(1.72)	(1.51)	(2.53)
High yielding varieties yield	321.7[f]	561.2[g]	NA	1001.9[h]
(1971 *rupees*/acre)	(384.3)	(353.3)		(500.4)
Annual rainfall (mm)	1,153.4[i]	1,012.1[i]	944.0[i]	1,004.3[i]
	(547.1)	(285.1)	(462.8)	(647.8)
Male agricultural wage	6.68[f]	9.99[g]	NA	16.7[h]
(1982 *rupees*/day)	(2.69)	(5.92)		(5.08)
Land price (1982 *rupees*)	8950.0[f]	8965.4[g]	NA	27218[h]
	(7910.3)	(9792.5)		(26395)
Household income (1982 *rupees*)	2,845.6[f]	3,071.3[g]	NA	5,213.9
	(1,451.5)	(1,806.8)		(7,738.0)
Paved (*pucca*) access road	NA	.290[g]	.706[e]	.731[h]
		(.455)	(.457)	(.444)
Factory in village	.135[f]	.622[g]	NA	.949[h]
	(.343)	(.486)		(.221)
Village in an Intensive Agricultural District Program district[f]			.215	
Proportion of land planted in rice in 1971[f]			.297	
Proportion of land planted in wheat in 1971[f]			.116	
Number of villages	253	242	234	253

[a]Landsat 1.
[b]Landsat 3.
[c]Landsat 4.
[d]Landsat 7.
[e]India Census.
[f]Additional Rural Income Survey, 1970-1971.
[g]Rural Economic Development Survey, 1981-1982.
[h]Rural Economic Development Survey, 1999.
[i]National Climate Data Center, monthly global surface data.
SOURCE: Foster and Rosenzweig (2003).

exactly what was observed—in the cross-section, a doubling of agricultural productivity is associated with a 5-point increase in the fraction of the village area that is forested. However, using differences and instrumenting to account for the fact that actual agricultural yields measure with error the true expected yields at a given point in time, we found that a doubling of agricultural productivity resulted in a 30-point decline in forest area.

Our results allow us to dismiss three of the primary hypotheses that might have been thought to govern this change based on the existing literature. First, there is no evidence that increased seed productivity in India has led to decreased need for agricultural land and thus the regrowth of forests. In fact, given that grain markets in India have been essentially integrated and tied to world prices over the study period, one would expect the opposite effect—as agricultural land becomes more productive due to higher yield, one has an incentive to move more land from forest to agricultural purposes and to export the surplus. As noted, this effect is readily evident in the data. Those areas experiencing the most rapid growth of agricultural productivity also experienced the most decline (or least growth) in forest cover. This result corresponds with those of the Yaqui Valley in Mexico (Matson et al., Chapter 10) and that of the Nang Rong area of Thailand (Walsh et al., Chapter 6), where the opening of an agricultural commodity market resulted in a substantial transition from forest to crop land.

Second, while there is some evidence that rural wages have risen in part as a consequence of growth in the nonfarm sector, there is no evidence that this rise in wages has importantly affected forest cover given household income, household size, and the returns to traditional agricultural land. It should be noted at the outset that whether one believes that rising wages should have an effect on forest cover depends very much on one's model of forest management. On one hand, if the primary source of forest decline is the nonsustainable extraction of forest resources (e.g., cutting of trees for firewood or fodder greater than the capacity of the forests to regenerate), then rising wages, by providing other opportunities for labor, will tend to decrease the extraction of these resources and thus increase forests. On the other hand, if forest area is being managed as an agricultural resource, then the effects of a rise in the wage, given household income and the returns to agricultural land, will depend on how sensitive the consumption of forest goods is to the effective price of these goods. The intuition here is that rising wages will reduce the amount of labor per unit area used in the extraction of forest resources. This, in turn, reduces the quantity of forest goods produced. If the demand for forest goods is fairly sensitive to price, then the price will rise a small amount but forest area will not be much affected. Alternatively, if the demand for forest goods is not much affected by their price, then the price of forest goods will have to rise a great deal in response to this higher cost of labor. There will be thus a high return to holding land as forests, and more land may be converted from traditional agriculture to forests.

Third, there is little evidence that income change at the local level importantly affects forest cover. Again, the theoretical effects are ambiguous and depend on how forest area is managed, as well as, in this case, on how responsive demand for forest products is to increases in household income. An increase in income may tend to increase demand for wood products for use in housing and furniture, for example, while decreasing demand for wood products in the form of firewood. If local demand must largely be met by local supply, then an income-induced increase in demand will have different effects on forest area depending, as before, on how forest resources are managed. If forest resource extraction is efficiently managed, then an increase (decrease) in demand will result in an increase (decrease) in forest area and conversely in the case of nonsustainable management. An additional income effect may be in place if higher incomes result in greater demand for environmental quality in terms of more or healthier forests or increased ability to pay for the protection of these resources.

Having examined these three hypotheses, we then proposed a rather different story—that growth in forest area is largely driven by demand for wood and paper products at the national level coupled with the trade barriers that, until recently, have discouraged the importation of these products into the country. There is ample evidence to support this view. First, there has been substantial growth in plantation forests in India—that is, a substantial fraction of forests are now literally being managed as agricultural commodities. Second, growth in demand for paper and wood products has substantially exceeded growth in net imports of these products. Third, given relatively low density of forest cover in most parts of the country as well as protections in place in others, there is little opportunity for suppliers to meet this demand through the cutting of old-growth forests. Finally, at the cross-national level, there is a strong relationship between income growth and forest growth among countries with relatively closed economies (i.e., those economies with significant barriers to trade) but no such relationship among countries with relatively open economies, in which changes in demand are largely met through trade (Foster and Rosenzweig, 2003).

Thus given the underlying market structures and conditions, population and economic growth have actually promoted growth in forest cover rather than decreasing it, as has generally been assumed. But this overall pattern of effects, which is driven through the national demand for forest products, does not necessarily imply that population does not have important adverse effects on forest cover at the local level.

In particular, our results suggest that population has a variety of effects on forest cover and that there is an important distinction to be made between population growth due to expansion of households and population growth due to an expansion in household size, a point also emphasized in Liu's work in the Wolong Nature Reserve of China (Liu et al., Chapter 9). As discussed in the theory section, how household size and the number of households affect forest cover is importantly governed by the structure of demand for, the technology of production of, and the process of management of forest resources and cannot in general be determined on theoretical grounds. Empirically, we find that the effects of an expansion in household size for given number of household is on average small. On net, a doubling of household size results in a 4-point decline in the forest area. By contrast a doubling in the number of households for a given household size results in a 9-point rise in the fraction of forest area. Moreover, this effect does not appear to be a consequence of the fact that an increase in the number of households increases the supply of labor, as the household effect is observed net of wages and land prices. These results suggest, as assumed in the baseline model, that local demand for forest products is met at least in part through local production, just as, at the national level, supply responds to demand. The fact that increases in household size have a different impact than do increases in the number of households suggests, in addition, that the organization of people into households affects the demand for forest products and thus forest area through scale effects. The fact that an increase in household size on average decreases forest area also indicates that there is an important sense in which forest resources are not efficiently managed.

In our second paper (Foster, Rosenzweig, and Behrman, 2003), we look at this issue more directly by focusing on how commons management of forest land impacts the local-level relationship between changes in agricultural productivity, population, and wages and changes in forest area. We find in particular that adverse impacts on forest area are stronger in those areas in which forest land is commonly held. In those areas in which forests are commonly held, we reject the implication of the benchmark model that an expansion in household size, which raises demand for forest products, should also raise forest area. But this implication is not rejected in areas in which forests are not commonly managed. These results suggest that a clear distinction needs to be drawn between forest area that is privately owned and managed, such as plantation forests, and more traditional forest commons.

Finally, consistent with results from other studies reported in this volume (Moran, Brondizion, and VanWey, Chapter 5; Walsh et al., Chapter 6; Fischer and O'Neill, Chapter 3), we find that the availability of high-quality roads tends to decrease forest cover. As a high-quality road does not significantly increase land prices but does push up wages, it appears that the primary effect of roads in India is not through an increase in the price farmers receive for agricultural commodities but through an expansion in labor opportunities outside the forest and the agricultural sector.

SCALE

The primary generalizable theme that has arisen in the context of this work is the critical link between the nature of the questions being examined and the scale at which the analysis takes place. This issue of appropriate scale is a major source of the underlying strength of this work as well as a basis for some of the key limitations.

In addressing this issue it is helpful to distinguish between the scale of analysis and the unit of analysis. For the purpose of this chapter, the scale of analysis refers to the overall geographical coverage of the data, whereas the unit of analysis refers to the underlying source of variation that is examined in a particular study region. Thus a unit of analysis may consist of an individual, a household, a village, a district, or a state, and the scale of analysis will in general consist of a collection of individual units at a higher level of aggregation.

The reason for making this distinction is that a given mechanism can be uncovered statistically only to the extent that mechanism is relatively fixed at the scale of analysis. Suppose one wishes to investigate a mechanism that links increases in village population to changes in forest cover. In this case, the unit of analysis must be the village, and the scale of analysis will be a collection of villages, say a country, with different levels of population growth. If the unit and scale of analyses are smaller than this, for example, then there is little basis for determining whether higher population growth puts pressure on local forests. Moreover, this analysis works only if the mechanism is relatively fixed across the scale of analysis. If the relationship between population and forest cover varies across villages, then an analysis based on a comparison across villages would provide little basis for inference about such a mechanism.

In the context of our work, the appropriate scale of analysis has been importantly governed by the size of the market as well as the availability of data. Table 12-2 provides a simple perspective on the different scales, units, and questions examined in our work. Consider first the question of whether increases in income increase or decrease demand for fuel or wood products. We assume that, for example, firewood is easily traded across households within a village but not easily traded between households in different villages. As a consequence of the first assumption, it is a reasonable approximation to assume that the unit cost of firewood is similar for households living in the same village. As a consequence of the second assumption, this unit cost varies from village to village. Given these two assumptions, and in the absence of direct measures of firewood price, the best way to measure the sensitivity of demand for forest products to income is through within-village variation in firewood consumption. Thus the appropriate scale of analysis is the village, and the appropriate unit of analysis is the household.

TABLE 12-2   Questions Asked and the Appropriate Scale and Unit of Analysis

Question	Unit	Scale	Comment
Effects of income on wood demand?	Household	Village	Tradability within village
Effects of HYV growth on forests?	Village	Country	One market within country, world price given
Demand for wood caused tree growth?	Country	World	Only linked in closed economies

Now turn to the question of the appropriate scale for examining the effects of technical change in agriculture in India on forest cover. In this context we assume that grains are fully tradable across villages and even nations so that, from the perspective of any given village and even India as a whole, the price of grains may be taken as given. In this context a comparison of rates of forest growth in regions with different levels of productivity growth in agriculture provides a reasonable basis of inference about decisions to allocate land between traditional agriculture and forests. The appropriate unit of analysis is thus the village, and the appropriate scale is the country. In the absence of the assumption that there is one market in the country, one would lose the ability to separate the production-side from the demand side effects. That is, the measured effect would reflect the direct effects of productivity in agriculture on the relative productivity of land devoted to agriculture minus an effect due to the declining local price, which is determined, in turn, by the price responsiveness of demand for the agricultural products. A similar convolution of demand and supply effects would occur to the extent that India cannot take world grain prices as given, because it is a relatively large producer and consumer of grains. In this case, the measured effect of the Green Revolution would only incorporate the production effect on forests and miss the fact that the Green Revolution in India may have helped, all else being equal, to lower world grain prices and thus decrease the incentive to convert forest land to agriculture.

Finally, consider the argument that overall demand for paper and wood products in India was largely responsible for the growth in forest cover over the 30-year study period. Under the maintained assumption, for example, that paper markets across India are reasonably well integrated, there is little basis on which to test the hypothesis that a rise in demand for paper products results in increased forest cover. This is because local demand for paper products in an integrated market is not linked to the supply in that area. There is, in effect, no systematic variation in demand for paper products across India. The only direct test of the idea is to turn to the unit of analysis of the country with the set of nations as the appropriate scale. Even this comparison, however, does not work in the case of relatively open economies—one needs the frictions created by a lack of openness in order to establish whether, indeed, increases in demand for paper products importantly drive forest cover.

From this perspective, it is clear that the process of scaling up and scaling down requires a great deal of conceptualization about the mechanisms in place. The finding that, for example, increases in household size at the level of the village tend to result in decreases in forest cover does not at all imply that increases in household size at the national level will decrease forest cover. To the extent that forest growth is driven by demand for paper products, a relatively tradable good, population growth at the national level may increase forest cover in a relatively closed economy. At the local level, however, increases in household size depress wages and increase rents, which may shift production from forests to more traditional agriculture, if the latter is relatively labor intensive.

FUTURE WORK

As noted at the beginning of this chapter, one of the primary motivations for this work was to examine issues of fertility externalities. First, in the early stages of the analysis, it became clear that, given existing data, we could do little more than conduct an indirect test through establishing whether changes in forest area reflected a commons tragedy as well as generally to determine whether increased forest area was associated with higher or lower fertility. A more direct test for the presence of a fertility externality required more detailed data on time spent by different household members in the extraction of forest products, as well as measurement of the relative importance of different fuel sources. This type of information has been incorporated into the 1999 round of the survey, and we hope to pursue this matter in some detail in the future.

Second, there is a need to understand and model the processes of demographic change and how this interacts with the land cover more generally. It is clear from our results that household size and the number of households, while both contributing overall to population growth, have effects on forest cover that differ in important ways. In other work (Foster and Rosenzweig, 2002), we have constructed a model of household division that relies importantly on the tension between the economic savings associated with joint consumption of a public good and tensions across subhousehold units over the preferred division of expenditures between public and private goods. Given that fuel and dwelling expenditures have a public component and may be influenced by land cover, there may be feedbacks operating between forest cover and household division that importantly impact population-environment relationships. There is also a need to better understand the role of migration as a source of change in household size and composition and how this interacts with changes in land cover, an issue raised by Walsh et al. (Chapter 6 in this volume) in the context of Thailand.

A third area in which more progress needs to be made is the identification of different types of forest growth. As noted, growth in plantation forests has played a major role in increasing forest cover in India generally. Thus much of the forest growth may have been in terms of a small number of marketable species. More generally, there is reason to believe that the species and diversity of forests in areas where forests are growing are substantially different from those in place in the early nineteenth century, differences that are also evident in the process of secondary secession in other regions, such as Brazil (Moran et al., Chapter 5). More detailed classification of the remotely sensed imagery may provide a basis for providing a richer perspective on changes in forest cover in India, thus assessing the extent to which the natural diversity is or is not being preserved.

CONCLUSION

This project shares much in common with other studies of population and environment that appear in this volume. First, the methodologies and even the questions asked have evolved importantly in the course of the survey. Our initial focus on issues of commons management have been retained, but we had no sense when beginning the analysis that a primary empirical fact to be explained was the rise in forest cover in India in the face of rapid population and economic growth. This is not to diminish the importance of the decline in forests in some areas or to suggest that changes in species and diversity of forests are not an important concern. It does suggest, however, that the field of research is at a stage in which an important component of any analysis will be to identify the salient issues and questions in a given research setting.

Second, the project involves the integration of local representative survey data with remotely sensed imagery. Given that the survey data that provided the starting point for our analysis did not contain detailed information on forest cover, the unique temporal frame of our study could not have been possible had we not been able to integrate into the analysis previously collected remotely sensed data. At the same time, however, the earliest remotely sensed images were of a different quality and in a different medium than those collected in more recent years. This raised possible issues of comparability and has limited to some extent our ability to carry out more refined analysis of forest cover. Methodological work on how best to integrate remotely sensed images of different quality and type across regions with substantially different agroclimatic conditions is clearly needed.

There are also two important aspects of our project that distinguish it from most of the other projects discussed in this volume. First, the temporal and geographical scale in our analysis is relatively large. This scale is, in my view, essential in that there is substantial local-level geographic and temporal spillover between population and environmental processes. Because of this, many important population-environment interactions can be examined only through studies at a very large scale. Patterns observed at lower scales may be interesting in their own right, but they are likely to provide little insight into these larger scale interactions. Conversely, however, there is likely to be variation in local-level processes, such as the constraints of biophysical processes and even the operation of markets or political systems. There is thus a clear need for a balance between large-scale studies such as ours that partially gloss over local-level variation and more local-level studies that focus on particular conditions and environments and help to identify the magnitude and significance of this local-level variation.

Finally, an important feature of our project has been the development of a specific analytic structure to focus attention on the critical mechanisms underlying population-environment interactions as well as to frame the empirical analysis. The fact that this project has used such a structure, rather than a more generalized characterization of pathways linking various types of conditions and outcomes, may be considered a potential weakness, in that many of the specific assumptions that have been incorporated may hold only approximately in practice. However, the use of specific structure has also played a very important role in allowing us to go beyond a characterization of empirical regularities. In particular, the approach has helped us to identify specific answerable research questions that we might otherwise have missed. As this research continues into a more detailed assessment of household-level processes and how they interact with environmental conditions, this structured approach will continue to play a critical role in guiding our research.

REFERENCES

Brown, C.
  2000 The Global Outlook for Future Wood Supply from Forest Plantations. (Working Paper No. GFPOS/WP/03.) Rome, Italy: Forestry Policy and Planning Division, Food and Agricultural Organization.
Cropper, M., and C. Griffiths
  1984 The interaction of population growth and environmental quality. American Economic Review 84:250-254.
Dasgupta, P.
  1995 An Inquiry into Well-Being and Destitution. Oxford, England: Clarendon Press.
Department of Agriculture and Cooperation
  1997 Agricultural Statistics at a Glance. New Delhi: Directorate of Economics and Statistics, Department of Agriculture and Cooperation, Ministry of Agriculture, Government of India.

Dyson, T., and M. Moore
  1983   On kinship structure, female autonomy, and demographic behavior in India. *Population and Development Review* 9(1):35-60.
Filmer, D., and L. Pritchett
  1986   *Environmental Degradation and the Demand for Children: Searching for the Vicious Circle.* (Policy Research Working Paper No. 1623.) Washington, DC: World Bank.
Firestone, L.
  2000   Land-Cover Change in Eastern Gujarat During the Green Revolution: A Case Study in the Use of Satellite Imagery in Social Science and Environmental Research. Unpublished undergraduate thesis, Brown University.
Food and Agriculture Organization
  2000   *Forest Resources Assessment 2000.* Rome, Italy: Food and Agriculture Organization of the United Nations.
Foster, A.D., and M.R. Rosenzweig
  2002   Household public goods, household division, and rural economic growth. *Review of Economic Studies* 69(4):839-69.
  2003   Economic growth and the rise of forests. *Quarterly Journal of Economics* 118(2): 601-637.
Foster, A.D., M.R. Rosenzweig, and J. Behrman
  2003   Population, Income and Forest Growth: Management of Village Common Land in India. Unpublished manuscript, Brown University.
Hardin, G.
  1968   The tragedy of the commons. *Science* 162:1243-1248.
Harris, J.M.
  2002   *Environmental and Resource Economics: A Contemporary Approach.* Boston, MA: Houghton Mifflin.
Jodha, N.S.
  1985   Population growth and the decline of common property resources in India. *Population and Development Review* 11(33):247-264.
Kumar, N., N. Saxena, Y. Alagh, and K. Mitra
  2000   *Alleviating Poverty Through Forest Development, Evaluation Country Case Studies Series.* Washington, DC: World Bank.
Lee, R.
  1990   Population policy and externalities to childbearing. Pp. 17-32 in *Annals of the American Academy of Political and Social Science,* special issue, S. Preston, ed. Philadelphia, PA: American Academy of Political and Social Science.
  1991   Evaluating externalities to childbearing in developing countries: The case of India. In *Consequences of Rapid Population Growth in Developing Countries,* G. Tapinos, D. Blanchet, and D. Horlacher, eds. New York: Taylor and Francis.
National Climate Data Center
  1997   *Monthly Global Surface Data.* Asheville, NC: National Climate Data Center.
Nerlove, M.L.
  1991   Population and the environment: A parable of firewood and other tales. *American Journal of Agricultural Economics* 73:1334-1347.
Nerlove, M.L., and A. Meyer
  1997   Endogenous fertility and the environment: A parable of firewood. In *The Environment and Emerging Development Issues,* P. DasGupta and K.-G. Mäler, eds. New York: Oxford University Press.

Ostrom, E.
  1990   *Governing the Commons: The Evolution of Institutions for Collective Action.* New York: Cambridge University Press.

Pender, J.
  1999   *Rural Population Growth, Agricultural Change and Natural Resource Management in Developing Countries: A Review of Hypotheses and Some Evidence from Honduras.* (Discussion Paper 48.) Washington, DC: International Food Policy Research Institute, Environment and Production Technology Division.

Richards, J.F., and E.P. Flint
  1994   *Historic Land Use and Carbon Estimates for South and Southeast Asia: 1880–1980.* (Environmental Sciences Division Publication No. 4174.) Oak Ridge, TN: Carbon Dioxide Information Analysis Center, Oak Ridge National Laboratory.

Rouse, J.W. Jr., R.H. Haas, D.W. Deering, J.A. Schell, and J.C. Harlan
  1974   *Monitoring the Vernal Advancement and Retrogradation (Green Wave Effect) of Natural Vegetation.* (Type III Final Report.) Greenbelt, MD: NASA Goddard Space Flight Center.

Sedjo, R.A.
  1995   Forests: Conflicting signals. In *The True State of the Planet*, R. Bailey, ed. New York: The Free Press.

Wulder, M.
  1998   Optical remote-sensing techniques for the assessment of forest inventory and biophysical parameters. *Progress in Physical Geography* 22:449-476.

Appendix

About the Contributors

Barbara Entwisle (*Chair*) is professor of sociology and director of the Carolina Population Center at the University of North Carolina, Chapel Hill. She is a social demographer interested in population dynamics and demographic responses to social change, mostly in developing countries. Her projects have addressed issues related to fertility decline, family planning program evaluation, communities as contexts for individual behavior, household change and social networks, and migration, household formation and land use change. An interest in methodology pervades all of her work. Her current research utilizes innovative data from Nang Rong, Thailand, which links prospective longitudinal social survey data on households, and links between households, to information about land use and land cover extracted from a time series of satellite images. She also studies topics related to data confidentiality and the ethics of social research. She is a member of the National Research Council's (NRC) Committee on the Human Dimensions of Global Change. She has an A.B. in sociology-anthropology from Swarthmore College and A.M. and Ph.D. degrees in sociology from Brown University.

Myron P. Gutmann is professor of history and director of the Interuniversity Consortium for Political and Social Research (ICPSR) at the University of Michigan. He has broad interests in interdisciplinary historical research, especially health, population, economy, and the environment. As director of ICPSR, he is a leader in the archiving and dissemination of electronic research materials related to society, population, and health. He is currently president of the Consortium of Social Science Associations and has served in the past as chair of the Social Sciences, Nursing, Epidemiology and Methods-3 Study Section of the National Institutes of Health, and as a member of the NRC's Committee on the Human Dimensions of Global Change, as well as other national advisory committees and editorial boards. He has a B.A. from Columbia University (1971) and M.A. (1973) and Ph.D. (1976) degrees from Princeton University.

Wolfgang Lutz has been the leader of the International Institute for Applied Systems Analysis's Population Project since 1992. He is also adjunct professor for demography and social statistics at the University of Vienna and served as a secretary general for the International Union for the Scientific Study of Population. His main interests are in population forecasting, family demography, and population-environment analysis. He has written or edited numerous books and scientific articles and book chapters. Lutz studied philosophy, mathematics, and statistics at the universities of Munich, Vienna, Helsinki, and Pennsylvania. He has a Ph.D. in demography from the University of Pennsylvania (1983) and a second doctorate (habilitation) from the University of Vienna (1998).

Emilio F. Moran is the James H. Rudy professor of anthropology at Indiana University, professor of environmental sciences, adjunct professor of geography, director of the Anthropological Center for Training and Research on Global Environmental Change, and codirector of the Center for the Study of Institutions, Population and Environmental Change. He is also lead scientist of the Land Use Cover Change (LUCC) Focus 1-Land Use Dynamics Office. His research has focused on the Amazon for the past 30 years. He is the author of numerous books, journal articles, and book chapters, and has edited several volumes. He is trained in anthropology, tropical ecology, tropical soil science, and remote sensing. He served for six years on the NRC's Committee on the Human Dimensions of Global Change and currently serves on its Geographical Sciences Committee. He has a Ph.D. from the University of Florida (1975).

Dennis S. Ojima is a senior research scientist at the Natural Resource Ecology Laboratory and an assistant professor in the Rangeland Ecosystem Science Department at Colorado State University. He teaches graduate and undergraduate courses in ecosystem modeling and land use change and lectures in a number of departments, including the anthropology, atmospheric, and natural resource departments. He has edited books and authored reports and papers on diverse topics related to ecosystem science. He has a B.A. in botany from Pomona College (1975), an M.Ag. from the

University of Florida (1978), and a Ph.D. from the Rangeland Ecosystem Science Department at Colorado State University (1987).

Steward Pickett had been on the faculty of Rutgers University until 1987, when he joined the Institute for Ecosystem Studies as a senior scientist. He is a fellow of the American Association for the Advancement of Science and of the American Academy of Arts and Sciences and has served as vice president for science of the Ecological Society of America, on the science advisory board of the National Center for Ecological Synthesis and Analysis, and on the board of the Defenders of Wildlife. He coedited *The Ecology of Patch Dynamics and Natural Disturbance* (1985), *Ecological Heterogeneity* (1991), *Humans as Components of Ecosystems* (1993), and *The Ecological Basis of Conservation* (1997). He has a Ph.D. from the University of Illinois, Urbana (1977).

Peter J. Richerson is professor of environmental science and policy at the University of California, Davis. He is a member of the Animal Behavior and Ecology Graduate Groups. He serves as treasurer of the Human Behavior and Evolution Society and is a member of the NRC's Committee on the Human Dimensions of Global Change. His research interests include the theoretical and empirical study of cultural evolution and aquatic ecology. His cultural evolution work was honored with the Staley Prize of the School of American Research. He has a B.S. in entomology (1965) and a Ph.D. in zoology (1969) from the University of California, Davis.

Mark R. Rosenzweig is Mohamed Kamal professor of public policy and director of the Center for International Development at Harvard University. His most recent work examines the consequences of the Indian Green Revolution for schooling attainment, household structure, and deforestation; the impact of local democratization on the distribution of public services in India; the effects of maternal schooling on children's human capital; and the consequences of low birthweight. During 1979-1980, Rosenzweig was the director of research for the U.S. Select Commission of Immigration and Refugee Policy and he is currently coprincipal investigator for the New Immigrant Survey, the first national longitudinal survey of immigrants in the United States. Rosenzweig is editor of the *Journal of Development Economics,* a member of the executive committee of the American Economic Association, and a fellow of the Econometric Society. He has B.A. and Ph.D. degrees from Columbia University.

Paul C. Stern (*Study Director*) is also study director of two NRC committees: the Committee on the Human Dimensions of Global Change and the Committee on Assessing Behavioral and Social Science Research on Aging.

His research interests include the determinants of environmentally significant behavior, particularly at the individual level, participatory processes for informing environmental decision making, and the governance of environmental resources and risks. He is the coauthor or coeditor of *Environmental Problems and Human Behavior* (2002), *The Drama of the Commons* (2002), and *New Tools for Environmental Protection: Education, Information, and Voluntary Measures* (2002). Stern is a fellow of the American Association for the Advancement of Science and the American Psychological Association. He has a B.A. from Amherst College and M.A. and Ph.D. degrees from Clark University.

Susan Stonich is professor of anthropology and environmental studies at the University of California, Santa Barbara. Her research concerns the human dimensions of global change, the human and environmental consequences of economic globalization, globalization of resistance to industrial shrimp farming, tourism and conservation, community conflict and environmental justice, poverty and food security, and grassroots environmental movements. Her research has been conducted in Asia, Mexico, Latin America, and the rural United States. She has a Ph.D. in anthropology from the University of Kentucky.

CONTRIBUTORS

Li An is a research fellow at the University of Michigan. His research interests and expertise range from modeling complexity in human-environment interactions, integrating social sciences with geographic information system/remote sensing and spatial analysis, to exploring methodology of quantitative landscape ecology. His approaches to addressing human-environment interactions are interdisciplinary and multiscale (time, space, and organization). He has published a number of papers on these areas in such journals as *Science* and *Annals of the Association of American Geographers*. He was the first recipient of Michigan State University's Outstanding Dissertation Award for Global Studies. He has a Ph.D. in systems modeling from Michigan State University (2003).

Sandra S. Batie is the first holder of the Elton R. Smith professorship in food and agricultural policy at Michigan State University. Her research area is the economics of agroenvironmental policy. Recent research projects include implementation of agroenvironmental water quality standards, the policy implications of the uncertain environmental impacts of biotechnology products, corporate environmental management strategies in the agricultural sector, and examining the influence of agricultural contractual arrangements on producers' financial and environmental performance. She does extension education, mainly with agencies and policy makers, and teaches a graduate environmental economics course. Active on commissions and boards that are related to her expertise, she is currently chair of the Board of Winrock. She has M.A. and Ph.D. degrees from Oregon State University.

Scott L. Bearer is a Ph.D. candidate in the Department of Fisheries and Wildlife at Michigan State University. His research interests include the effects of timber harvesting and fuelwood collection on wildlife habitats, and he is continuing the search for a method to balance these necessary activities with endangered habitat preservation.

Eduardo S. Brondízio is associate professor of anthropology, assistant director of the Anthropological Center for Training and Research on Global Environmental Change, and faculty associate with the Center for the Study of Institutions, Populations, and Environmental Change. His work has focused on sociocultural, economic, and land use change among Amazônian rural populations particularly, of *caboclo* and colonist populations of the Brazilian Amazon, where he has carried out long-term ethnographic research. His research integrates ethnographic methods and survey instruments, historical remote sensing, and ecological measurements aimed at spatial-temporal analysis of social and environmental processes. He has a B.A. in agronomic engineering from the Universidade de Taubaté, Ciências Agrárias, Brazil (1987) and a Ph.D. in environmental anthropology (1996) from Indiana University.

Ingrid C. Burke is professor and university distinguished teaching scholar in the Department of Forest, Rangeland, and Watershed Stewardship in the College of Natural Resources at Colorado State University. Her professional interests include soil organic matter dynamics, ecosystem ecology, biogeochemistry, regional modeling, and global change. Current areas of research include influence of land use practices on carbon and nitrogen cycling, interactions between regional and global scale biogeochemistry, remote sensing of fire fuel load, and the carbon and nitrogen consequences of wildland fire. Recent publications include (with coauthors) *The Effect of Climate and Cultivation on Soil Organic C and N* (2004) and *Functional Traits of Graminoids in Semi-Arid Steppes: A Test of Grazing Histories* (2004). She has a B.S in biology from Middleburg College and a Ph.D. in botany from the University of Wyoming.

Aphichat Chamratrithirong is associate professor at the Institute of Population and Social Research (IPSR) at Mahidol University in Thailand. He is a social demographer interested in population change in the context of social and economic development. His published work focuses on fertility decline, contraceptive choice, family arrangements, and migration. He has played a key role in the design, implementation, and analysis of population surveys in Thailand, including Thailandís National Contraceptive Prevalence Surveys, the National Migration Survey, and the Nang Rong longitudinal surveys. Chamratrithirong was director of IPSR from 1988 to 1996 and advisor on Population Census and Survey Data Analysis for the Country Technical Services Team for East and South-East Asia of the United National Population Fund. He received a B.A. in political science from Chulalongkorn University and M.A. and Ph.D. degrees in sociology from Brown University.

Xiaodong Chen is a Ph.D. candidate in the Department of Fisheries and Wildlife at Michigan State University. His research interests include integrating socioeconomics with ecology, spatial pattern analysis in plant ecology, and applying geographic information systems and remote sensing in natural resources management.

Geoff Cunfer is associate professor in the Center for Rural and Regional Studies at Southwest Minnesota State University. He teaches environmental history, rural and regional studies, and geographical information systems. Previously he was assistant professor at Southwest Minnesota, and prior to that he was an assistant instructor at the University of Texas. One of his current research projects explores the historical connection between people, land use, and natural systems in an agricultural setting. He received the Social Science History Association's 2003 President's Book Award, for the best unpublished manuscript by a beginning scholar, published as *On the Great Plains: Agriculture and Environment* (2005). He has an M.A. from Texas Tech University and a Ph.D. from the University of Texas, both in environmental history.

Günther Fischer is a research scholar in the Food and Agriculture Program at the International Institute for Applied Systems Analysis (IIASA). Previously he was part of IIASA's Computer Sciences Group. He participated in the formulation of a general equilibrium framework and the implementation and application of a global model of the world food systems, known as IIASA's Basic Linked System. He was a major contributor to two studies, one on the welfare implications of trade liberalization in agriculture (*Towards Free Trade in Agriculture*, 1988) and one on poverty and hunger (*Hunger: Beyond the Reach of the Invisible Hand*, 1991). He participated in a multinational research project on climate change and world agriculture. He was coauthor of a major study on *Potential Population Supporting Capacity of Lands in the Developing World* (1983). Since 1987, he has coordinated the joint efforts of a worldwide network of collaborating institutions, the Food and Agriculture Network, which shares common interests in the development and use of tools for national and international policy analysis.

Andrew Foster is professor and chair of the Department of Economics and professor of community health at Brown University. He is an empirical microeconomist whose research considers issues in labor, population, development, health, and the environment. Previously he was associate professor in the Department of Economics at the University of Pennsylvania. He received the Dorothy Thomas Award from the Population Association of America in 1987 and a fellowship with the Population Council in 1986, among many other fellowships, scholarships, and honors. He has a Ph.D. in economics from the University of California, Berkeley (1988).

Debbie L. Fugate is a Ph.D. candidate in the joint doctoral program in geography at San Diego State University and the University of California, Santa Barbara. Her dissertation research focuses on the development of geodemographic models for estimating the size, distribution, and characteristics of data poor populations using remote sensing and geographic information systems.

Richard E. Groop is professor and chair of the Department of Geography and former director of the Center for Remote Sensing and Geographic Information Science at Michigan State University. He has published numerous research articles and book chapters and contributed to a number of atlases, including the Digital Atlas of Michigan. His research interests include internal migration within the United States, computer cartography, and human applications of geographic information systems. He has a B.S.Ed. (1965) and an M.A. in geography from Bowling Green State University (1967) and a Ph.D. in geography from the University of Kansas (1976).

Guangming He is a Ph.D. candidate in the Department of Fisheries and Wildlife at Michigan State University. His research interests include the integration and application of web-based geographic information systems, remote sensing, system modeling, and decision support systems in natural resource management.

Dennis P. Larson is a senior GIS (geographic information systems) technician with the San Diego Association of Governments and its chartered consulting agency, SouthPoint. He manages short-term GIS projects for member agencies and contributes to detailed research studies, examining the demographics and economics of local jurisdictions, growth management policies, and regional marketing strategies. His research interests include the use of spatial statistics in urban economics, the role of GIS in public policy, and the analysis of community and economic development strategies.

Zai Liang is associate professor of sociology at the State University of New York at Albany. He serves as chair-elect of the Asia and Asian American Section of the American Sociological Association and codirector of Urban China Research Network based at Albany. His major research interests are in internal and international migration. He recently finished a project on market transition and internal migration in China. His current research projects include a major study of international migration from China's Fujian Province to the United States and an examination of the social and health consequences of internal migration in China. He has a B.Sc. in mathematics from Jilin University, China (1983) and M.A. (1988) and Ph.D. (1992) degrees in sociology from the University of Chicago.

Marc A. Linderman is a National Science Foundation postdoctoral fellow in the Department of Geography at the University of Louvain in Belgium. His research interests include remote sensing, geographic information systems, landscape modeling, and human impacts on wildlife habitat. He has coauthored several journal articles, including "Ecological Degradation in Protected Areas: The Case of Wolong Nature Reserve for Giant Pandas," published in *Science*. He has a Ph.D. from Michigan State University.

Jianguo (Jack) Liu is the Rachel Carson chair in ecological sustainability in the Department of Fisheries and Wildlife and Director of the Center for Systems Integration and Sustainability at Michigan State University. His research interests include conservation ecology, landscape ecology, and human-environment interactions. He is interested in integrating ecology with socioeconomics as well as human demography and behavior. He has served on various committees and panels and is currently on editorial boards of six journals. He has received the National Science Foundation's CAREER Award, the Aldo Leopold Leadership Fellowship of the Ecological Society of America, and Michigan State University's Teacher-Scholar Award.

Amy Lynd Luers is a climate impacts scientist for the Global Environment Program at the Union of Concerned Scientists in Berkeley, California. Her research has focused on assessing vulnerability of agricultural farmers and coastal communities in northern Mexico to global environmental changes. Her current research explores climate change impacts in California. She has an M.A. in international policy studies and a Ph.D. in environmental science from Stanford University.

Pamela Matson is the Richard and Rhoda Goldman professor in the Department of Geological and Environmental Sciences and the Stanford Institute of International Studies and the Naramore dean of the School of Earth Sciences at Stanford University. She is a member of the National Academy of Sciences, a MacArthur fellow, and cochair of the National Academies' Roundtable on Science and Technology for Sustainability. Her research focuses on land use changes and their effects on biogeochemical cycling and trace gas exchange in tropical forests and agricultural systems. Ongoing interests include integrated analyses of sustainable resource use and vulnerability of human-environment systems to environmental and policy changes. She has a B.S. in biology from the University of Wisconsin (1975), an M.S. in environmental science from Indiana University (1980), and a Ph.D. in forest ecology from Oregon State University (1983).

Angela G. Mertig is associate professor of sociology in the Department of Sociology and Anthropology at Middle Tennessee State University. Previously at Michigan State University, she has worked extensively with the Michigan Department of Natural Resources Wildlife Division in researching the human dimensions of wildlife management. She specializes in sociological research methodology and statistics, social movements, especially the environmental movement, and in the study of public opinion and attitudes regarding the natural environment. She has a Ph.D. in sociology from Washington State University (1995).

Rosamond L. Naylor is the Julie Wrigley senior fellow at the Center for Environmental Science and Policy at Stanford University. Her research focuses on the environmental and equity dimensions of intensive food production. She has been involved in a number of field-level research projects throughout the world concerning issues of high-input agricultural production, biotechnology, climate-induced yield variability, aquaculture production, and food security. She was named a fellow in the Aldo Leopold Leadership Program in Environmental Sciences in 1999 and a Pew fellow in conservation and the environment in 1994, and she serves on the oversight committee for the McKnight Foundation's Collaborative Crop Research Program. She has a B.A. in economics and environmental studies from the University of Colorado, an M.Sc. in economics from the London School of Economics, and a Ph.D. in applied economics from Stanford University.

Brian C. O'Neill is a research scholar in the Greenhouse Gas Initiative and in the World Population Project at the International Institute for Applied Systems Analysis in Austria. He is currently on partial leave of absence from the Watson Institute for International Studies at Brown University. His research focuses on population-environment interactions and the science and policy of global climate change. In 2004 he received the European Young Investigator Award for research on demography and climate change. He has a Ph.D. in earth systems science from New York University.

J. Ivan Ortiz-Monasterio is a senior scientist in the intensive agroecosystems program at the International Maize and Wheat Improvement Center and consulting professor at Stanford University. He is a member of the Mexican Academy of Sciences as well as the National Academy of Agricultural Sciences. He has been working on ways to improve nutrient use efficiency in wheat-based cropping systems, looking at crop management as well as breeding approaches. He is also currently serving as wheat crop leader of the Consultative Group in International Agriculture Research Biofortification Challenge Program. He has a B.S. from the Monterrey Institute of Technology in Mexico and M.Sc. and Ph.D. degrees from the University of Illinois at Urbana-Champaign.

Zhiyun Ouyang is professor and director of the Key Lab of Systems Ecology and associate director of the Research Center for Eco-Environmental Sciences in the Chinese Academy of Sciences. His research interests include ecosystem services, ecosystem assessment, and ecological planning, biodiversity conservation, as well as applications of geographic information systems in ecology and environmental sciences.

William J. Parton is a senior research scientist and professor of rangeland and ecosystem science at the Natural Resource Ecology Laboratory at Colorado State University. His major research interests include ecosystem modeling, nutrient cycling, and trace gas fluxes. Previously, he was the director of the Ecosystem Studies Program in the Division of Biotic Systems and Resources at the National Science Foundation. He is a member of the Ecological Society of America. He has authored or coauthored numerous reports, papers, and articles, including *Modeling Soil Organic-Matter in Organic-Amended and Nitrogen-Fertilized Long-Term Plots* (2002), and *Regional and Temporal Variability in Aboveground Net Primary Productivity and Net N Mineralization in Grasslands* (2002). He has M.S. and Ph.D. degrees in meteorology from the University of Oklahoma.

Pramote Prasartkul is professor at the Institute of Population and Social Research (IPSR) at Mahidol Univeresity in Thailand. He is a social demographer interested in population dynamics, with particular reference to the population of Thailand. Dr. Prasartkul is the author of the major demography textbook used in graduate level training in Thailand. He has published descriptions of the age-sex structure of the Thai population, assessments of trends in survival curves, generation life tables for five-year cohorts, and population projections for the country. He is now leading a study to develop verbal autopsy as a tool to identify causes of death as part of a larger ongoing longitudinal study based in Kanchanaburi, Thailand. He has played a key role in the design, implementation, and analysis of the Nang Rong longitudinal surveys. Dr. Prasartkul is president of the Population Association of Thailand. He received a B.A. in political science from Chulalongkorn University and M.A. and Ph.D. degrees in sociology from Cornell University.

Jiaguo Qi is associate professor in the Department of Geography and the Center for Global Change and Earth Observations at Michigan State University. His primary research areas include theoretical development and applications of remote sensing technologies to study the dynamics of the earth system and their environmental impacts at variable spatial and temporal scales. His specific research interests focus on quantitative assessment of ecosystems health and their biophysical attributes, such as forest density, fragmentation, rangeland productivity, degradation, and spatial patterns of land use and land cover dynamics. He has a B.S. in physics from Harbin Teacher's Normal University in China (1981) and M.S. (1989) and Ph.D. (1993) degrees in water and environmental sciences from the University of Arizona.

Charles L. Redman is professor in the Department of Anthropology and director of the Center for Environmental Studies at Arizona State University. Previously, he taught at New York University and at the State University of New York-Binghamton. Redman's interests include human impacts on the environment, historical ecology, the rise of civilization, archaeological research design, and environmental education and public outreach. The author or coauthor of numerous books, including *Explanation in Archaeology, The Rise of Civilization, People of the Tonto Rim* and, most recently, *Human Impact on Ancient Environments,* he has directed archaeological field projects in the Near East, North Africa, and Arizona. He is a founding member of the Southwest Center for Education and the Natural Environment, a member of the board of trustees of the Museum of Northern Arizona, as well as the Arizona chapter of The Nature Conservancy, and a member of the science advisory committee of Biosphere 2 and the Wenner-Gren Foundation. He has a B.A. from Harvard University and M.A. and Ph.D. degrees in anthropology from the University of Chicago.

Ronald R. Rindfuss is the Robert Paul Ziff distinguished professor of sociology and fellow of the Carolina Population Center, University of North Carolina, Chapel Hill. Together with colleagues at Mahidol University and the University of North Carolina, he has been actively researching population and environment issues in Nang Rong district in northeast Thailand. Other research interests include family and fertility behavior in developed countries. He is a past president of the Population Association of America and a current member of the Science Steering Committee of the Land Use Cover and Change Program, the International Human Dimensions Program and the International Geosphere-Biosphere Program. He has a B.A. in sociology from Fordham University and a Ph.D. in sociology from Princeton University.

Karen C. Seto is assistant professor in the Department of Geological and Environmental Sciences in the School of Earth Sciences and a Fellow in the Center for Environmental Science and Policy at the Stanford Institute for International Studies at Stanford University. Her research focuses on monitoring urban growth trajectories, understanding the causes of land use change, and evaluating the social and ecological impacts of land use dynamics. She is particularly interested in the spatiotemporal patterns and social interactions at the agriculture-urban land use interface. She is on the scientific steering committees of the International Human Dimensions Programme's project on urbanization and global environmental change, and the World Conservation Union's Commission on Ecosystem Management. She has a B.A. in political science from the University of California, Santa Barbara, an M.A. in international relations, resources, and environmental management from Boston University, and a Ph.D. in geography from Boston University.

Leah K. VanWey is assistant professor of sociology at Indiana University and is a faculty fellow at the Anthropological Center for Training and Research on Global Environmental Change and at the Center for the Study of Institutions, Population and Environmental Change. She is a social demographer with research interests in household demography, migration, and population and environment relationships in Brazil, Mexico, and Thailand. She has a Ph.D. in sociology from the University of North Carolina, Chapel Hill.

Stephen J. Walsh is professor of geography, director of the Landscape Characterization and Spatial Analysis, and research fellow of the Carolina Population Center at the University of North Carolina, Chapel Hill. Previously he was the Amos H. Hawley professor of geography and organizer and director of the Spatial Analysis Unit at the Carolina Population Center. He is on the editorial boards of *Plant Ecology* and the *Journal of Geography*. He has coedited a series of books: *GIS and Remote Sensing Applications in Biogeography and Ecology* (2001), *Linking People, Place, and Policy: A GIScience Approach* (2002), and *People and the Environment:*

Approaches for Linking Household and Community Surveys to Remote Sensing and GIS (2003). Specific research foci are on pattern and process at the alpine treeline ecotone, biocomplexity, scale dependence and information scaling, land use and land cover dynamics, spatial simulations and change modeling, health care delivery, and population-environment interactions. He has M.S. and Ph.D. degrees in resource and physical geography from Oregon State University.

John R. Weeks is professor of geography and director of the International Population Center at San Diego State University. His research focuses on the application of remote sensing, spatial analysis, and geographic information system techniques to demographic phenomena. He is currently directing a project analyzing Arab fertility transitions, and another analyzing intraurban health in Accra, Ghana. His textbook, *Population: An Introduction to Concept and Issues*, is now in its ninth edition and has been the bestselling text in the field since the first edition appeared in 1978. He has a B.A. in sociology (1966) and M.A. (1969) and Ph.D. (1972) degrees in demography, all from the University of California, Berkeley.

Hemin Zhang is director of the China Conservation and Research Center for the Giant Panda, Wolong Nature Reserve. He is senior author of a recent book (in Chinese) entitled *Reproductive Studies of the Giant Panda*. He has an M.A. in wildlife management from Idaho State University.

Shiqiang Zhou is a research scientist in the China Conservation and Research Center for the Giant Panda, Wolong Nature Reserve. He is interested in the study of panda habitats, bamboo ecology, and socioeconomic issues.